WEATHER HISTORY AND CLIMATE GUIDE TO THE LOWER HUDSON VALLEY

JEROME S. THALER

GEORGE CANDREVA ENVIRONMENTAL CENTER
OSSINING, NEW YORK

This work is dedicated to the 20th century volunteer weather observers and to my grandchildren; Rebecca, Diane Ruby, Noah, Mark, Maxwell and Anna Rose who should witness the 21st century warming

Weather History and Climate Guide to the Lower Hudson Valley
First Edition

Published by
George Candreva Environmental Center, Inc.
820 Pinesbridge Road
Ossining, New York 10562
914-962-4352 • Fax 914-962-1714
Copyright © 2000 by Jerome S. Thaler

ISBN 0-9705688-0-0

LCCN 00-092452

Acknowledgments

Without the input of many individuals a book of this nature would not have been possible. By far the most important are the unsung daily weather watchers of the 19th and 20th century who have provided the raw data and observations that have made this book a reality, with its diaries and climate summaries. I am in total debt to them for their years of dedication.

Other individuals who contributed important aspects of this study were; Mary Azarian, of East Calais, Vermont for her seasonal and monthly woodcut illustrations, Tom Boden of the Oak Ridge National Laboratory for his interest and hard copy weather station climate summaries, John Chase of the Pennysaver and North County News who donated the assistance of his organization through Robert Townsend - art director, for the computer graphics contained, Keith Eggleston of the Northeast Regional Climate Center for monthly station summaries and Storm Data back issues, Wray Runninger of the Purple Mountain Press for his publishing knowledge and Eleanor Arnold for editing the text.

Organizations that have provided material for this book were: the staff of the New York City Department of Environmental Protection - Katonah office who provided a place for me to copy their many years of the Croton Watershed precipitation record, the John C. Hart Memorial Library of Shrub Oak that obtained many references, the Hudson Valley Climate Service for the use of its 20th century monthly climatological files and collection of daily extremes of temperature, rainfall and snowfall, and members of the Hudson Valley Weather Observers for their interest and encouragement. Finally I am grateful to the George Candreva Environmental Center for their years of financial support and commitment to publish this book and its predecessor.

The George Candreva Environmental Center Inc. (Publisher) is a non-profit organization that for over 30 years has been devoted to research and education. Over the years it has funded water quality and local climate studies, and has given scholarships to high school seniors pursuing careers in envrionmental science. its present activity is giving mini-grants to elementary and secondary schools to engage students in environmental education and service projects.

Introduction:

Westchester— A County With A Split Personality

"And just as we came to the Hawthorne intersection driving north on the Saw Mill Parkway the rain changed to snow."

These words are repeatedly related by Westchester parkway travelers in many winters, and they tell the story of a county with a split climate personality.

There is a special significance to this rain-snow transition area which is located near the Westchester waistline. This is the line stretching eight miles westward from the most westerly tip of Connecticut to the Hudson River and across to the southern boundary of Rockland County. South of this line lies three quarters of Westchester's population and greatest urbanization but only one quarter of its land area.

By Westchester standards, south of that line it is warm, north of it, it is cold. When crossing this few miles wide boundary from south to north you are moving from a warmer region to a colder one. South of that line lies the Coastal Climate Division of New York State containing all of New York City and Long Island. North of the line including all of Rockland County is the Hudson Valley Climate Division with its own characteristic colder climate. The climate split of Westchester has long been recognized by the U.S. Weather Service and is shown in the monthly publication Climatological Data - New York which gives the daily weather facts of over 200 weather stations throughout the state. Northern Westchester, Rockland and Putnam comprise the only segments of the New York City metropolitan region that lie within the Hudson Valley climate division making them the coldest suburban orphans of the region.

The temperature differences between the northern and southern parts of Westchester, although recognizable throughout the year, are especially evident in the winter (See Figures 23 & 24). For example, in February, a month that often records the coldest temperature of the year, the normal coldest in the south is three below zero, but ten below zero in the north. At Central Park in New York City it is three degrees above zero.

During the coldest week of the year, the normal daily low temperature in the Scarsdale/Ardsley area is 20°F, but is five degrees lower in the town of Carmel. Average snowfall for the winter season is about five inches greater in the north. (See Figure 31).

Another measure of the north-south difference is through the use of the Heating Degree Day Unit. The Degree Day unit is the basis on which fuel consumption is measured. The greater the number of degree days, the colder the average daily temperatures and the greater the fuel required to heat homes and businesses above 65 degrees. In a normal winter, the south county accumulates 5500 degree day units while the north county registers 6000 units.

In the spring, the average date of the last freeze is April 20 in lower Westchester, but is as late as May 1 in the upper county and Putnam. In the fall, 32 degrees Fahrenheit normally comes on October 20th in the south, but normally arrives ten days earlier in the north. In the settled lower elevation part of Rockland County the last and first freeze dates are April 20 and October 20.

The source of all the temperature and snowfall data comes from nine weather stations. All but one of these are part of the cooperative observer network of stations of the National Weather Service that have taken daily temperature, precipitation and snowfall readings at least 30 years. Those within the Coastal Climate Division are Dobbs Ferry/Ardsley, Westchester Airport and the former Scarsdale with 86 years of daily observations ending in 1990. In the north are the Peekskill and Carmel/Yorktown Heights stations. When temperature monitoring ended in Carmel in 1980 after 92 years its record was merged with that of Yorktown Heights. Formerly in operation were Bedford Hills (82 years of daily observations) and Shrub Oak (19 years). These have all contributed to a detailed 20th century climate portrait of Westchester and Putnam County. The climate profile of Rockland is based on the long-term station record from Suffern and West Point and other unofficial stations with less than 30 years of records.

While the greater number of homes, businesses, traffic and people in the south county do contribute to make a warmer climate regime in that part of Westchester, they are but one factor. The influences of Long Island Sound and the Hudson River are warming during the fall and winter and some cooling in the spring and summer. Higher elevations in northern Westchester and Putnam also act to create a temperature differential by greater cooling.

With the expected increased urbanization of the northern Westchester and Putnam in the 21st century, the temperature differential between northern and southern Westchester should decrease, however the "heat dome effect" of the northerly expanding New York City metropolitan region plus the carbon dioxide produced "Greenhouse Effect" will create a warmer temperature regime for all parts of the region of this study.

Westchester

Westchester's coordinate location on the planet Earth are 40°53' 41°22' N latitude and 73°25' - 73°58' W longitude. It occupies a place in southeastern New York State immediately north of the Bronx, the most northerly of New York City's five boroughs, the only one that is part of the mainland. Westchester County is bounded by the Hudson River (one to three miles wide) on the west, Putnam County on the north, Fairfield County in Connecticut on the east and New York City on the south. These boundaries encompass an area of 450 square miles. The county stretches 33 miles from north to south, 25 miles from east to west at its maximum width along the Putnam County boundary line and 7 miles at its narrowest along the New York City boundary line.

Within the county are three cities, two of which, Yonkers and Mount Vernon located in the south continue the urbanization of New York City, lying immediately to the south. Smaller adjoining towns - New Rochelle, Pelham Manor, Larchmont, Mamaroneck, Rye and Portchester, lie in a belt to the northeast along Long Island Sound up to the Connecticut line. These are connected by Route 1, the original Boston Post Road. Within the north-central part of lower Westchester is the county seat of White Plains surrounded by the communities of Scarsdale, Hartsdale, Tuckahoe, Eastchester and Harrison. In all of the lower county one town blends into another with little to distinguish one from the other. Only a local resident can know the borders of each community. This is typical of the megalopolis pattern in the northeastern United States from the Boston region to that of Washington D.C.

North of the city of Yonkers along the Hudson River lie the river villages of Dobbs Ferry, Irvington, Tarrytown, Sleepy Hollow, Scarborough, Ossining, Croton-on-Hudson and the City of Peekskill. These towns are connected by Route 9, or Broadway, the original Albany Post Road dating back to colonial times and by the Hudson Line Railroad running along the river, serving the many residents commuting into New York City.

In the north central part of the county going north from White Plains are the villages of Valhalla, Hawthorne, Thornwood, Pleasantville, Chappaqua, Mount Kisco, Bedford Hills, Katonah, Goldens Bridge, Purdys, Somers and Croton Falls. The common connector for these communities is the Harlem Railroad that serves as a feeder to southern Westchester and New York City to the south for the increasing number of resident commuters. Nearby Interstate 684 also serves vehicles from most of these villagers.

Other small unincorporated communities, villages and hamlets denoted with 105- postal zip numbers make up the total bulk of human habitation of the county.

The transportation road system carrying the increasing number of vehicles has proved to be quite adequate for north-south traffic. The Bronx River, Saw Mill, Hutchinson and Sprain Parkways have been satisfactory for non-commercial traffic in the south county. The New York State Thruway (Interstate 87), also provides good commercial service in the south. In the north, the Saw Mill and Taconic Parkways together with the newer Interstate 684 have also been satisfactory to date. The latter major road has greatly contributed to the urbanization of the north central part of the county.

East-west roadways have proved to be far less satisfactory. The Cross County Parkway in the south provides adequate non-commercial service. The Cross Westchester Expressway (Interstate 287) which links the Tappan Zee Bridge in the west to Rye in the east is a highly traveled route that during peak commuter time is severely congested. Light industry growth along this route since 1970 has only aggravated the condition. In the north county only Route 35 from Peekskill to Ridgefield, Connecticut completely crosses the county and this road in many places is inadequate for the need.

The population of Westchester County in 1997 has been estimated at 890,000. The 1990 census showed that the number of residents had only increased by 1% over the previous 1980 census. Census figures revealed that in the southern part of the county there was a 5% decrease in population from 1970 to 1980 and a 1% decrease in the period from 1980 to 1990. This percentage decrease has been more than offset by the increase in the north county. The 1980 census shows a 5% increase from the previous 1970 figures and an 8.8% increase over that number in 1990. The 2000 census should show about 900,000. Particularly revealing of the rapid population increase in northern Westchester is the large number of railroad stations on the Hudson and Harlem Lines that have had to add additional parking space areas for commuters.

The trends for the early 21st century that these figures reveal are a static population in the south and a rapid population growth in the north within a few miles east and west of the major roadways. This can only result in a slow but steady urbanization with its attendant average temperature increase.

The effect of the colder temperatures in the higher elevated northern part of Westchester and Putnam is to increase the number of hours of sub-freezing temperatures and the frequency and duration of freezing rain or snow. These conditions combine to significantly increase the time of hazardous driving conditions during the winter months.

Under some weather conditions, the normal decrease of temperature with elevation is reversed. During these times which usually occur on calm, clear nights, the coldest air is found at the lowest elevations. This condition is known as an inversion. One Westchester example of an inversion is that shown in Yorktown where there is a two to four degree temperature difference resulting from the 250 foot elevation difference between the Yorktown Heights weather station (670 feet) and the former station located in Shrub Oak. Under inversion conditions Shrub Oak and other sites at lower elevations will be colder. This will also be the case in bowl shaped valleys.

Normally within northern Westchester and Putnam, temperature differences·between hilltop and lowland are relatively unimportant as large scale agriculture is no longer practiced. However, it can become very significant on days when the temperature is near freezing and precipitation is falling. It is not unusual under these circumstances to have icing and even snow (road and air temperatures below freezing) on the hilltops and north facing slopes, but only wet roads at the lower elevations. Winter drivers should be alert to their local topographical or micro-climate that can often create hazardous conditions.

Rockland has more uniform temperatures in its bowl shaped, settled central region. Significant elevation caused temperature differences are generally restricted to the higher Palisades Interstate Park region where because of the higher irregular terrain the overall climate is much like that of Putnam County. On the east the influence of the Hudson River is paramount for nearly all of the year where it acts to moderate any temperature reduction of the higher Palisade ridges. This region however is subject to greater than normal windy days.

There is little doubt that average temperatures have increased in Rockland since the surge of urbanization beginning in the mid-20th century. A determination of the exact amount is not possible as daily readings of temperature at the only station in the county at Suffern did not begin until 1940. The closest station to Rockland that can provide part of the answer is located about five miles north of Rockland's most northern point at West Point. Twentieth century annual temperatures there show a gradual increase of temperatures of one and one half degrees Fahrenheit through the mid 1950s followed by a cooling of one degree through the 1970s. Since then there has been a rapid increase of nearly two degrees.

TOPOGRAPHY, DRAINAGE and GEOLOGY

WESTCHESTER

In the southern part of Westchester County the terrain is relatively flat with occasional small hills and ridges, few of which are over 300 feet in elevation above sea level. There is a gradual increase in elevation as one proceeds northward from Long Island Sound. This increase is fairly uniform up to five miles from the Sound when other factors such as the hardness of the bedrock produce different land contours. Westward along the Hudson River a north-south ridge stretches from Yonkers to Peekskill with breaks at Tarrytown and Croton-on-Hudson.

Roughly paralleling this ridge is a series of valleys and hills that become increasingly prominent as one goes from south to north. While the hills and ridges in lower Westchester are rarely over 300 feet in elevation, there are about twenty peaks and ridges over 800 feet and four over 900 feet in the north county. This kind of topography causes differences in local climate.

Average elevations in southern Westchester are from 50-150 feet and 350-450 feet in the north. Detailed local maps giving exact elevations are available from the U.S. Geological Survey through the Internet (see address below) and from other sources. The following thirteen 7.5 minute quadrangles cover the county: Yonkers, Mount Vernon, Mamaroneck, Glenville, White Plains, Ossining, Mount Kisco, Pound Ridge, Peach Lake, Croton Falls, Mohegan Lake, Haverstraw and Peekskill,.

Peak elevations greater than 300 feet for Westchester townships are as follows: Bronxville - 330 feet; Yonkers - 390 feet; Harrison - 470 feet; Greenburgh (east of East Irvington) - 543 feet; Mount Pleasant (Sarles Hill) - 710 feet; North Castle (on Bedford boundary line) - 730 feet; Somers (Round Top) - 730 feet; New Castle (Chappaqua Hill) - 730 feet; Bedford (near Guard Hill) - 800 feet; Yorktown (Turkey Mountain) - 830 feet;; Pound Ridge (Bouton Hill) - 860 feet; Cortlandt (Anthony's Nose) - 900 feet; Lewisboro (north of Lake Rippowan) - 910 feet; and North Salem (Bailey Mountain) - 980 feet.

Bodies of water within the county, while numerous are generally small. Except for the reservoirs and lakes created by intentional damming of water, most free flowing water bodies are of the brook, creek or stream variety (See Figure 28). The principal ones are as follows: Saw Mill River - flows approximately 15 miles south from a point about three miles southwest of Mount Kisco (elevation 350 feet) into the Hudson River at Yonkers; Grassy Sprain Brook - flows six miles south before joining the Bronx River in Mount Vernon; Bronx River - flows south from the Kensico Dam outlet twelve miles south to the Bronx and then into the salt water East River, mostly through a narrow strip park alongside the Bronx River Parkway in the south central part of the county; Hutchinson River - flows four miles south into the Bronx and then into Eastchester Bay; Blind Brook - flows seven miles from Westchester Airport to Long Island Sound through Harrison and Rye. The Croton River in northern Westchester is the major body of water and with its attendant watershed encompasses about half the total land in the upper county plus a major part of Putnam County (See Figure B). Retention dams built in the later part of the 19th century by New York City for water supply have formed lakes, namely the Amawalk, Cross River and Titicus reservoirs. The largest dam located three miles northeast of Croton-on-Hudson created a lake that stretches about ten miles northeast to Purdys. These bodies of water with their usual band of surrounding evergreens have a distinct effect on the climate adjacent to the reservoirs (within one mile) particularly in the late fall when the warm water creates fog on many days and also acts to melt any early snow. Peekskill Hollow Brook - flows through Putnam County for six miles and then four miles in northwestern Westchester to the Hudson River at Peekskill.

The above mentioned streams are all subject to flooding for generally short periods of time when 24 hour precipitation is greater than three inches or when one inch or more falls on three or more successive days. Increased acreage covered by buildings and pavement have caused a higher incidence of local flooding due to the increased speed of run-off water. This is especially true of the the Saw Mill River and Blind Brook watersheds (See Floods).

PUTNAM

Gradually higher elevations continue northward into the highlands of Putnam County. While the highlands are intersected in many places by narrow lower elevation valleys, the overall topographical complexion of the county is one of hills and ridges more rugged and elevated than any in Westchester. The county appears to act as a large rectangular high hat on top of Westchester. In the western part of Putnam, geologic faults and fractures in the underlying bedrock running from southwest to northeast determine the drainage pattern of many of the streams.

Elevations greater than 1000 feet are not unusual - all six Putnam townships except in Southeast. By township nearly all of these are PHILIPSTOWN: Fort Defiance Hill - 1000', East Mountain - 1060', Round Hill - 1080'. Bull Hill (ridge) - 1420', Trout Creek region - many areas over 1000', highest 1226', Fahnstock Park - 1000' -1140', Breakneck Ridge - 1000' to 1540' (Scofield Ridge) the highest in the county. PUTNAM VALLEY: Kiah Hill - 1038', Moose Hill 1089', Prospect Hill - 1101', north of Barger Lake - 1016', Fahnstock Park - about ten sites up to 1205'. KENT: California Hill - 1173', Mt Nimham - 1244', Bare Hill - 1055', Sedgewood Club - 1030', Lake Carmel area - 1094', Richardsville area - 1096', Kent Cliffs area - 1060', West of White Pond 1090', South, east, and west of Westminster Lake - 1040', CARMEL: North, south, and southeast of Lake Ossi 1120'. PATTERSON: North of Haviland Hollow and east of Route 22 -1220', northwest corner of township - 1040'. These highest elevations are significant in that they create different precipitation patterns. In the late fall and early spring, lower temperatures will also produce snowfall at these elevations when not seen elsewhere in the county.

The Appalachian Trail crosses the county from the Bear Mountain Bridge through the townships of Philipstown, Putnam Valley, and Kent.

Complete Putnam county elevations are given in the U.S. Geological Survey 7.5' topographical maps of Peekskill, Mohegan Lake, Croton Falls, Peach Lake, West Point, Oscawana Lake, Lake Carmel and Brewster.

The major drainage streams in the county are the Croton River, Peekskill Hollow Brook, Clove Creek, Canopus Creek, Muscoot Creek, Foundry Brook and Horse Pound Brook. Most of these streams have drainage areas of less than ten square miles. The Croton River with its attendant dams form the East Branch, West Branch, Middle Branch and Boyd's Corners Reservoirs, the major water bodies of the county. Together with the other reservoirs in Westchester it provides a significant if not major portion of the water supply to New York City and many Westchester and Putnam communities. Peekskill Hollow Brook drains a major portion of Putnam Valley and smaller parts of Kent and Philipstown and supplies Peekskill with its water supply. It is subject to flooding in times of heavy precipitation.

There are 116 lakes, ponds and reservoirs in the county with a surface area of approximately 28 square miles and just over 237 miles of shoreline. Major lakes besides the New York City reservoirs are Lake Mahopac, Oscawana Lake, Putnam Lake and Lake Carmel.

Nearly all smaller lakes and ponds are the result of the last ice sheet that in its last recession about 17,000 years age blocked the normal drainage by forming dams which have resulted in the numerous smaller bodies of water. By township some of these are: PHILIPSTOWN: Dales Pond, Cat Pond, Nelson Pond, Reeves Pond, Lake Valhalla, Cold Spring Reservoir, Barrett Pond, Beacon Reservoir, Lake Wicopee, and Jordan Pond. PUTNAM VALLEY: Lake Peekskill, Indian Lake, Barger Pond, Bryant Pond, Wiccopee Reservoir, Mud Lake, Clear Lake, Stillwater Pond, State Lake, Canopus Lake, and Roaring Brook Lake. CARMEL: Lake Secor, Kirk Lake, Long Pond, Lake Gilead, Lake Gleneida, Wixon Pond, and Cranberry Pond. KENT: Sagamore Lake, China Pond, Barrett Pond, Pine Pond, White Pond, and Drew

Pond. SOUTHEAST: Peach Lake. PATTERSON: Lost Lake.

With the many vacation homes around these lakes having been converted to year round dwellings, the sewage effluent from their septic systems have caused eutrofication of many of these smaller bodies resulting in an unpleasant algae bloom by mid-summer.

ROCKLAND

The drainage patterns within Rockland have been determined by the bowl-like configuration of the county with the highest elevations to the north and east. Northern branches of the Hackensack River drain much of the eastern county. Three of the largest lakes of the county, DeForest, Congers and Swartwout flow into this river, which then flows about four miles south into the Lake Tappan Reservoir. In the extreme west the Ramapo River drains the southern segment of the Palisades Interstate Park and flows through the county for about five miles near the villages of Sloatsburg, Ramapo, Hillburn and Suffern. Just south of the New Jersey line it is joined by the Mahwah River which flows southwest for nine miles mostly in Ramapo township along the base of the elevated south eastern side of Palisades Interstate Park. The villages adjoining these western small rivers can be subject to flooding as nearby steep slopes during heavy rain events cannot retain the precipitation. North of the Palisades in the Haverstraw, Stony Point, Thiells area, two small streams drain into the Hudson River - Minisceongo which drains Lake Welch about six miles to the west and Cedar Pond Brook which drains Lake Tiaroti in Orange County about seven miles from the Hudson River at Stony Point.

Some of the other smaller lakes that add to the beauty of Rockland are Lake Sebago, Breakneck Pond, Second and Third Reservoirs in Haverstraw Township; Lake Wanosink, Minsi and Pine Meadow Lake in Ramapo Township; Rockland and Lucille Lakes in Clarkstown and Hessian Lake in Stony Point Township.

Topographically Rockland is shaped most like a dust pan. The flat lower elevation central region tips towards the southwest. In this central region elevations are generally about 200 feet above sea level. At Tappan the elevation is as low as 80 feet while at Pomona there are 450 feet elevations. Lowest elevations are along the Haverstraw River. Along the eastern Palisades, escarpment rim elevations rise above 500 feet with the highest peaks in Haverstraw township at High Tor (820') and Little Tor (680'). The highest elevations are located within the Palisades Interstate Park in the northwest part of the county within the townships of Stony Point, Haverstraw and Ramapo. There are at least two dozen peaks or ridges over 1000 feet elevation.

Three peaks over 1200 feet are in RAMAPO township with the highest of these Diamond Mountain

(1240'). The highest peaks in the county are located in STONY POINT township- Rockhouse Mountain (1283') and West Mountain (1257'). Conklin Mountain (1201') is the highest in HAVERSTRAW township. The Appalachian Trail runs a few miles from the Bear Mountain Bridge through northern Stony Point township.

For information on specific site elevations and how to obtain topographical maps, contact the U.S. Geological Survey on the Internet at mapping.usgs.gov/esic/usimage/dealers.html. The 7.5' topographical maps that cover Rockland are Nyack, Haverstraw, Peekskill, Thiells, Popolopen Lake, Park Ridge, and Sloatsburg.

GEOLOGY

The topography of our three counties and their accompanying drainage system is largely determined by the strength and weakness of its underlying bedrock. The different bedrock of Westchester and Putnam are principally metamorphic in character. A metamorphic rock is one that has been changed in structure and composition by folding and twisting forces in the presence of intense heat and pressure taking place miles deep in the earth. These processes were brought about by crustal movements that occurred hundreds of millions of years ago. The resultant varied topography and elevation particularly of northern Westchester and Putnam was caused by erosion of these rocks. These elevation and topography differences create significant local temperature differences. Precipitation differences are also caused by topographic variations.

Most of the bedrock in Westchester is composed of three distinct types of rock that lie in a sequence known as the Manhattan Prong. The oldest of these is known as Fordham gneiss, first named for exposures in the Bronx. This formation makes up a low ridge that extends along the east bank of the Hudson River 1-3 miles wide running from New York City and then swinging northeastward south of the Croton Reservoir and continuing up to the North Salem area. This rock, originally a mix of sands, clays and sediments of volcanic origin now appears as wavy bands of light and dark rock. The time of origin of the Fordham is uncertain but it has been placed at about 1100 million years ago.

The multiple metamorphic processes that transformed this rock into its present form took place well before any visible life had evolved. At some time before 650 million years ago the original Fordham was lifted above sea level long enough for an erosion surface to be created.

Following this erosion period of uncertain duration, earth crustal movements forced the Fordham below sea level on top of which a thin layer of sandstone was deposited followed by a thick bed of carbonate sediments produced by marine invertebrates (shell forming animals). This bed is known as the Inwood Limestone or Marble after its metamorphism, and is dated about 500 million in age (Cambrian Period). It is named after exposures in the Inwood section of Manhattan and appears now as a chalky whitish rock with little or no structure. The bedrock lies in the lowest elevations of the county and makes up many of lake and stream beds such as the Saw Mill River. Streams and lakes over many eons of time have tended to more rapidly erode this body of rock because of its relative softness and solubility. Exposures of this rock can be seen in Elmsford, Croton-on-Hudson, and Yorktown Heights and other low elevation areas.

The third and youngest bedrock of the Manhattan Prong series is the Manhattan formation, a hard rock characterized in many places by shiny bits of mica (Muscovite). Like the Fordham formation it also makes up many of the hills and ridges of the county. The origins of this bedrock are complicated as there are three varieties of this formation. The clear ocean that produced the underlying limestone changed in character about 460 million years ago (Ordovician Period) with the tectonic approach of an island arc such as that of Japan off the Asian coast. Erosion from this volcanic land mass produced dark muds that were deposited on top of the limestone. This continental shelf deposition lasted about 20 million years before the island arc was thrust up against ancient North America. About the same time deep ocean deposits were also accreting onto ancient North America to form the metamorphic Hartland Formation that makes up the present eastern part of the county along Long Island Sound and the Connecticut panhandle. These deposits formed a dark shale and sand sedimentary rock. The subsequent folding and buckling of this continental shelf produced the ancestral Taconic mountains about 440 million years ago during which the three Manhattan beds were stacked up in huge overlapping slices with the lower portion thrust above the youngest. The entire Manhattan formation was then thrust 9 - 15 miles into the earth with the resultant metamorphic transformations of sandstone/ clay into granite, then granite into gneiss, limestone into marble, and shale/slate into schist.

The above formations comprise nearly all of the Westchester County bedrock. The remainder consists of a few small but important pieces.

The northern Westchester-Putnam line in Cortlandt, Yorktown and Somers and most of western Putnam County including Philipstown, Putnam Valley, Carmel, and Kent, consists of Hudson Highlands granite-gneiss complex bedrock. This unit includes the Palisades Interstate Park across the Hudson River in northern Rockland County and contains some of the oldest bedrock of New York State dated from 1000 - 1300 million years in age. In Rockland County the Ramapo fault separates this ancient bedrock from the

THE CROTON WATERSHED

The Croton River watershed is located principally in the northeastern section of Westchester County and eastern half of Putnam County (See Figure B). Within northern Westchester, the watershed basin includes all of the townships of Somers, Bedford, New Castle, and North Salem. Significant segments of Yorktown, Lewisboro, Cortlandt and Pound Ridge are also included. In Putnam County, the entire townships of Patterson, Southeast and major parts of Carmel and Kent are included. Small segments of southeastern Dutchess County and western Fairfield County in Connecticut are also part of the watershed. At present there are about 100,000 people residing within the area.

The bedrock in which the basin lies is known to be part of the Manhattan prong. This geological province consists of a complex suite of changed form sedimentary and igneous rocks that were altered by heat and pressure through plate tectonic crustal movements over 350 million years ago when the original formations were thrust about ten miles deep into the earth.

Precipitation falling into this catchment basin ultimately flows into the ten collecting reservoirs that supply about ten percent of the water supply for New York City. Many Westchester and Putnam communities also rely on all their water supply from the Croton reservoir system.

The largest reservoir, Croton Lake was formed by the Cornell Dam constructed in 1907. Together with the New Croton Aqueduct, they replaced the Old Croton Dam and aqueduct built in 1842. The dam, located about two miles east of Croton-on-Hudson, creates a lake stretching about 16 miles to the northeast, almost to the Putnam County line. This reservoir, located about 30 miles north of New York City covers an area of about 5.6 square miles. Before the dam was built, the Croton River flowed unimpeded to the southwest into the Hudson River. From the end of the 19th and into the early 20th century a network of smaller reservoirs was created by damming up tributaries of the Croton River. In Putnam County, these are Boyd's Corners, East Branch (Sodom), Middle Branch, West Branch (Carmel) and White Pond. In Westchester, besides Croton Lake , they are Amawalk, Cross River, Croton Falls and Titicus.

Daily monitoring of precipitation by the New York City Water Department, presently known as the Department of Environmental Protection began at Croton Lake in 1860 and at Boyd's Corners in 1866. These were followed by West Branch (1888), East Branch (1895), Amawalk and Titicus (1903), Cross River and Croton Falls (1907), Middle Branch and White Pond (1924). The Boyd's Corners and West Branch precipitation record has numerous months missing in the 19th century. The White Pond gauge was terminated in 1983. At the present there are nine gauges in operation, (Figure B), routinely monitored by employees of the DEP. (See Figure 33 and Appendices M - V). The rain gauges are sited for convenience of reading at the reservoir outlets or dams and are at elevations ranging from 210 to 580 feet above sea level.

Differences in annual precipitation are the result of the varied elevations and topographical configuration differences. Average annual precipitation ranges from 44 to 48 inches. There is a uniform variability of annual precipitation centering about a standard deviation of seven inches. Average Annual watershed precipitation totals have ranged from less than 40 inches to over 52 inches (See Figure 27). Average annual differences between the gauges of less than 2.6 inches are not statistically significant. Within the watershed, precipitation of 0.10 inches normally comes on five to eight days during each month of the year. April and May show the greatest number of such days while October has the least.

The water quality of these picturesque reservoirs is presently being threatened by the increasing surge over the past 50 years of residential urbanization surrounding these bodies of water. The population increase in the watershed area has been inexorably accompanied by septic system failures, fertilizer runoff, sewage and pesticide spill, and other noxious human produced chemicals. Unless timely steps are taken to shield the reservoirs through land acquisition of sensitive buffer areas and through rigorous enforcement of city, town and state zoning laws, further deterioration of the water quality will result, requiring drastic and expensive measures to insure water quality. The entire aqueduct, after 90 years of use would also benefit with a new relining.

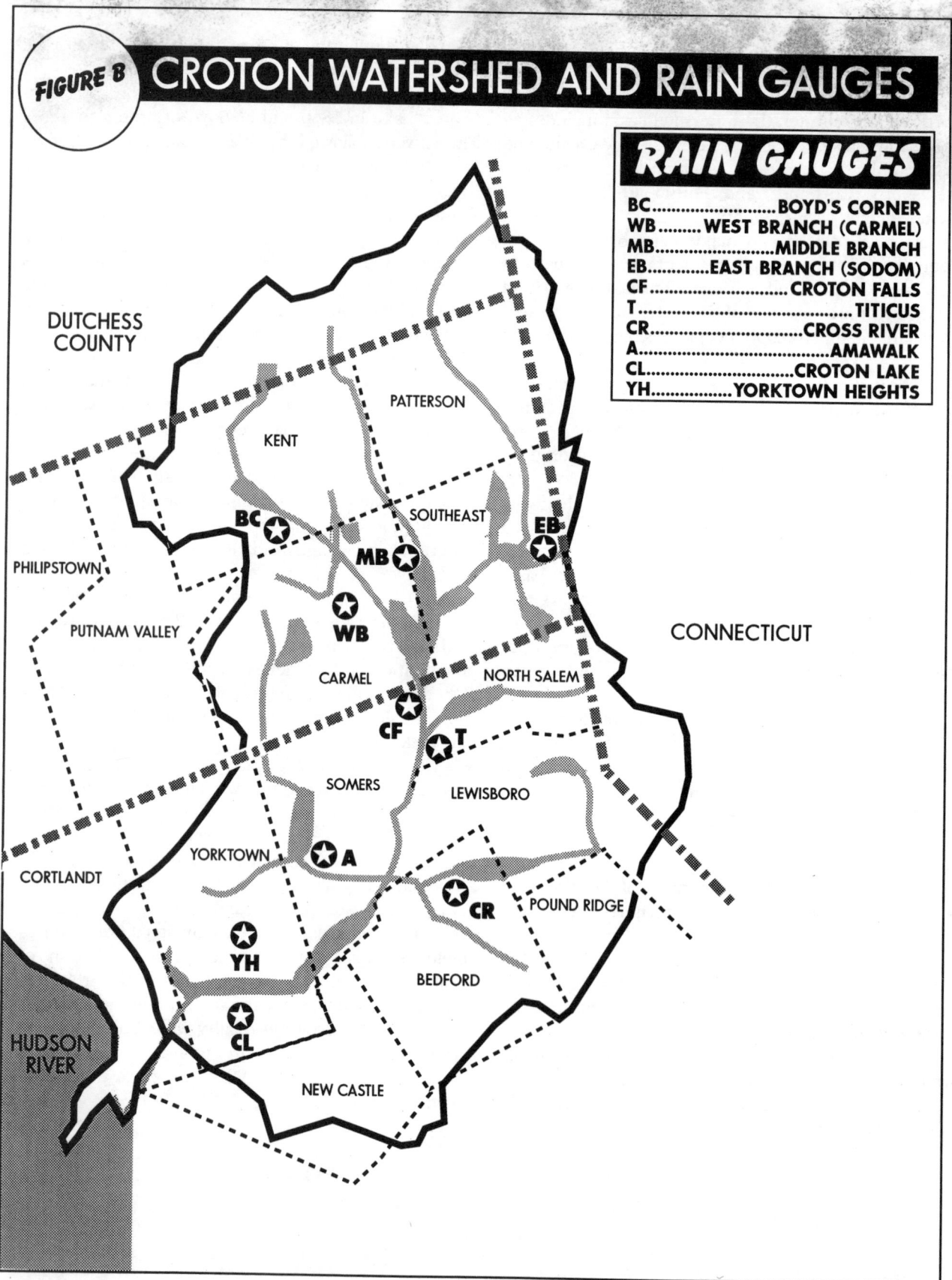

FIGURE 8 CROTON WATERSHED AND RAIN GAUGES

RAIN GAUGES

BC	BOYD'S CORNER
WB	WEST BRANCH (CARMEL)
MB	MIDDLE BRANCH
EB	EAST BRANCH (SODOM)
CF	CROTON FALLS
T	TITICUS
CR	CROSS RIVER
A	AMAWALK
CL	CROTON LAKE
YH	YORKTOWN HEIGHTS

CLIMATE HISTORY
Prehistoric Climate and the Ice Age

A backward view of history in the Hudson valley deals first with human events since the United States was formed, then the colonial era of English dominance, followed by the land grants of the Phillippes and Van Cortlandts , the early Dutch settlers in the lower Hudson Valley, the purchase of Manhattan Island by Peter Minuit, then Hendrick Hudson's trip in his ship Half Moon up the river now bearing his name, and earlier of Verrazano and his discovery of upper New York Bay.

Prehistory before the written word concerns the millennia of time when the many tribes of the Mohican branch of the Delaware nation that occupied our counties, ate oysters and fish from the river and had small scale farms before the European arrival. Prehistory takes us back even further, to the time a few thousand years earlier when the first nomadic hunters arrived following the glacier recession about fifteen thousand years ago. Before these humans all that existed was an unnamed area of land through which a river flowed towards an ocean to the south.

While we know from the earliest colonial writings that our local climate has been essentially the same for the past 500 years, other sources of information are required to determine what it was before then. Within the last century, scientific disciplines of glacial geology, anthropology, paleobotany, fresh and salt water biology and isotopic dating have enabled researchers to obtain an increasingly clearer picture of the prehistoric climate of our counties. From this knowledge we are now able in a rough manner to glean the paleoclimatology of our region.

If we could in some way be transported back in time 50,000 years and see our home counties in a different age, we would view a land that looked and felt like present-day Greenland. It was one of the coldest times of the last ice age. The time is known to glacial geologists as the early Wisconsin period of the Pleistocene era. It was just after the start of the fourth glacial advance and all three of our counties were covered by ice hundreds of feet thick. We would see a region totally forbidding and uninhabitable, not only in our region but for the entire northeast. Northern New Jersey and much of the Midwest also lay buried under this continental ice sheet. A quick imaginary flight would reveal that in the New York City area only small parts of Staten Island and Brooklyn were not ice covered. On the present Long Island, the frontal edge of the ice stretched eastward to Orient and Montauk Points all the way to Cape Cod and beyond.

The ice that covered our counties in this early phase of the Wisconsin Ice Age era (named for classical glacial deposits in Wisconsin) lasted from about 55,000 to 45,000 years ago and is believed to have come from a north-north east direction as is evidenced by gauged grooves in bedrock. A tentative radiocarbon date of 43,800 has been made of organic material from western Long Island indicating that the ice sheet had begun to recede from there just before that time.

Following the recession of this glacial ice from the lower Hudson valley, the climate warmed over a period of about 13,000 years. At about 31,000 years ago pollen analysis from bogs and ponds shows forest vegetation very much like the present. However this climate regime did not last long (geologically speaking). By 28,000 years ago pollen analysis from regional lake bottoms reveals a colder climate with spruce, birch and alder pollen predominating. Other radiocarbon dating about 27,000 years before the present, confirms the return to a cold moist climate regime. This evidence indicates that ice from the north had not reached the local area. However climate conditions did exist here for a few thousand years that were cold and wet enough for the growth of the spreading continental ice sheet to reach its maximum extent. This period is believed to have taken a few thousand years. Locally, this marked the start here of the late Wisconsin glaciation. A tundra-like environment existed locally for about 2000 years before the ice sheet arrived. A dating of spruce wood at 23,000 years ago indicates a rough arrival date of the ice sheet to our two counties of about 24,000 years ago. The ice that returned to the area obliterated nearly all evidence of earlier glaciation. Because of this we are dependent on an analysis of Long Island glacial deposits pushed by the ice past the edge of the last ice margin or terminal moraine to give us an idea of what conditions were immediately before the glacier arrived.

Recent studies have shown that the time span from temperate to arctic cold climate conditions need not be thousands of years but could take place over hundreds of years or even less. The major trigger mechanisms starting an ice age are currently believed to be the earth's path around the sun (eccentricity of orbit), tilt of the earth's axis, and wobble or precession of its axis. These inherent earth characteristics plus the present configuration and elevation of the continents on the surface of the earth and changing ocean currents have created climate conditions in which periodic coldness has been a regular event for the last four million years and should continue well into the future.

In any case, at about 24,000 years ago the advancing ice, this time from the north-north west was covering our three counties and advancing southward. At the time it reached its most southerly extent on present Long Island about 21,000 years before the present, there was no Long Island Sound. Sea levels had retreated a good 300 feet vertically since the ice covering much of North America and Europe had resulted in a significant lowering of sea level. The Atlantic Ocean shoreline was about 100 miles south of its present location. Before ice covered it, Long Island Sound was a bowl shaped valley with a small river flowing eastward past the Orient Point region. The advancing ice crossed this valley and finally stopped moving southward along a line roughly parallel to the present north shore of Long Island. At this point in time the melting of the ice each summer was equal to the ice advance resulting in a buildup of glacial rubble or till that the ice was depositing at its southern edge. The material of this glacial debris forms the terminal moraine that makes up the present two fins of the eastern part of Long Island.

Within Westchester, Rockland and Putnam during the period of maximum advance, the ice again attained a depth in many places hundreds of feet deep and again scraped bedrock bare at the higher elevations. These scrapes or striations mark the generally north-south ice movement. The ice also carried south many boulder sized rocks called erratics, some of which were moved hundreds of miles, plucked from their bedrock origin and deposited in some cases on the tops of hills with a totally different bedrock makeup.

Glacial ice recession began some time earlier than 19,000 years ago when the earth's orbital and orientation positions had changed to a more warming configuration. The initial stages of melting began with a downwasting (melting in place) of ice when a further supply was no longer coming from the north. This downwasting of stagnant ice first exposed most of the higher elevations. By about 18,000 years ago Long Island is believed to have been ice free.

Because of the weight of the ice, the land underneath had been depressed, leaving unglaciated land to the south relatively elevated. This resulted in a huge lake abutting the retreating ice. Within the Hudson River basin the thick tongue of ice that had occupied the present river bed melted, and back up water formed a long elongated glacial lake called Lake Hudson extending beyond Haverstraw and up to 80 feet higher that the present river level. An analysis of yearly clay deposits in this area shows that the lake remained for over 1500 years. An estimate of the average glacial ice retreat at that time was about 100 feet each year. It is believed that it took a good two thousand years for the ice to leave Westchester and

Rockland. As the ice front receded to the north an elongated freshwater lake (Lake Albany) persisted to about 13,000 years ago. The ice retreat was an uneven one, as is indicated by remains of a moraine at Croton Point where the ice front must have stabilized long enough to build up a mass of till. At about the same time, just south of the ice front, the present Croton River was depositing large amounts of eroded sand and gravel carried by melting ice water from most of northern Westchester and eastern Putnam County. The remains of both the rock rubble moraine and the sand and gravel delta form the present Croton Point peninsula. Some glacial geologists believe that but for the protective rubble-till moraine, Croton Point would have been eroded long ago by currents in the Hudson River. This moraine could have been put in place between about 18,000 years ago.

By about 17,000 years ago Westchester and Rockland were clear of ice. The Hudson Highland parts of Putnam may have contained a few ice pockets on north facing slopes at that time. A bleak ice scared landscape was revealed at this time with characteristic tundra-like vegetation. Glacial till, sand and gravel blocked many stream beds with many large lakes resulting, especially in the north. All of the natural lakes of Putnam and northern Westchester are glacial in origin. Some of these are Peach Lake, Waccabuc, Mohansic, Mohegan and Kitchawan.

The vegetation that grew in the tundra pre and post glacial period at lower elevations near lakes, as shown by lake bottom pollen was initially non arboreal with moss, sedge, low grasses and shrubs, but as the climate gradually warmed to a boreal temperature regime, birch, willow and spruce pollen made their appearance. July average temperatures in such an environment were more typical of April climate (50 degrees Fahrenheit) in our two counties. In summer, wooly mammoth or mastadon and caribou could be seen feeding on the small low vegetation growing between the rocks and boulders left by the melting ice. Archeological investigations have paleo-indian activity first present within a few thousand years of this time. During this climate stage up to 13,000 years ago there were two or three minor ice readvances, and while none of these even came close to Putnam County they did continue the tundra and forest-tundra climate regime with trees no higher than eight feet as in present day northern Canada., the northern limit of spruce.

The southern edge of the forest-tundra has an average July temperature of 55 - 60 degrees. This is typical of early May in our region. After 13,000 years ago, the amount of spruce, birch and willow pollen increased to produce a boreal forest with spruce, birch, fir, and some pine. The southern limit of this forest type in present day Canada shows a July average temperature of 60 - 65 degrees, typical of our area in late May. The above two climate regimes lasted for about 3000 years. At about 12,000 years before the present, some oak pollen appeared in southern Connecticut bogs. Ice retreated from New York State about 12,500 years ago and from Canada 10,000 years ago. The Hudson River assumed its present character about 11,500 years ago when its supply of ice meltwater ended. At the latter time a distinctly warmer and drier period began with pine becoming the predominant tree type. This was followed by the mixed evergreen-hardwood forest that prevails over most of present day northern New England.

By 7000 years ago the waters of Long Island Sound had risen to within 50 feet of the present shoreline and the present deciduous forest made its appearance locally. Pollen studies show that there have been variations in temperature and moisture since 6000 years ago with a slightly warmer than present climate five to eight thousand years ago and a cooler period about one thousand years ago.

Most of the 20th century has experienced significant worldwide reduction in glacier size following small fluctuating glacier expansion from 1500 to 1850. Except for dips in average temperature in the first, sixth and seventh decades of the 20th century, there has been a two degree Fahrenheit increase for the century as a whole (see figure 19). This increase has been greatest in the last two decades and is attributed by nearly all climatologists to greater human produced greenhouse gases.

This short sketch of prehistoric climate shows that for less than 10,000 years our lower Hudson valley has been an inhospitable place to live, more typical of present day northern Canada.

THE OLDEST WEATHER OBSERVATIONS

While even the earliest of the European settlers took note of the vagaries of American weather on the east coast, there were no continuous numerical observations until the latter part of the 18th century when the first crude weather instruments were sent to the American colonists by European instrument fabricators. In the 1640s, the chaplain of a Swedish military expedition, John Campanius Holm kept a daily journal of the weather at what is now Wilmington, Delaware. His records, the earliest known, were largely descriptive. Before the arrival of the thermometer, invented in the early 1700s, the determination of temperature was a very subjective judgement. Extreme heat would be noted by its effect on crops, live stock and people. Coldness was noted in diaries in terms of ice thickness on local bodies of water, the earliest or latest frost of the season and its effect on crops, animals

and travel. These qualitative observations, while useful could not give any objective comparison of climate from one year to the next, or from one month of one year to the same month of a different year. An example of this kind of weather reporting is taken from "The Journal of Reverand Silas Constant" in Yorktown over 200 years ago:

January 1, 1784 - Great snow on the earth.

April 14, 1784 - Springlike weather, planted peas.

March 29, 1785 - Cloudy, snow about 16 inches deep in the woods; and blue birds return April 19, 1785 - Snow and hail 3 inches deep.

April 21, 1794 - Very dry; peach trees blossomed; may the Lord send rain.

December 31, 1794 - There has not been any sledding this season, snow one inch. It has been a warm season not one hard storm, nor very cold day. So ends the year. God's name be praised for all his mercies.

January 28, 1795 - Warm day

January 29, 1795 - Hard rain and wind; roof of loom shop blew off:

February 1, 1795 - Two inches of snow.

May 18, 1797 - Apple trees in bloom.

February 18, 1801 - Rainy day; snow gone so as to spoil sleighing; muddy riding.

March 6, 1801 - 8 inches snow.

August 3, 1801 - Cool morning; some frost in some places.

The first continuous instrumental weather observations were taken at a few of the oldest educational institutions located in the populated centers of the original colonies. Harvard in Boston and Yale at New Haven were recording daily temperatures from the mid 1700s, thus providing some data which forms the basis of determining the climatic normals and variability of that time. After the American Revolution, nearly all of the major cities had thermometers and were recording temperature.

Within Westchester continuous daily weather observations did not begin until about 80 years later. In the rural sparsely populated region such as Westchester in those times, the earliest weather observations of an ongoing nature were of rainfall. The oldest published records were of measurements taken at North Salem in 1829 and Mount Pleasant in 1831 by academies sponsored by the New York State Regents. (See Discontinued Stations). Little is known regarding the type, quality and accuracy of these early thermometers and rain gauges.

Following these, other precipitation measuring stations were set up. White Plains began in 1853 and later temperature was recorded there beginning in 1862. In 1860, Tarrytown and the original Croton dam in 1860 started measuring precipitation, followed by Yonkers in 1878, and Kensico Reservoir in 1884. Only two of these 19th century precipitation stations (Croton Lake and Kensico) have maintained unbroken records continuing to the present. They are serviced by the New York City Department of Water Resources and are located within the Croton and Bronx River watersheds which provide part of the city's and Westchester's water supply. With the length of their record they are invaluable as benchmark stations in determining long-term averages, trends, periodicities, and for comparison studies within and outside the county (See Appendices H, P, R).

Since 1900 there are 20 sites within Westchester that maintain rain gauges or have done so in the past. An additional six stations have in the past 50 years at one time or another monitored precipitation on an hourly basis through the use of automatic equipment. Daily temperature readings began at Carmel in 1888 and Bedford Hills in 1896.

The standard rain gauge used at the present time by the cooperative stations of the U.S. Weather Service throughout the country is the eight inch diameter copper cylinder with its inner copper tube and funnel that can measure amounts as small as one one-hundreth of an inch. Measurements are normally taken once a day.

There are at present weather stations that record temperature daily and about 17 stations that monitor precipitation. Twelve of these latter are maintained by the New York City Department of Water Resources for the Croton and Bronx River watersheds at their dam sites. The others are serviced by different municipalities within the county. Many volunteers and amateur weather buffs affiliated with TV networks also monitor daily temperature and precipitation.

HISTORICAL WINTER EVENTS

In his monumentally researched two volume work "Early American Winters," America's foremost climate historian, David Ludlam roamed through diaries, journals, newspapers and other records of the 17th, 18th and 19th centuries. In his searches of winter weather events, much of the information relating to cold, snow and ice concerns the major eastern seaboard cities. Our interest concerns itself with New York City because of its proximity to Westchester County.

References regarding extreme cold for a day, week, month or season for New York City would apply to Westchester and Rockland as well. Similarly, references to Hudson River ice along the New York City banks would certainly hold true for that part of the Hudson River adjoining both counties and for points further north. Concerning severe storms and snow depths, there is less certainty, since coastal storms can be much more severe than inland in regard to wind speed and its damage. Estimated snowfall amounts for Westchester based on New York City figures also need to be carefully examined for the path of the storm wind direction if available and particularly for temperature.

New York City before the 19th century nestled in the lower part of Manhattan island without the network of suburban weather observers that our late 20th century is accustomed to. With delays in transportation a common occurrence in the winters of those times, and few newspapers reporting such events, little of what was happening in Westchester and Putnam weather wise or otherwise was mentioned in the New York City newspapers. The keeping of diaries was also not common in an adult population where fewer than half the adults were able to read.

One of the earliest reports of unusual winter weather in New York City was a cold wave preceded by a northwest gale that grounded a ship near Sandy Hook. In the extreme cold and wind, 132 passengers froze to death before assistance arrived. The Hudson River froze over completely and continued "fast" for several days after this tragedy on December 30, 1705.

In a severe winter of 1740-41, heavy snow was reported in New York City at the end of December followed by cold so extreme that the ink in a pen was freezing while the author was attempting to write. In that winter the Hudson River was closed to navigation from December 28 to January 21 and during the second and third weeks of February 1741. North of Westchester at Esopus the ice was thick enough to permit loaded teams to cross the river as late as April 1. A report from Stratford, Connecticut stated that Long Island Sound there was frozen over "three leagues across so that people ride every day thence to Long Island." The narrower section of the Sound opposite Westchester would have also been frozen over.

The winter of 1764-65 was the snowiest since the one cited above. On December 30, 1764 "the mercury dropped to zero in New York City and after three days of such conditions the river and harbor became clogged with ice." The upper and lower bays were so jammed with ice floes that small boats could not pass through. Large ships were still detained at their docks as late as January 23rd. Newspaper accounts mention zero temperatures or below for over two straight days (January 26-28, 1765). The Hudson during this latter period again froze over almost solid to the Jersey shore opposite Manhattan Island and was certainly frozen opposite the Westchester shore.

The winter of 1765-66 was one of four winters in a century in which the Hudson River was frozen over at Paulus Hook (lower Manhattan to Jersey City).

On May 4, 1774 snow fell from New York City to Poughkeepsie~with an estimated 2 - 4 inches in Westchester.

"The Hard Winter" of 1779-80 ranks as probably the most severe in American history in all parts of the eastern United States. Winter began with eight inches of snow falling on November 26th and December 5, 1779. The severity of cold and snow restricted military activity to a minimum. In that year, as with most of the years during the American Revolution, British troops

HARPERS WEEKLY: FEBRUARY 1, 1879

FIGURE 1: ICE YACHTING ON THE HUDSON

FIGURE 2: ICE YACHTING ON THE HUDSON   **HARPERS WEEKLY: FEBRUARY 1, 1879**

occupied New York City. The American forces were encamped that winter in Morristown, New Jersey. Following these introductory snowstorms another major fall of 10-17 inches came on December 18th, Westchester Estimate- (WE) . Following this, three severe northeasters came within a ten day period. Storm 1 on December 28th accompanied by high winds deposited 12-18 inches (WE). Storm 2 on January 2, 1780, again with very strong winds, deposited about 12 inches (WE). The third storm January 5-7, 1780 brought high winds but only intermittent snow. The principal effect of this storm was to cause drifting of the previous snowfalls. Total snow depths of this period are estimated to be three to four feet in the New York City area.

In January 1780 about eight days during the month are estimated to have had temperatures of zero or below and a greater number in Westchester, with temperatures never rising to 32 degrees. Six of the last seven days of January had below zero minimums with the coldest (-20°F) on the 19th (WE). New York City harbor pedestrians were able to walk from Manhattan to Staten Island, a distance of five miles. The British were able to move large cannon across the ice to reinforce their positions on Staten Island that had been subject to cross-the-ice raids from General Washington's outposts in New Jersey. The solid ice-locked harbor persisted from December 20th to February 20, 1780.

Needless to say, the Hudson River was ice bound for an even longer period opposite Westchester. By January 14, 1780, the East River and western Long Island Sound could be crossed on foot for several days. Some Hessian mercenary soldiers deserted their regiments by this route. It can be surmised that the area from western Long Island Sound near the East River (Triboro Bridge) northeastward 25 miles almost to the Stamford area was frozen over from shore to shore. This includes the twelve mile section of Westchester shoreline on the Sound (WE).

It is believed by climate historians that January 1780 along with January 1857 jointly hold the dubious distinction of being the coldest months in the northeast since Europeans first arrived. The winter cold of 1779-80 persisted to February 11, with 6 - 10 inches of snow on February 8, when the first thaw occurred in over eight weeks. From then on the snow gradually melted, interspersed with additional 4-8 inch amounts falling on the 16th and 31st of March (WE).

Other single day winter events of note were:
January 23, 1781 - 9- 12 inches of snow
January 29, 1782, 15 - 20 below zero in the north county (WE).

Another long, hard winter occurred in 1783-84, the year that ended the American Revolution. Severe near zero and below cold from February 10-17 closed the New York City harbor with the Narrows (the site of the present Verrazano bridge) choked with ice for ten days. Another cold spell came late that month to insure that February 1784 will rank as one of the ten coldest months of the last 250 years.

The winter season of 1791-92 featured snow in northern New Jersey on October 17-19, 1791 (up to three inches) and in all likelihood in northern Westchester as well. In January 1792, the New York City Observer reported temperatures below 30 degrees from the 7th to the 30th of the month. The coldest of that period came on the 23rd when five below zero was reported.

The start of winter in 1798 came with the famous "Long Storm" of November 19-21. Starting as rain the storm culminated in 12- 18 inches of snow in New York City. The snowstorm is accorded the distinction of the heaviest November storm in the recorded weather history of the coastal northeast.

Significant 19th century winter events were as follows:
May 8, 1803 - a late touch of winter gave 2-6 inches of snow (WE).
February 23rd to March 2, 1804 - snows during this period left one to two feet of snow on the ground (WE).
October 9, 1804, - 6-12 inches of snow fell on the higher elevations of the county (WE) and most likely more in Putnam. During the following winter months, January had 4-5 feet of snow (WE), (the 20th century's greatest monthly total for a Westchester January is about three feet).
January 1-23, 1805 - There were only two to three days with above freezing temperatures at noon during this period (WE). The Hudson River was frozen over opposite Hoboken on January 23rd.
April 11, 1807 - 6-12 inches of snow fell in a gale force windstorm (WE).
January 19, 1810 - known as "Cold Friday" started four successive days of zero to 10 below temperatures.
December 23, 1811 - The pre-Christmas storm with gale winds and near zero temperatures left many ships foundered or aground in Long Island Sound. 12 inches of snow was deposited in most of the county (WE).
January 16-22, 1812 - Five of these days had below zero temperatures (WE).
May 3-4, 1812 - 4-8 inches of snow fell (WE).
November 11, 1820 - Winter began early when 6-8 inches of snow fell (WE). This early onset of winter froze the upper Hudson River at Coxsackie on November 13th. The river was blocked by ice for ten days. In January 1821 at New York City the Hudson River was frozen over during the last week of that month. Thousands were able to cross on foot to and from Jersey City. The upper bay was mostly frozen from Manhattan to Staten Island. Temperatures were below zero (in the minus teens) for most of Westchester on

January 24,25, 1821 (WE).

March 30, 1823, 6- 10 inches of snow fell in the south county (WE).

January 15, 1831 - a slow moving "northeaster" deposited 1-1.5 feet of snow in the south county (WE).

December 1831 - the coldest December of record, (about 15 degrees below normal) had below freezing temperatures on all but two days of the month (WE).

May 16, 1834 - Light snow and ice on ponds were reported in northeastern Westchester with temperatures between 23 and 29 degrees.

January 4-10, 1835 - A cold week with below zero temperatures was reported (WE). The standard thermometer of the Regents Academy system reported 31 below zero at sunrise at North Salem on the 4th for the coldest recorded Westchester temperature. On that day Poughkeepsie reported 35 below zero.

The winter of 1835-36 was the outstanding cold season of the first half of the 19th century. The early freeze of the last week of November held steady for the area until early April 1836. Snow of an indeterminate depth fell on the county on the 23rd of November.

December 16, 1835 - 15-20 below zero was reported (WE). The ground was snow covered after the first week of January for over nine weeks. Three major storms occurred in January: on the 9-10th - 1.5 - 2.5 feet; (WE); on the 24-25th - 6 inches (WE), left 3.5 to 4 feet (WE) of snow in the county that month.

February 5, 1836 - reported 10-15 degrees below zero (WE). The Hudson and East Rivers froze over on February 6th as hundreds crossed over the ice at all hours. A Long Island Sound ice barrier at Throgs Neck remained until March 9. Lower Hudson River navigation reopened on March 24th when a steamboat arrived from Sing Sing. The first northbound boats reached Poughkeepsie on April 5th.

December 27,28, 1839, 2-2.5 feet of snow fell in the north county (WE).

April 12 1841, about 1-1.5 feet of snow fell in the south county (WE).

October 23, 1843, snow was reported at North Salem.

January 20-24 1852 - The East River in New York City could be crossed on foot with temperatures as low as eight below zero recorded there.

January 5, 1855, 1 - 1.5 feet of snow (WE) permitted sleighing for eight weeks.

February 5, 1855 - White Plains had below zero for 24 hours.

In the snowy winter of 1855-56, 4 - 8 inches of snow fell on December 28,29 (WE). Below freezing temperatures caused the snow to persist. The Throgs Neck area of Long Island Sound was frozen over from January 25th to February 27th and during this period the East River in New York City could be crossed on foot. During this period, Peekskill's Highland Eagle weekly newspaper reported on February 10 that "the thermometer was 12 below zero on Tuesday and Wednesday of this past week. Snow commenced falling on Wednesday and continued descending until Friday afternoon when it had attained a depth of 12 to 15 inches."

December 24, 1856 - A coastal storm laid down about a foot of snow on the county, setting the stage for the bitter and coldest January of 1857. Below zero temperatures for 24 continuous hours "zero day" took place on January 18, and on the 23rd in the north county (WE). The Hudson River froze over solidly as far south as Yonkers. During the week of the 18th the Times observed "Hundreds of both sexes availed themselves of this novel mode of crossing, thereby defrauding the Ferry Company of a considerable number of pennies." The thickness of the ice varied from one to three feet, and a floe was brought up against a shelf of thicker ice in the East River on an incoming tide. Needless to say, it presented a great temptation for the adventuresome as hundreds rushed to the wharves to enjoy the pleasure and dangers of crossing the river on an ice bridge. One account described the scene: "Not gentlemen alone, but Ladies - with and without crinolines, youths with and without protectors, representatives of all classes but the sensible." Western Long Island Sound was closed for one month to ship traffic after February 18th. Up to one foot of snow fell in the south county during the great cold storm of January 18,19 when the temperature never rose above zero (WE). Peekskill's Highland Eagle reported "that the wind blown snow lay in windrows along stone walls and fences or filled up roads and cuts up to a depth of 15 feet closing up all avenues of public transportation." The town was blockaded for two days after which farmers with the aid of oxen were able to open the road to Mohegan Lake and Shrub Oak.

January 10, 1859, A "zero day" was recorded at White Plains with a sunrise reading of 13 below zero; 10 below zero at 2 PM and 15 below zero at 9 PM.

October 26, 1859, Snow in the New York area showed 1 -3 inches (WE).

February 8, 1861, a 50 degree drop in temperature occurred in 12 hours from 40 degrees to about 10 below zero (WE). On May 4, 1861 snow was reported in New York City.

January 8, 1866, 15-20 below zero was reported (WE).

January 1867 - About 20 inches of snow fell in the county. February 1867 - About 15 inches of snow fell during the month (WE).

March 3, 1867 - Below zero temperatures were noted countywide (WE).

March 21, 1867 - 12-15 inches of snow was measured.

In the snowy winter of 1867-68 over 80 inches of snow fell in the county (WE). This estimate is based on the same amount that fell in New York City.

December 12,13 1867, one foot of snow fell (WE).

January 9, 1875, six below zero low temperature was reported in New York City.

February 1885 - Early 20th century Weather Bureau records note this month to be the coldest February.

March 12,13 1888, - Known as "The Blizzard of 88" this famous unexpected storm has had books written about it. Very little has been reported of its impact on Westchester. The basic statistics of the storm are well documented. Maximum wind speeds were from 30 to 50 miles per hour on the 13th. Total snow amounts for local sites estimated because of drifting were: 23 inches at New Rochelle, 24 inches at Mamaroneck, 24 inches at Tarrytown, 26 inches at Peekskill, 30 inches at Carmel, 32 inches at White Plains, 36 inches at Croton Falls, 36 inches at Mount Vernon, 36 inches at Boyd's Corners and 48 inches at Cold Spring. Coldest temperatures of the storm on the 12th ranged from five degrees in the north to ten degrees in the south.

A few stranded Westchester commuter stories are worth repeating. On March 12th, the Spuyten Duyvil railroad cut, 150 feet deep and 500 feet long at the top of Manhattan Island became so heavily drifted so that no trains could get through. The morning local into the city from Croton hit a mountainous drift and went no further. The Peekskill local and eight following trains nearly a mile in length were stalled there for nearly three days. At Mount Vernon, thousands of stranded commuters took refuge in the train station. The owner of the only restaurant in town had just filed a bankruptcy petition. The price of sandwiches suddenly jumped to five dollars each. The hungry travelers snapped up this only food available. An estimated 6000 sandwiches were served. Two days later the bankruptcy papers were torn up.

February 12 -13, 1899 This major storm, while depositing about six inches less snow than the 1888 blizzard had far lower temperatures. Peekskill's Highland Democrat weekly newspaper reported two days of blizzard conditions with high velocity winds and falling snow after a week of zero temperatures. No mail and no trains, high drifts blocked highways and business was suspended.

Before the 20th century era of iron hulled boats that could break though the ice, the Hudson River was the scene of ice boat races in many winters (see Figures 1, 2).

HISTORICAL WINTER STORMS

"There is nothing quite like the promise and anticipation of a good snowstorm. It makes Christmas pale, birthdays insignificant, and is rivaled by only by Election Day for the joy of anxious hope"

...... Source unknown

18th Century

February 27 - March 7, "The Great Snow of 1717." A series of four snowstorms, two relatively minor and two major left depths in excess of five to seven feet with drifts about 40 feet.

March 24,1765, two to three feet of snow fell in many places from Pennsylvania to Massachusetts.

December 26, 1778, "The Hessian Storm" Named for the troops occupying Rhode Island during the American Revolution, this was a severe blizzard with heavy snow, high winds and bitter cold that struck from Pennsylvania to New England with drifts reported up to 16 feet.

December 28, 1779 - January 7, 1780, three storms during one of the coldest winters of the past three centuries produced deep snows. In Westchester the first resulted in about fifteen inches. The second was a violent snowstorm (depth not determined) with extremely high tides. The third was mainly in New England. Total snow depths from Pennsylvania to New England ranged from two to four feet.

December 4-10, 1786, "The Great Snow," A succession of three crippling snowstorms came during this period from Pennsylvania to New England with total depth between two and four feet.

November 19-21, 1798, "The Long Storm." This was the heaviest November snowstorm of the coastal Maryland to Maine with eighteen inches reported in New York City.

19th Century

January 26-28,1805, snow fell continuously for 48 hours in New York City, where a two foot depth was reported.

December 23, 24, 1811, temperatures during this period fell from well above freezing to near zero as blizzard conditions prevailed with a foot of snow deposited in New York City.

January 5-7, 1821, an extensive snowstorm spread from Virginia to southern New England leaving fourteen inches of snow in New York City

April 17, 1821, up to three inches of snow was measured in New York City. Amounts to the north are uncertain.

January 14-16, 1831, up to that year this was the heaviest snowfall over the greatest area, west to Ohio and south to North Carolina. In New York City fifteen to twenty inches was measured.

January 8-10, 1836, this storm buried areas from Philadelphia to western New England with fifteen to eighteen inches of snow deposited in New York City.

December 27, 28, 1839, approximately two feet of snow fell in Northern Westchester and Putnam.

April 12, 1841, twelve to 18 inches of snow fell in the New York City area, from a northeaster storm that ranged from Philadelphia to Cape Cod.

March 16, 17, 1843, this great storm left heavy snow from Washington to Portland. In New York City it was reported as the most violent storm of the season leaving twelve inches of snow.

January 5, 1856, fifteen to 18 inches of snow in the New York City area came from a major coastal storm. Westchester amounts are uncertain.

January 18, 19, 1857, "The Cold Storm." Blizzard conditions (high winds, heavy snow and near zero temperatures) from North Carolina to Maine with a foot of snow in New York City (see early winters).

March 11-14, 1888, "Blizzard of 88," In this historic storm New York City was particularly hard hit, with widespread destruction of shipping and communications. The storm generated snow amounts of two to four feet depth with drifts many time greater (See Early Winters).

November 26,27, 1898, This early in the season storm deposited ten inches of snow in New York City.

February 12-14, 1899, "Blizzard of 99," This storm formed along the edge of one of the greatest outbreaks of Arctic air ever experienced in central and eastern United States. Snow fell from Florida to Maine with amounts of ten to twenty inches common, from the Carolinas northward with severe impact in the lower Hudson Valley (See Early Winters).

20th Century

March 1, 2, 1914, near hurricane force winds and slightly below freezing temperatures in both counties produced just over one foot of snow in this intense storm. Some newspaper reports had this storm as the worst since the Blizzard of 88.

April 3, 4, 1915, this spring storm produced ten to sixteen inches of snow in our region.

February 4-7, 1920, fifteen to twenty inches of snow fell in the New York City area stalling traffic for weeks.

February 19, 20, 1934, during this coldest February on record, this storm produced blizzard conditions and left about twenty inches in southern Westchester and a lesser amount to the north.

January 22-24, 1935, this widespread storm left about one foot of snow in our area.

December 26, 27, 1947, in this heaviest snowstorm of record, most of the snow came within a

12 hour period. At White Plains, six inches fell in one hour, with twelve inches in a six hour period.

Within our region from 25 to 30 inches was measured.

November 25, 1950, "Wind Storm" with sustained wind velocities of 50 - 60 miles per hour struck the entire New York City area with peak gusts between 75 and 94 mph. These winds caused extensive damage to power and telephone lines and roofs, besides uprooting many trees. Two to three inches of rainfall was measured at four Westchester rain gauges.

March 19, 20, 1956, over a foot of snow covered much of Westchester and Putnam with Dobbs Ferry measuring nineteen inches. In the New York City metropolitan area thousands of autos were stranded. Twenty deaths due to over-exertion and heart failure were reported.

February 14-17, 1958, this was one of three storms that affected New York State that month in one of the snowiest winters of the previous half century. Between one and one and one half feet of snow fell in Westchester with fourteen inches at Shrub Oak and seventeen inches at Dobbs Ferry.

March 18-21, 1958, this storm, with relatively high temperatures produced the same snowfall amounts in our area as had the storm of the previous month. Surprisingly both Dobbs Ferry and Shrub Oak also had the same amounts. The month had three times the normal amount for March.

March 3-5, 1960, this storm, following the classic path up the east coast, produced eighteen to twenty seven inches as measured at Dobbs Ferry (the greatest amount), Scarsdale and Shrub Oak.

December 12, 13, 1960, heavy snows from Virginia to Maine came from this, the first of three major storms in the 1960-61 winter season. Locally about eighteen inches was measured at Shrub Oak, Scarsdale and Dobbs Ferry. The storm had gale winds and temperatures in the teens. In New York City, 19,000 workmen were engaged in snow removal.

January 19, 20, 1961, sixteen to eighteen inches of snow fell at the three reporting U.S. Weather Service Cooperative Stations in Westchester. The storm effect was made more severe by gale winds in excess of 50 miles per hour and much blowing and drifting snow with temperatures as low as the single digits. Communication and transportation channels were severely affected.

February 3-5, 1961, this third major storm of the winter came after a prolonged cold spell recording many below zero lows. After the previous storms, this resulted in near record snow cover from the unmelted falls of the two previous months. Local reporting weather stations measured 22 inches at Dobbs Ferry, 17 inches at Shrub Oak and 16 inches at Scarsdale.

February 6, 7, 1967, sixteen inches of snow was deposited in all parts of Westchester, Rockland and Putnam in this two day coastal storm that paralyzed the region for at least two days.

February 9, 10, 1969, this Hudson Valley and New England poorly predicted storm produced snowfall amounts up to two feet. Within New York and Northern New Jersey, Westchester received the greatest total, with Scarsdale measuring that amount. Sustained wind speeds of 25 miles per hour with gusts over 40 mph were recorded on both days. Surface and air travel did not return to normal till the 13th. The New York Thruway was closed for twelve hours, the first time in its history. More than 1000 cars were stranded at the Tappan Zee Bridge.

February 6, 7, 1978, twelve to sixteen inches blanketed the two counties with the greater amount to the south. Many people in the New York City area were stranded on roads as they were going to work during the rush hour.

April 6, 1982, this unusual late-season storm produced near-blizzard conditions over much of Pennsylvania, New York and New England. The snow and cold forced the postponement of the opening day of the baseball season in some cities. The ten inches of snow that fell in Yorktown and Dobbs Ferry was the greatest single day's amount so late in the season since those stations started in the 1940s.

February 11, 12, 1983, the lower Hudson Valley was buried in eighteen to twenty five inches of new snow. The heaviest totals of about two feet were from northern Westchester north-eastward into Connecticut. Many areas of the heavily populated Northeast urban corridor were severely affected.

March 13,14, 1993, known as the "Superstorm" for its dire effects on every east coast state, its effects on our two county region were not as severe as some of the past snowstorms. The dubious distinction that the storm produced for Westchester was in recording the storm's lowest barometric pressure at White Plains (28.40"). Hurricane speed winds over 75 mph were recorded to the south. Snowfall and sleet amounts ranged from ten to seventeen inches, greater in the north where temperatures were below freezing for a longer period of time.

January 7, 8, 1996, Westchester and Putnam residents had fourteen to twenty inches deposited on them. Greatest amount was measured at Westchester Airport.

April 1, 1997, the seventeen inches of snow that fell was the greatest April amount in Putnam and Northern Westchester. Unofficially, greater amounts up to two feet were reported at higher elevations in Putnam County. The second greatest but later in the season occurred on April 11, 1907 at Carmel when fourteen inches was recorded.

SELECTED AGRICULTURAL EXCERPTS FROM THE DIARY OF JOHN C. HART

May 1, 1864 Shrub Oak - Weather pleasant, grass green but not enough for pasture, fire still necessary nights.

June 10 Sharp frost injuring beans, pumpkins etc, but not killing them.

June 26 Thermometer 92 in shade at noon, no rain for 17 days - the county parched - prospects gloomy, everything wilted down.

July 1 A slight shower doing much good but not wetting the earth more than an inch.

Early potatoes dying.

July 20 Copious rains - the ground is glad. Corn fit for the table, would have been earlier but that it is wilted down every day with the almost intolerable drought.

July 23 The rain, although considerable, falling on ground on which rain had not fallen for more than four weeks, seemed absorbed at once, and when it ceased to fall, the ground was dry again and now after more than two weeks heat with drying almost scorching winds, it is no wonder that pear trees laden with fruit are dying. I have never seen such a discouraging drought. Thermometer 63 - sun looking like brass and no prospect of rain.

July 25 Rain has come at last, not enough but yet enough to make us all rejoice. Corn is now safe for a good crop and potatoes will be a fair one.

August 1 A few drops of rain, enough to lay the dust.

August 2 Commenced to rain at dusk - toward morning rained heavily - since the rain of July 25th, the country has suffered terribly for want of rain and many say we have never had so dry a time - we have never had so dry a time - we have almost literally been without rain for more than 7 weeks, the first showers only wetting the surface and doing little or no good and we have had no dews all summer and besides a high wind has prevailed most of the time, sometimes almost like a sample of the desert.

August 13 After eleven days of severe heat without rain, it has rained again refreshing the earth so fully that we are almost sure of corn, potatoes and buckwheat - all of which were despaired of a short time ago. In fact, it is almost marvelous but appearances indicate a full crop - the grass is as green in all fields as ever, and the hopes of all men are bright. Fruit has grown rapidly, and now promises to be a fair crop.

August 17 Rain again, almost a flood.

November 13 First snow storm, very light, succeeded by severe cold; ground frozen hard.

November 15 Snow three inches deep, milder weather.

December 9 Last night was bitter cold with a furious gale - brook nearly frozen over, eggs frozen in carriage house.

December 11 Cold at 9 a.m., the thermometer stood at 14 - every window in the house covered with ice.

December 19 Snow fell last night 6 inches deep then turned to rain, cleared off in the night.

December 21 More snow, now fully 1 foot deep.

December 23 9 a.m. thermometer 12.

Dec. 25 - 31 Weather moderate, snowing and raining with dense fog - snow nearly gone, but snowed hard on 31st all day.

January 1, 1865 sleighing good, weather clear and cold but snow thawing in the sun, 13 at night.

January 7 Rain all the forenoon succeeded by hail and snow which fell in great quantity accompanied with a great gale and very cold.

January 8 Thermometer at 9 a.m. 5, perfectly clear and still, 10 a.m. 9.

February 12 Very cold storm with slight snow. Thermometer 10 above zero.

February 13 Thermometer zero.

March 14 Frost nearly out of the ground. Blue birds and robins have arrived.

March 22 Weather like summer - roads dry and dusty - planted hot beds today.

April 25 Warm and pleasant - planted most of the garden today.

(edit. - end of Civil War this month).

May 21 Continued rain and absence of sunshine keep things back much.

May 28 Set out second lot of eggplant - rain today, ground wet.

June 1 Season backward - tomatoes not commenced to grow since transplanting, potatoes in the field not yet up - corn so small that we hesitated about hoeing.

June 8, 9 Torrents of rain doing much damage by washing

October 1-3 A sharp frost.

October 12 No rain of consequence for nearly 2 months - rills drying up, pasture gone.

November 6 Thermometer 24, barometer 29.3.

November 23 First snow to whiten the hills.

Thanksgiving Snow about 3 to 4 inches - weather mild and up to now delightful, so all farm operations could go on.

December 16 9 p.m. thermometer 20.

December 19 Snow

December 21 Thawed

December 22 Sleighing

December 23 8:30 p.m. thermometer 10

December 24 Snowing hard 10 p.m.

December 25 Sky bright & clear, thermometer 50 to 60 all day; snow melting fast and nearly gone

December 30 Snow all day.

December 31 Bright and clear and beautiful - nothing can surpass the wondrous beauty of the landscape with the mantle of snow resting so kindly everywhere.

January 5, 1866 Thermometer 6, barometer 30 at 9 a.m. The weather has been unusually mild from Christmas 'til now.

January 7 4 p.m. thermometer 0, intensely cold with fierce wind; 9 p.m. 6 degrees below zero.

January 8 9 a.m. 14 below zero with fierce gale - pump frozen - difficult to keep warm - plants all frozen stiff and dead.

January 9 8 o'clock a.m. 6 above zero - wind still continuous and cold very bitter but not as severe as yesterday.

January 10 More moderate - thermometer 18 above zero.

January 11 Thawing finally.

January 12 Still mild, snowing slightly - no sleighing as yet but for one day and that poor. January 14 Thawed in the sun but cold.

January 15 Thermometer said to be at zero at sunrise - very cold.

January 16 Mild

January 18 Thawed all day, streets all slushy.

February 6 Since last report close winter weather, scarcely thawing at midday and very cold at midnight. Thermometer at 8 a.m. zero. Neighbors say 1 below zero at sunrise.

February 8 Snowed last night, 6 inches but so soft that there will be but little sleighing.

February 11 Thawing fast, snow will soon be gone.

February 12 Rained all day causing a flood, the brook (Shrub Oak) rose higher than ever before.

February 15 Cleared off, very cold, at sunrise 4 above zero.

February 18,19 Heavy rain with great floods. Ice very troublesome almost impossible to walk

February 20-22 Springlike and clear, ice fast disappearing and frost coming out of ground - walking bad but otherwise most pleasant. Bluebirds have come but only a few are seen. A prospect for an early spring. Winter has passed away without sleighing of consequence.

February 23,24 Pleasant and warm with heavy rain; frost out about 6 inches

February 25 Cleared off cold; thawed in the middle of the day but became very cold before night

February 26 Thermometer at 8:30 p.m. 14 above zero, but the sun was so clear and bright that it was warm in the middle of the day. Blue birds are getting quite plenty.

February 27 Snowed all day, about 6 inches but no sleighing.

February 28 Warm and thawing, most of the snow gone.

March 1 Overcast and prospect of rain - roads muddy.

March 5 Cold wind - thermometer 22 at 8 o'clock a.m.

March 10 The last 6 days have been most disagreeable, a furious gale of wind has been blowing most of the time and although not very cold yet it has been the most unpleasant period of the winter. The wind has ceased now and it promises to be pleasant - the ground is frozen stiff and spring work is hardly thought of. Thermometer has ranged from 22 to 30 for the last week.

March 12 Commenced to thaw and rain - roads bad and growing worse.

March 15 Springlike - robins, bluebirds, meadow larks in abundance; grass looks even a little green. Dug out hot beds and filled with manure. Frost about 2 feet deep but coming out rapidly; the roads will soon be settled.

March 18 8 a.m. thermometer 18, a howling gale has been blowing all night. Froze water in tank and pipes in attic so that water will not flow, has not occurred before this winter.

March 19, 20 Cold all the time.

March 21 Thunder and hail, ground frozen hard again and surface slippery; What will become of the birds?

March 23 It's now thawing and rain has commenced so that we can hope for Spring.

March 25 On awakening this morning it was snowing hard - about 3 inches has fallen and now it is clearing up with a high wind - it was cold last night and this morning it looks as dreary as in January. Alas! for the robins, larks, and bluebirds that yesterday were merry with their Spring songs.

March 26 Last night the thermometer got down to 18 before bed time but stood at 22 at 8 a.m. It is bitter cold with a howling gale as much like Winter as any time for six months past.

March 30 Planted hotbeds today but as it freezes every night quite hard, fear they will do but poorly.

April 3 Froze quite hard last night but is bright and clear and looks spring like.

April 8 Snowing hard (9 a.m.) and up to 2 inches on level but no wind and it is not cold and so we can look for pleasant weather before night; the season is backward.

April 9 Snow from yesterday is almost all gone now (6 p.m.); it froze hard last night and the Turnpike is exceedingly muddy today. It will freeze again tonight - we had to break out the manure in the barnyard with a crowbar it is so frozen, very little plowing as yet and none with us.

April 11 Cold and frosty nights and pleasant days. The frost is not wholly out of the ground and there are patches of snow in the shade.

April 13 Planted peas and set out onions today, the weather is pleasant but not hot; nights are cool but no frost.

April 22 The weather is now delightful and the landscape is a picture of beauty - had a refreshing shower last night and this morning the grass is as green as emerald.

April 25 Ice formed last night and the ground was slightly frozen, perhaps again tonight.

April 27 Frost for the last 3 nights with violent winds, planted potatoes, onions and beets.

April 28 Ice thin at 7:30 a.m. on glass of hotbed.

April 29 Has been blowing a gale all day and we fear it will freeze hard tonight.

May 2 Rained hard all last night and snowed this morning - cleared off cold with high winds, 9 p.m. thermometer 44; it is seldom we have so backward a Spring - we have nothing up in th garden but peas and but little planted.

May 4 Very cold yet - last night we supposed it must freeze and kill the fruit blossoms - the wind was violent and fire most acceptable.

May 9 The weather is pleasant but so cool and cloudy that nothing seems to grow.

May 12 Planted the balance of the garden today, melons, cucumbers and a few tomatoes

May 15 White frost last night killed tomatoes to the ground. There will be frost tonight.

May 22 Last night at bed time the mercury stood at 50 - the same this a.m. and at noon it is but little above. The sky is overcast - ground very dry with a violent gale blowing - we go about shivering in the cold wind quite discouraged. Should the wind abate, it must freeze tonight. Thermometer 46 at 9 p.m.

May 23 Cold and very disagreeable but did not freeze last night as we feared - is a little warmer tonight and no wind, mercury 48. We have had but one rain since May 1 and that but little; grass is very short and nothing grows.

May 24 Frost last night killing outright about every thing. It is sad to behold. Ground dry as powder - no grass for cattle. Meadows nothing - oats the same - garden also

May 27 Commenced to rain early this a.m., a steady copious rain which has completely saturated the parched earth - our hopes are raised.

June 4 Rained steadily all day yesterday and part of last night - a soaking rain - grass will now be a good crop.

June 9 Frequent rains and no sunshine - the air is cold; grass and oats look well but corn is very small. Garden is so wet that we have not hoed it, and it is suffering badly.

June 13 Ground is moist and is warm enough for things to grow. The foliage of the trees has never been surpassed and the color is perfect. The whole face of nature is exquisite in color and form and feature. I never tire in gazing on it. To study merely the different form of trees, to analyze their outlines, position of leaves, sprays, branches etc., affords me almost the greatest pleasure I know of. Early morning and sunset are the times to see light and shade, color and form in nature to the best advantage - softness - mellowness - rest - peace and calm prevail then, except in a storm. In a thunderstorm nature is the most picturesque but when the storm is past most beautiful.

June 18 Heavy rain last night with violent wind - no warm weather yet to make corn grow.

June 20 8 a.m. thermometer 62, commenced to have corn, it is quite small.

June 25 Thermometer 90 nearly all day.

June 27 After 5 days of excessive heat, a heavy shower set in with much thunder - it has rained unceasingly for 5 hours and the ground is saturated, in fact too much rain has fallen to be taken up by the ground and it flows to the full brooks.

June 30 More rain - a small shower with wind and thunder, weather cool, crops are fine.

July 4 A light shower - weather hot.

July 8 Intense heat - thermometer reaching 92; thunder shower - but little rain.

July 15 Excessive heat continues and the crops are burning up - potatoes will be killed, thermometer above 90 nearly every day.

July 17 Thermometer 96 at half past 3 p.m.; the heat has been almost frightful for nearly the whole month and we have had but little rain since June 27th. Everything scorched and burned nearly to death - several showers have gone by us in all directions and at last we have had a small dash which is most acceptable but will do no good unless followed by more.

July 18 Heat still most oppressive - showers all around us and a small dash here

July 19 A change, thermometer 76 at noon; rained a little in the night and the surface of the earth is moist.

July 26 After seeing many showers go by, we have a good one to fall on us here wetting the ground several inches down. The whole country looks green.

July 28 A soaking shower - rivers of water - delightfully cool and pleasant.

August 4 Heavy shower - ground pretty well soaked.

August 28 The month of August has been very wet and cool - not one hot day - corn does not ripen neither do tomatoes.

September 11 Weather clear and warm - rains have been frequent since August came in.

September 21 A heavy shower; thermometer 78 - no frost yet; it has rained nearly half the time for the last 2 months, country looking very fresh and green.

October 1 Weather warm and delicious.

October 5 On the 3rd we had a slight frost and hoped we should escape for a season but alas! last night we had a black frost killing about all vegetation. The flowers are all gone save the petunias and verbanas. We feel sad as even as if we had lost a friend.

October 14 Made a fire in the hall stove; it was not so very cold but there is a strong north- east wind and it rains and is quite chilly and disagreeable. As we look out of window we see great flocks of yellow and scarlet leaves go scudding by, borne by Autumn into great piles, even as the sea piles up heaps of sand, but the evergreens grow seemingly greener - and oh! how grateful we feel to them for their faithfulness, their stability, may we not say their loyalty? Now the birds have deserted us and all the tribes of insects have passed away - the flowers alas - how few remain. The deciduous trees with their bare branches look like the shipping in a great boat when all the sails are down. But the evergreens (Hemlock, Kalmas, Rhododendron, Hollies, Spruce, Pines and Fir) how beautiful in form - how soft and refreshing and cheering in color. How they reassure our faith in the eternity of matter - of nature - of truth of God. And as the dead leaves go scudding by and as the wind sighs among the evergreen branches, the evergreen seems to say to the leaves "farewell" we will tarry here till you return.

This is a season of sadness, yet I am not wholly sad or, if I am I would not be otherwise, for it is a sadness which does not make me unhappy. On the contrary I love to hear the winds moan, to see the changing season accompanied with so much beauty and giving us a reassurance of the stability of all nature's laws - and the body surely feels refreshed with the bracing winds, and recuperates what it lost in the enervating days of summer.

October 27 The weather for the past month has been beautiful with the exception of two or three frosty nights, but the frost was so severe that the trees have become bare and the country now looks as if prepared for Winter and today it is really cold and raw.

November 3 Froze ice last night 2 inches thick. Thermometer 26 this morning.

November 11 Most delicious weather with slight exceptions for two months past - now promising rain.

November 22 Snowed all day whitening all things but at night all gone and mild up to now - the season has been most delightful, only 4 or 5 rains for 6 weeks past and they all in the night, clearing off beautifully and balmy in the morning.

November 24 Cold - ground froze hard.

November 25 Quite cold - Winter fairly set in.

November 26 Thermometer 26 at 8:30 A.M. Froze badly in the new cellar - very cold at night.

December 1 Clear and cold - finished covering raspberries today. We are ready for Winter.

December 2 Sunday - a most beautiful day, bright, clear and mild like Spring - the face of nature is very clean! All the leaves have gone long ago and the grass on hillside and plain is quite brown. I sat on a mossy stone wall by the orchard today and cracked nuts which were left by the squirrels under the Hickories close by and mused and gazed afar along the quiet scene. I was all alone as I would wish to be unless I should have for company one or two other (alas not more) human brothers and them I cannot have, and I am contented, yes almost happy, without them. Once I thought I could not be happy unless some friend were with me, but long practice with flexible natures makes possibilities. I have found in life scarce one who cares to walk afield for the mere love of nature and not one who sees in woods and fields a thousandth part of what is there spread out - and to ask one to accompany me through hill and dale whose eyes and ears and soul and thought are not interested is violence to him and me.

December 9 Weather pleasant - no frost

December 12 Very cold - thermometer 20 at sunrise.

December 15 8 A.M. 14 still and clear, but oh! how cold.

December 16 Noon - has commenced to snow and will be a heavy fall from appearances -
wind from the east, ground frozen hard - roads smooth.

December 17 Snow fell yesterday and today 6 inches deep.

December 18 Cleared off with violent gale of wind from NW which fell before morning. Today has been thawing all day - no sleighing of consequence.

December 19 Slushy streets - colder with light snow at bedtime.

December 20 Cleared off cold in the night with brisk wind. Thermometer 40 at 8 P.M. Wind still steady but not so violent but the cold is bitter, we wish ourselves in the Tropics. It will be a terrible night. Lord have mercy on the poor.

December 21 Sunrise - thermometer 2 below zero. At 9 A.M. 8 above zero, hazy.

December 22 Noon - thermometer 32 - a thaw in prospect.

December 23 Rained all night and now a heavy fog hangs on hill and dale, our usual Christmas thaw.

December 24 Mild as Spring - drizzling all day but clearing off without wind blowing and still warm.

December 25 Bright sunshine - still and mild -

thawing all day and muddy everywhere - only a few patches of snow left but there is much ice

December 27 A fearful snow storm has raged all day with fierce gale - heavy fall of snow much drifted, not very cold.

December 28 Cold all day, sleighing good

January 1 1867 Snowed all day and thawed some.

January 2 Clear and cold in the morning but thawed all day in the sun - looks like rain

January 3 Cold but thawing all day in the sun. At 10 P.M., 10 above zero, sleighing perfect.

January 5 Clear & mild, thawing in the sun all day & making bare ground in the roads.

January 8 Clear and cold with high winds which makes it appear colder than it is, thermometer 26 at 8 o'clock p.m.

January 13 Thermometer 14 at 9 o'clock a.m. Snow falling fast but fine - at 6 p.m. thermometer 22 has been snowing all day - sleighing will be good again.

January 16 Very cold, thermometer 4 above zero at sunrise but is now 1 p.m. overcast & mild brought our plants down stairs and increased the fires last night on account of the intense cold. At 8 p.m. 12 perfectly still and clear.

January 17 Violent snowstorm - thermometer 16 at 9 a.m., 22 at sunset. Snow had fallen to a depth of more than a foot and as the wind is violent it has drifted in huge piles.

January 18 Cleared off cold with wind. Thermometer at sunrise 10. At 9 a.m. the wind is fearful, bright and clear - the snowstorm of yesterday was one of the heaviest in years and long to be remembered, The roads are almost impassable.

January 19 Cold very severe - thermometer at sunrise 10, but the wind has fallen and the sun shines bright. Turned out with teams to break the roads - temp.18 at 9p.m.

January 20 Thermometer 8 at 9 a.m. - still & cold but clear & the sun cheerful - indications of a change. A southeaster of snow of great violence has set in this evening, thermometer 26 at 9 p.m. Prospect that it may turn to rain.

January 21 Thermometer at 32 at 9 a.m., raining slightly - has snowed and blown all night, giving us more than we care for, but we are grateful to have it so moderate after such protracted cold. 10 p.m. still above the freezing point with prospect of thaw. Teams to break roads again today. Removed potatoes from new cellar to house.

January 23 Thawing all day in the sun and mild at 11 p.m. Snow about 18 inches on the level and drifts 6 feet deep. Cross roads filled up full.

January 24 Thawing all day and sleighing bad in spots already.

January 29 Very cold but clear, thermometer 18 at bed time.

January 30 Very cold weather - thermometer at 8 o'clock a.m. 8, clear & sun shining - at 11 p.m. thermometer at 8 again and overcast.

January 31 Snowing slightly, wind east.

February 2 Raining with gale from the southeast - snow melting fast. 11 p.m. furious lightning and loud thunder with very heavy rain.

February 3 Rain has ceased. Thermometer 40 all day. Water in the streets 6 inches deep Snow half gone, side hills half bare, almost looks like Spring.

February 9 Raining hard - brooks very high and mud everywhere. It seems like the breaking up of Winter and yet it seems scarcely possible that it should be so at this early period but the great amount of cold weather we have had leads us to hope that the Winter is nearly past.

February 10 Rained in torrents nearly all night and cleared off with bitter cold terrific gales, thermometer 17 at sunset.

February 13,14 Springlike & thawing all day - raining all day - mud getting deeper, 56 mid day.

February 15,16 Warm all day, thermometer near 60. Raining all day, thermometer 33

February 21 Thermometer 24 overcast & cold. Heavy snowstorm all day - about 12 inches have fallen, will be good sleighing.

February 23 Thermometer 12 above zero, still & overcast. Spring is evidently postponed.

February 25 Thawing all day, freezing at night - the ground is more than half snow covered

March 3 This morning at 8 a.m. thermometer at 22 - at 7 p.m. winds east and quite cold, A furious snowstorm has set in, thermometer 26.

March 7 Two inches of snow and sleet have fallen in the night - drizzled all day - ground is now covered with slush about 3 inches deep - thermometer 34

March 9 A few flakes of snow, thawing in the middle of the day. Blackbirds have come and perched in a tall tree by the brook are whistling furiously to each other and seem to be surveying the prospect for a summer's visit. I wonder what they see that looks changed since they left last Autumn and how they are pleased with the look of things. They evidently have a thought about it and are talking it all over in an eager manner as if it was quite important business.

March 12 Snowed all night and drizzled all day - the snow still was upon the ground but a few hours sun would melt it. A few robins and bluebirds have come and one bird sang in the distance most cheerfully today.

March 15 Froze very hard last night and has been cold all day - snow banks lie along the walls yet 2 feet deep and the brook has a good deal of ice in it yet.

March 16 Commenced to snow this p.m. - 6 inches or more have fallen and still it comes in blinding masses. Is not cold and probably it will soon melt.

March 17 More than 24 hours of steady snow - falling 12 inches thick - now clear & cold with high winds - very much like Winter. Oh! how long and dreary it seems.

March 18 Clear but cold, thermometer 20 at 10 p.m. sleighing never better.

March 23 The roads are breaking up and frost coming out of the ground, but there are great snow drifts 6 feet deep in places. No Spring yet.

March 29 Violent winds yesterday and today - frozen hard at night. The roads are getting quite dry but it freezes so hard at night that the frost cannot come out of the ground and consequently cannot settle.

March 31 A peerless day - warm, bright and beautiful. Robins have sung and frogs have peeped for the first time - the green grass is springing and the roads are dry. What a relief to have escaped from the clutches of the long and tedious Winter - How we all rejoice!

April 5 March weather with heavy winds and cold nights.

April 14 Raw and chilly and overcast but not much frost since March.

April 16 Warm rain which was much needed.

April 23 Heavy shower with violent thunder & lightning yesterday, today now delightful.

April 24 Heavy snow squall and quite cold and disagreeable.

April 26 Froze quite hard last night but it is pleasant today - nothing planted but peas.

April 28 Very cold last night - freezing hard. We fear the fruit is killed, especially pears which were all quite near in blossom.

May 2 Very cold - snowed last night and will freeze tonight. Have not planted garden yet except peas, potatoes, beets and onions.

May 4 Froze last night and will again tonight, fruit must suffer.

May 8 Raining very hard all night, season very backward - fruit trees not yet in blossom - 9 p.m. still raining. It has been a most violent north-easter and floods of water have fallen. Much damage must ensue. No corn has been planted yet and the ground is so wet it must be delayed much later than usual.

May 14 Rained very hard all night with thunder and lightning. There was a slight frost on the night of the 12th.

May 17 Finished planting corn today and set out house plants and a few Egg-plants and tomatoes but alas! it is so chilly that nothing grows but grass & that but slowly. We have not had a single warm day this year so far and the ground is very wet.

May 21 Still cold and overcast - in constant dread of frost, can scarcely remember so backward a Spring - much planting has got to be done.

May 26 Heavy rain - crops very backward except grass and oats which look well

June 3 Heavy rain last night and rain again today - ground oozing wet.

June 5 Set out rest of tomatoes.

June 6 Hot 80 in the shade - planted sweet corn today for late use.

June 9 Made a fire to keep us warm - rained hard all night and this forenoon

June 13 Hot and dry - corn and potatoes fine, everything in fact looks remarkably well except for fruit which has mostly been blighted we think by cold winds

June 27 Rain! Rain! Rain! Too wet for the general good.

July 4, 5 Rain again - heat as high as 86.

July 13 Frequent showers - bad hay weather.

July 20 Almost constant rain spoiling much hay and preventing the getting it so that the work is hardly begun - wind northeast nearly the entire month.

July 25 Rain again - the farmers look blue and complain very much, but the country looks very green and luxuriant.

August 3 Ground saturated with rain - hay rotting in the fields.

August 7 Shower again - one third of the hay is yet to get in this section and over half oats.

August 15 Rained all day and now raining hard - so wet a season I cannot remember

August 16 Rained all night till now, half past 9 a.m., a violent east storm, floods of water.

August 22 Rain again - alas! it rains nearly one half of the time. Thermometer not over 80.

September 5 Heavy thunder storm - rained very hard yesterday and is raining a deluge as I write. This will be known as the wet year - so much rain has not fallen since the memory of the present race as has fallen thus far this year - upwards of forty inches on a level.

September 9 Clear at last with westerly wind.

September 19 Hot and dry for some days past - thermometer 80 at noon - corn all cut, got in two loads of it last week without rain.

September 24 Last night we had a pretty sharp frost injuring many things in the garden - corn suffered a good deal in many places, a great deal being uncut as yet, Lima beans were slightly injured as well as Tomatoes cucumbers, etc. Pumpkins were nearly all killed - on higher ground everything escaped. It is now very dry.

October 18 Six weeks of most delicious weather - An occasional shower with loud thunder but clearing off warmer. Have had but two frosty nights as yet - thermometer 70 in the shade.

October 29 I am motherless. She died peacefully this morning at 5 o'clock after being confined to her bed for less than two weeks.

May 22, 1868 Just arrived from the city (New York) for the season. No corn planted yet and very little garden. Very wet all the month so far and cold.

May 29 Planted corn and potatoes 2 days ago - today set out tomatoes and planted Lima beans, cucumbers and Sweet corn.

June 11 A violent north-east storm all day - cold - so backward a season we have never known, much planting is not yet done and no hoeing has been commenced not even in the garden.

June 13 First clear warmth of the season.

June 16 Heavy thunder shower - we have had three dry hot days, not 1 field in 10 hoed..

June 20 Hot 88 - corn grows apace.

June 24 Showery all day - few have hoed their corn the first time - it stands 8 inches high.

June 27 Today it is clear and settled and hot - good hay weather.

July 3 Heavy shower with terrific lightning & thunder- 5 or 6 loads of hay mostly wet.

July 5 Heat oppressive, 89 - peas yesterday, no beans, beets or potatoes yet.

July 7 Heavy showers - 5 -6 loads of hay out in cocks.

July 14 Hot and dry - thermometer 88 at noon and 91 at 2 o'clock.

July 17 Cooler but very dry - ground is parched and plants wilting, pastures drying up

July 21 A fine shower this morning doing a vast amount of good - cucumbers, squash and beets today for dinner - tomatoes an inch in diameter, Sweet corn in silk

July 25 Rained steadily all night, a most welcome rain- the country is very green

August 9 Heavy showers again yesterday and day before - more rain today - much hay cut and rotting, oats mostly in the swaths - a very light crop.

August 20 Heavy and continuous rain - have just gathered a nice mess of ripe tomatoes, all there were - had corn twice and Lima beans.

August 31 Rain again - it has been a rainy season and yet it has been so evenly distributed that while the amount of rain which has fallen has been very small yet the ground has been almost constantly moist.

September 12 Very heavy shower yesterday with sharp lightning and loud thunder - terrific rainfall last night - lowland flooded but no damage - weather hot and sultry September 18 Sharp frost last night injuring tomatoes, pumpkins, etc but not killing them quite. Corn suffered but little, but it was a narrow escape for all green things - but how sad the reflection that summer is gone again. How short the Summers and how long the Winters.

September 23 Rain again last night and now warm and spring-like.

September 28 Nearly continuous rain for four days and nights but very light in the day and heavy at night - wind easterly - warm.

October 12 Pleasant weather - very little frost so far.

October 18 Rained yesterday morning and cleared off with violent wind and became very cold at night freezing the ground stiff enough to bear one's weight and making much ice, also killing all vegetation and the leaves fell in showers.

October 21 Rain again, tomorrow we go to the city. I am sad. I would prefer to stay here.

May 15, 1869 Just arrived from the city. Showers today - ground moist - weather warm, garden about half planted but nothing much up.

June 1 Frequent showers - grass growing finely - has been hot for a few days but is now chilly. Lima beans, cucumbers, and beets just up, peas in blossom.

June 6 Heavy showers yesterday with hurricane (tornado ?) a few miles east destroying houses and trees.

June 8 Showers this morning and now very cool with north-east wind, feels like frost

June 20 Overcast and looks like rain - ground dry - corn very small and yellow.

July 3 Fine shower - very much needed - finished hilling corn today.

July 7 Overcast or cloudy with high wind - got in 4 loads of hay.

July 9 Copious showers - much hay out - sweet corn in silk for 2 days past, oats fine

July 15 Fine shower - had 3 loads of hay out in cock. Cucumbers for dinner today

July 21 Had a copious shower in the night for which we are glad notwithstanding we had the whole of the orchard of hay out in cock and an acre in barn lot in swaths.

July 31 Cool night and no rain - pastures drying up, exceedingly dry.

August 3 Fierce wind - heat 82 - barometer falling - country parched up - looking for rain - cisterns both dry - pastures dead - garden dying, gloomy in the extreme

August 5 It rained last night a goodly shower - oh! how welcome, immense good.

August 13 It is now showering a little - just enough to lay the dust - in fact, we are having the second drought of years and this section is dried up. Corn and potatoes, Buckwheat and meadows are literally burnt up. Thermometer ranging from 70 to 80 - wind fresh from the south-west - the cisterns gave out nearly two weeks ago and we have had to draw water from the brook.

August 15 Close and sultry - it must rain before night but we have looked so long for for every sign that we almost give up hope. There is nothing so sad in the country as a drought ..... and we have not had a heavy rain since April.

August 20 Noon thermometer 96 - hot wind from the

south-west, hot enough to take your breathe away as you breathe it - an intolerable drought - 112 in the sun.

August 21 The heat at midday was scorching - the corn literally burnt in the sun, the leaves of the pear tree fairly wilted. Tomato vines lay flat on the roasting ground - thunder was heard in many directions but the rain was not for us.

August 29 The rain of last night which gave so much promise ceased as soon as it commenced, not laying the dust and today it has been clear and hot.

September 1 No rain yet and cold enough for fire with northwest winds all the time. Corn is dried up half grown and will be but half a crop. The brook is dry for more than half its length and all the fish are dead.

September 8 Copious rains last night and today and already the grass begins to grow.

September 20 The showers of the 8th did not wet the ground more than 2 inches deep and although the grass gave a little effort to grow yet the heat and drought ever since have burned it up entirely - so little rain in 5 consecutive months.

September 26 Commenced raining this morning a 5 o'clock. Wind south-east - rainfall is heavy and continues. To sum up the drought which we now consider ended we may say that since May 15th no rainfall has wetted the ground more than 2 inches and for 9/10 of the time the ground has been perfectly dry to any depth you might go short of depth sufficient for a well. It can fitly be called a great drought.

September 28 The rain of the 26th continued for nearly 24 hours thoroughly soaking the earth and filling the streams. Alas! another summer gone - how soon will all our summers be gone?

October 3 Heavy rains all day - our neighbors have had a slight frost.

October 11 Rained all day yesterday, now mild and beautiful, fields are green and foliage is fine in color.

October 13 Terrible thunderstorm last night with hail - it is now almost cold enough to freeze with keen north-west wind. Tomorrow we leave for the city.

June 3 1870 Arrived from the city yesterday for the season - it is very dry and the meadows are looking very bad - oats and corn look well

June 7 A fine rain has set in and we are glad

June 14 It has rained every day for 4 days past - all crops promise well

June 21 Yesterday and day before it was hot reaching 85 - last night there were several copious showers with vivid lightning - it is now quite cool with a high breeze.

June 28 Hot - 90 at 2 o'clock and 82 at 9 in the evening - heavy showers all about but none here - commenced haying & cut nearly one field and got

in part of a load.

July 3 Rained a little this A.M. - looks like more - got in 9 loads of hay thus far

July 8 Heavy rain from southeast last night soaking the ground to our great joy

July 15 Finished haying today - 19 loads in the new barn in all from the big field

July 17 Hot - 92 for several hours and still 90 at 6 p.m.

July 23 Heat oppressive 90 for hours - a gale blowing from the south-west - yet stifling.

August 4 No rain for 14 days with heat and heavy winds - late in day rain finally came and heavily for 2 hours and may rain all night.

August 14 Fine rains - it is the greatest fruit year since 1860.

August 22 Fearfully dry - cistern gave out today and the well yesterday.

September 1 Terribly dry rivaling last summer in intensity.

September 10 A light shower - grass has not grown at all since the latter end of June.

September 12 No rain and very dry - a repetition of last year's drought.

September 20 Very slight frost last night - The rain of 3 days ago did very little good and it is terribly dry again - warm in the middle of the day.

September 30 Has rained hard all day and the drought is ended. Of course we are glad and regret that it was not sooner but it is all for the best no doubt.

October 3 Rained again quite hard in the night - mild - even the grass is springing up finally. Have had no frost as yet to do any hurt. I shall go to town tomorrow.

June 1 1871 Just arrived from the city - yesterday there was a fine shower previously to which it was fearfully dry and grass for hay is much less than last year - thus we have 3 successive Mays very dry followed by two summers with excessive drought which will, we fear, come again

June 3 Thermometer 84 - the earth roasted and a famine in sight unless we have rain.

June 4 A fine shower lasting 20 minutes and wetting the groung an inch or so.

June 8 It rained nearly all night and the ground is thoroughly soaked.

June 15 Heavy showers with hail sufficient to whiten the ground and much lay unmelted for half an hour.

June 18 Very heavy rain storm from south-east lasting all night and still continuing at 10 1/2 p.m. Nearly finished plowing side hill next to wood for Buckwheat.

June 24 Rain again - easterly wind - had beets today.

June 29 Commenced to go through corn third time (hoed) - it looks well, nearly waist high - no haying yet.

July 4 Fine showers in the night before last -

Raspberries very fine and plentiful- corn high enough to stretch to my eyes- grandson born yesterday in N.Y.C.

July 10 Fine shower last night - got in 2 loads of hay.

July 15 Heavy thunder shower at noon - much hay out - Cucumbers for dinner.

July 19 Finished haying yesterday about 30 loads in all, the smallest crop I can remember. It took 9 days in all to get it for 3 men.

July 20 Heavy mist all day yesterday with much rain in the night - nothing has lacked rain for six weeks past - previous to which the country suffered for it.

July 31 Heavy rain yesterday and today saturating the ground and standing on the surface - small sweet corn nearly fit for the table.

August 4 Heavy showers again - heat oppressive - sweet corn on table.

August 15 Light showers in the night - ground moist and the meadows and pastures as green as in Spring - garden fine - tomatoes and Egg plants in great plenty.

August 24 Heavy rain all night raising the brook (Shrub Oak) and saturating the ground - this may be called the wet year as the two previous ones were two dry ones.

August 28 Very heavy rains last night, almost a flood.

September 1 Cleared off at last cool and delicious.

September 13 Rain set in before 7 o'clock, the first in a fortnight - ground had got quite dry.

September 22 Hard frost last night - killed everything dead - ground frozen stiff and remaining so till 8 o'clock in the shade. September 26 Heavy rain - cold all the month.

September 30 Rained yesterday and hailed hard - foliage turning finally.

October 6 1871 Expect to go to town tomorrow (last diary entry).

John C. Hart never returned to his house in Shrub Oak (now the Hart Memorial Library). He died on May 3, 1872, aged 42 after an extended period of pain and failing health and is buried near the new church he had struggled hard to build.

SOME 19TH CENTURY WEATHER EVENTS FROM WEEKLY NEWSPAPERS

Thursday, January 20, 1831

The snowstorm of previous Friday to Sunday drifted into heaps by force of the wind which rendered the roads impassable, so much so that in some cases where horses had plunged into these banks, they were literally covered over and were with difficulty rescued by digging them out. Westchester and Putnam Sentinel - Peekskill

Tuesday, May 20, 1834

During the greater part of last week, the weather was extremely cold, so much so that we fear great damage has been done to all kinds of fruit, particularly the early. We have examined the currant, cherry, gooseberry, plum and peach and found nearly two thirds destroyed by the heavy frost. Our oldest inhabitants do not remember such weather during the month of May. On Thursday and Friday morning we had ice of considerable thickness and during the whole of those days, cloak and a good fire were absolutely necessary. Westchester and Putnam Sentinel - Peekskill

May 12, 1840

We have experienced for six or eight days past a series of cold, damp and disagreeable weather and some nights attended with frost which it is feared may injure the coming fruit, a greater promise of which we do not recollect of ever before witnessing. We have not seen a fruit tree which has appeared in full bloom. Westchester and Putnam Sentinel - Peekskill

Saturday, February 10, 1855

VERY COLD WEATHER - The thermometer was 12 below zero on Tuesday and Wednesday of this past week. Snow commenced falling on Wednesday and continued descending until Friday afternoon when it had attained a depth of 12 to 15 inches. Highland Eagle - Peekskill

Saturday, August 28, 1886

The water in the Peekskill village reservoir got down so low last week that it was deemed best to start the Engine and this was done and it has since been going steadily, when the flow of water permitted. It will be recollected that we have had no rain of any consequence in several weeks and the indications are that the drought will last for some time longer. As much economy as is possible in the use of water should be practiced by our citizens as a precautionary measure. The Democrat

Saturday, August 16, 1896

It seems entirely unnecessary to tell the people of Peekskill through the columns of the DEMOCRAT that the weather was extremely warm the present week and that the atmosphere was well charged with humidity. But such was the case and it has been many years since Peekskill has experienced a hot wave for so long a continued period of time. Highland Democrat

Saturday, July 24, 1897

Peekskill has been exceptionally exempt from the heat fatalities which have occurred elsewhere during the hot spell. The Democrat

Saturday, March 1, 1902

About a week after an all day snowstorm with high winds and a subsequent one on February 21 with several more inches of snow, McGregor brook overflowed its banks yesterday, flooding Park and Division streets in Peekskill. This was the third flood of that site in two years (March 12, 1901 and August 1901). Highland Democrat

FIGURE 3

SPRING

One of the problems of Spring is defining just when it is. In the lower Hudson Valley this presents difficulties. If we think of spring as the transition period between the frosts of winter and the heat of summer there is no problem. There is also no problem if we consider Spring as that period between the Vernal Equinox and the Summer Solstice. The problem arises when we name the Spring months as March, April and May. Weather-wise, March never seems to fit as a spring month and at least a portion of June is certainly spring.

One criterion for the start of spring is the "ice out" date. This is the date that the last ice melts from local lakes and ponds. This date is of greater importance in the north where larger bodies of water such as the Great Lakes serve as ship highways. Locally this date is important for boating and fishing. Three bodies of water in northern Westchester and Putnam have been observed for many years and in spite of a great degree of variability from year to year, a good idea of what is normal has been determined. For Mohansic Lake in Yorktown the average date is March 17, and up to three days later for Amawalk Reservoir and Lake Mahopac. For northern Westchester and Putnam at least, the lakes and reservoirs appear to be close to the calendar season (See Table 14). An estimate of the "ice out" date for lakes in southern Westchester would be one to two weeks earlier.

Following the annual "ice out" date comes the mud season, the length of which is related to how deeply the ground was frozen during the previous winter. Any period of rainfall or snow during this time will of course prolong this mud season. By early April this unpleasant time has ended for most of the county.

As can be seen, the start of Spring varies greatly and cannot be tied to a specific month or calendar date.

The period between the ice out date and the first unfolding of greenery is one of hope for warmth, but also of frustration and disillusionment. It is a tease of occasional outdoor shirt sleeve warmth along with chilling overcast days. It is Spring by the calendar but not by the feel of the air. This variable, tease weather is the product of conflicting movements of cold and

Listen buds, it's March twenty first
Don't you know enough to burst
Come on birds, unlock your throats!
Come on gardeners, shed your coats
Come on zephyrs, come on flowers
Come on grass and violet showers!
And come on lambs in frisking flocks
Salute the Vernal Equinox
Twang the cheerful lute and zither
Spring is absolutely hither!
Yester eve was dark despair
With winter, winter everywhere
Today upon the other hand
Tis spring throughout this happy land
Oh such is nature's chiaroscuro
According to the Weather Bureau
What though the blasts of winter sting!
Officially, at least, it's Spring

Ogden Nash

warm air and is typical of our month of April. In 1976, April gave us a summer day with over 90 degree temperatures county-wide, while only one week earlier the magnolia blossoms were freezing with temperatures in the 20s.

The normal date of the last freeze in mid Westchester and Rockland occurs about April 20, ten days earlier in southern Westchester but nearly two weeks later in most of Putnam. The earliest gardening normally begins about this time, when the ground has dried enough to become workable. The length of this normal growing or freeze free season, is about 200 days in southern Westchester, 190 days in the mid Westchester and Rockland, 170 days in northern Westchester and 160 days in Putnam.

While commercial farming is a thing of the past, the intensity and devotion of homeowner flower and vegetable growers make up for this loss. Most of the daylight hours of the weekends of April and May for many are filled with tilling, fertilizing and seeding of gardens of all kinds. It's also the busiest time of the year for local nurseries. Adequate precipitation is the key factor for native vegetation as well as for those gardeners not relying on sprinkler systems. On the other hand excessive rainfall, particularly over weekends during this time can set back many gardening schedules.

Spring droughts of the past have occurred from April to June in 1903 and 1913 with no rainfall for 40 to 50 days during most of that time period. More recently the growing periods of 1964, 1965 and 1966 had extreme drought conditions unequaled in the 20th century, causing severe damage to much to both native and cultivated vegetation.

While there can be wide differences of temperature on individual days during springtime between southern and northern Westchester, average differences are about three degrees with combined spring temperature averages for April, May and June ranging from about 57 to 60 degrees.

Just as the "ice out" date each year can range over a five week period, the average date of the last frost also has a high variability. The normal county last frost of the season is from April 24th to May 6th

(See Table 13). However, temperatures freezing and below have been recorded in southern Westchester as late as the second week in May and as early as the last week in March.

A late spring can be a frustrating time for fishermen, golfers, tennis players and campers. The normal six month period of indoor confinement is bad enough. When it is prolonged longer than normal we feel cheated of our share of springtime. Too often the comment is heard that we seem to jump from winter to summer, from too cold to too hot with not enough comfortable outdoor weather in between.

The variability of temperatures within the months of March, April and sometimes May is one of the striking aspects of spring in our three county area. Monthly averages can be quite deceiving in perceiving the exact temperature quality of a spring month.

Spring is that time of the year when average daily temperatures become warmer inland than along large bodies of water. Land areas warm up faster than oceans, which require a good two or three months to warm up to their peak heat. The time in early spring when the ocean waters begin to exert a cooling effect on the adjacent land in called the "sea turn." The air over the land rises when warmed and the resultant lower pressure draws inland the nearby cooler, heavier air from over the water. This sea breeze while welcome in summer is not always appreciated in the springtime. This "sea turn" change of wind direction mainly along the Long Island Sound shore begins sometime in April or May.

The warmest springs (March, April, May) of the 20th century, when the average temperature topped 51 degrees in the north county were 1903, 1921, 1945, 1977, 1985 and 1991. In the south, Scarsdale in 1945 had the warmest spring with an average of 54.6 degrees.

The coldest springs in the north, when the average temperature was 44 degrees or below occurred in the years: 1893, 1907, 1916, 1917, 1926, 1956, 1967, In the south at Scarsdale 1916 had the coldest of its 1904-1990 record with an average of 44.5 degrees.

Whatever uncertainties there are regarding warm weather, these are mostly ended by mid May. Frosty setbacks become a faded memory and all are able to garden and sport without fear of cold. The woods are fine for hikers and campers to take to the trails and the sun delivers enough heat for sun-bathing.

SUMMER

With almost a sigh
The bee trades blossoms
With the butterfly.

FIGURE 4

SUMMER

I sing of brooks, of blossoms, birds and bowers
Of April, May of June and July flowers
I sing of Maypoles, Hockcarts, Wassails, Wares
Of bridegrooms, brides and the bridal cares
Hesperides 1648 - Robert Merrick

If winter in Westchester, Rockland and Putnam can be thought of as the qualified period of discomfort in the quality of life, then summer is the qualified period of pleasantness. Qualified is added to both seasons, since just as our winters are never a complete zero on a scale of zero to ten, in like manner summers are never a complete ten in terms of the ideal quality of life.

Summer means no heavy garments or fuel bills for heating, warm nights and sunbathing days, all outdoor activities unhampered by any cold. All these and other positives give our summers a rating of nine on the scale of "ideal liveability or quality of life." The rating of the county is thus not a perfect ten. Our summers, except for a few short periods are rarely perfect. The concept of a perfect summer day is one with a cloudless sky with high temperatures in the mid 80s and a low humidity. This kind of day, splendid for all occasions from June weddings to Labor Day picnics, is actually not that common. In other parts of the country, such as the southwest, this kind of a day can persist week after week. Persistent clear, dry days and nights however indicate a dry climate. These areas have little or no summer greenery. Any vegetation there, has to be artificially watered on a regular basis. Any water has to be pumped to the surface from wells or piped in from sources many miles away. Our three counties and the northeast generally do not have this as a problem. We are thus assured during the growing season of a lush green of forest and field that is the envy of much of the country. Normally the wettest months of the year are those of summer, insuring us of more than adequate rainfall.

This greenery however, comes at a price. Rainfall comes in the daytime as well as at night. It can come as a steady all-day rain or as a torrential downpour. It can come with dangerous lightning. Potential rain can remain as clouds screening out the sun for days. On many summer days a warm temperature and high humidity combine to make nearly all people very uncomfortable. Relative humidity normally ranges from 57 percent in the evening to 80 percent in the morning in most parts of the county during the summer months. Summer relative humidity is rarely under 50%. Under these conditions at work or at home, we are forced into the artificial environment of indoor air conditioning.

Along with the moisture supported greenery comes a surge of insect life. From no-see-ums to mosquitos to bumble bees, all insects are dependant on moisture and water at some vital stage in their life development.

These negative aspects of our summer combine to give us less than a perfect 10 for "ideal liveability." The summer outdoor weather is very good but has its unscheduled interruptions and annoyances.

Meteorologically, summer can be defined as the warmest 91 consecutive days of the year. This period of time begins the second week of June and ends at the end of the first week of September. The third week of July normally gives the county the greatest heat of the year. While the hottest days of summer with highs in the 80s usually end by mid August (See Tables 7, 8, 9), the cumulative effect of the sun's high altitude and the relatively long duration of sunlight keeps average temperatures over land areas within 4-5 degree of the summer maximum until the last week of August. The heat waves of summer with 90+ high temperatures usually last two or three days before cooler air brings relief.

Of the 30 thunderstorms that normally cross the county during the year, most occur during the summer. Hail stones, the product of severe thunderstorms, can be expected once or twice a year. Rainbows also have the same frequency and are usually seen to the east following an late afternoon storm.

The average duration of the growing season is 190 days. The average temperature is above 65 degrees from May 1 to September 30. During the five month growing season about 21 inches normally falls in the county. In addition to greater daylight, the average twenty one clear days during the summer is greater than that of any other season. Also greater than any other season is 62 percent sunshine during the daytime hours.

Summer, like winter, has a paradox that comes from our using an arbitrary calendar to determine seasons. The longest day comes at the beginning of summer rather than in its midst. As a consequence, all summer long we are losing daylight, rather than building to a peak and then tapering off. In winter, the greatest amount of darkness also comes at the beginning of that season. These seasons seems to stand somewhat out of gear.

Based on the longest available records at Carmel and West Point for the last third of the 20th century, the period of warmest summers was between 1935 and 1955 until the 1990s. This last decade and 1999 have given our area its warmest summers of record (See Figure 21). The coldest summers came during the first three decades of the century. The warmest summers came during the years of 1900, 1901, 1908, 1939, 1943, 1949, 1952, 1955 and 1999 with average temperatures between 72 and 74 degrees. The coldest summers were during the years of 1903, 1927, 1958, 1960 and 1962 ranging between 66 and 68 degrees.

WINTER

With the arrival of winter (December, January, February) comes the yearly topic of weather conversation. "Are our winters getting warmer and less snowier?" The subject is a difficult one as even the experts cannot provide a conclusive long-term answer. For most of us, one experience with bitter cold weather, be it with a stalled car stuck in a snowdrift or without heat in a home without electric power can color one's perception of an entire season. After many years of weather watching and weather talk this writer has long ago concluded that one can never rely on the memory of people regarding the severity of weather.

Climate historians generally believe that the coldest winters worldwide came during the period of 1650 - 1850, a period often referred to as "the little ice age" since this was a time of worldwide glacier advances. The subsequent period has seen a gradual warming up to about 1950 when temperatures leveled off. In the 1960s and 70s there was a drop in winter temperatures. For the last 20 years however, winter temperatures have resumed their upward trend, with some of the century's warmest in the 1990s. (See Figure 21).

The warmest 20th century winters locally, all averaging above freezing at Carmel/Yorktown Heights were those of 1931-32, 1932-33, 1936-37, 1948-49, 1952-53 1974-75, 1982-83, 1990-91, 1994-95, 1997-98 and 1998-99. The warmest of these was that of 1931-32 with an average of 35.4°F with 1997-98 only slightly less warm. In southern Westchester at Scarsdale, 1931-32 averaged 37.8°F. Another warm above freezing 19th century winter was that of 1889-90.

Locally the coldest ten year period came during the first decade of the 20th century. The winters of 1903-04 and 1904-05 were only slightly surpassed in coldness by the winter of 1917-18 (19.7°F) at Carmel. At Scarsdale, that winter averaged 22.1°F and Bedford Hills showed 23.1°F. Other cold 20th century winters were those of 1947-48 and 1960-61.

One measure of the coldness of a winter season is through the use of Degree Days. Degree days are based on the difference between 65 degrees, and the daily mean or average temperature. Thus a normal winter day averaging 25 degrees would have 40 degree day units. Heating normally has to be supplied when the average outside temperature drops below 65 degrees in order to maintain and indoor temperature of 70 degrees.

A normal heating season in Putnam and northeastern Westchester measures about 6000

He who marvels at the beauty of the world
in summer
Will find equal cause for wonder and admiration
in winter

John Burroughs

heating Degree Day units. In Rockland and most of Westchester it measures about 5750 Degree Days. South of the Westchester waistline, 5500 are measured. Degree Day data is used as a basis for planning heating and insulation requirements where heat losses can be calculated. It is also used to estimate fuel consumption to regulate the delivery of fuel by the distributor to the consumer.

Degree Day unit accumulation is not confined to the winter months. Almost half of the normal yearly totals come in other than winter months. At Carmel/Yorktown Heights, January shows an average of 1250 units, December shows 1125 units and February 1085 units. February shows fewer units than December not because it is warmer but because of its lower number of days. Even the summer months of July and August normally give us about a dozen Degree Day units in Putnam County. Like Putnam County and northern Westchester, Boston, Hartford, Providence and Poughkeepsie show 6000 Degree day unit totals, while New York City and Philadelphia show about 5000, and Baltimore and Washington show about 4500.

Another measure of the severity of a winter is through a count of the number of extremes of coldness. For weather stations with a record of 50 or more years, any winter season with over five record breaking cold minimums would result in a cold winter, while an excess of five record daily high temperatures would result in a warmer winter season. Such extremes are generally not used by climatologists in determining climate trends. As the length of the instrumental climate record lengthens the significance of the extremes of weather phenomena increases and assumes greater importance. Assuming no climate change, extremes are a measure of the variability of climate for a specific locality. Where climate is changing, as is presently believed, extremes can herald and portend the direction and amount of change.

The coldest day of the winter is yet another determination of a winter's severity. An examination of yearly minimums of most of the 20th century shows that three degrees below zero is the average coldest in southern Westchester, while at Carmel the average coldest is close to ten below zero. At Scarsdale 10 below zero can be expected every 10 years and 15 below zero is a once in 40 year event. In Putnam, 18 below zero is a once in 10 year occurrence and 23 below can happen every 25 years (See Tables 15 & 16). These return frequency events assume that no warming or cooling trends are occurring.

Winter is the time of cold waves. Despite less storminess and more sunshine in January than in December, the ground is generally snow covered thus limiting any warming, and the slanting sun's rays hardly warm the atmosphere which is constantly receiving cold reinforcement from the north.

The first night of a cold wave is usually windy and the sky may be covered with broken, streaking clouds. On the second night additional cooling adds increased frigidity to the air. A large high barometric pressure air mass called an anti-cyclone (with pressures about 31.00 inches) moves southeastward from Canada providing the force for the coldness to come. When this high pressure air mass moves over our area, the winds drop to near calm, the sky is cloudless and radiation cooling begins. The ground surface loses more of its remaining heat. With a snow covered terrain the cooling process is enhanced. Temperatures under these conditions may drop 10 to 20 degrees Fahrenheit (6 to 11 degrees Centigrade) or more after nightfall. The cold air at the surface becomes denser and heavier and drains downhill to form pools of colder air in the valleys and hollows. Hilltops on some of these clear, still nights can be 20 or more degrees warmer than valley bottoms.

Winter is the driest time of the year. Total precipitation of the three winter months is closer to 20 percent of the annual total than the 25 percent that would be expected if precipitation were equal throughout the year. Locally, winter is the only time of the year that energy can be derived from wind power, since average wind speed at the hilltops is about 11 miles per hour. A steady wind speed of 8 miles per hour would be needed year round to make the electricity produced, economically feasible. Prevailing winter wind direction is mostly from the northwest.

In our region, the odds on having a clear sky is one chance in four. A cloudy sky is defined as one in which cloudiness is greater than 30% of the sky most of the day. The cloudiest winter period is the week of December 6 to12 and the clearest is January 10 to 16. During the winter months 3/4 of the precipitation that falls comes as snow for inland areas (Hudson Valley Climate Division). In the south (Coastal Climate Division) the ratio is reversed with only 1/4 coming as snow.

Hal Borland the former New York Times nature writer captured the essence of winter in his description of winter light and snow.

"Each season has its own light, its own sunrise and sunset ... With the southward shift of the sun, the sky clarifies itself with frost, and the light begins to shimmer. Late dawn with a long slanting light that touches the leafless hillside with a brief rosy glow. Then comes the cold, and the icy green at sunset; and after that the snow, and the winter light on the snowy land is full of blue and purple, which lie like lakes among the drifts."

"One of the penalties of modern life is the loss of appreciation of snow. The country man realizes that snow nourishes and protects his fields and pastures and even helps to seal and insulate his house and barns against the cruelest bites of winter. The youngster with a sled and the grownup with a pair of skis know the satisfaction of a snow clad slope. But in the city and suburbs, snow has become a cold and slushy nuisance when it isn't a costly problem. To travelers everywhere, snow is a blinding slippery hazard to foot, wheel and wing. Yet the snowflake, of itself, is a thing of fragile evanescent beauty. It is a delicate water crystal, one of the most transient of all natural forms, a wisp of mist that has briefly acquired tangible shape. A snowfall can transform a woodland into a place of magic, meadow into a shimmering wonderland. A snowdrift is the frozen grace of wind, perfection of line and curve and form. Snow can temporarily restore the lost innocence to a scarred and naughty world of disillusionment and folly. We know these things. We can believe in them for a little while at the beginning of any winter. Then our comfort and our convenience are threatened and we forget."

Plant Hardiness Zones

Hardiness zones are used to determine whether specific shrubs or trees will survive winters and thrive in a given area. The zones are based on the average coldest winter temperature. At nurseries, each species of plant is rated as to the zone where it will grow the best. An extreme example of its usefulness would be knowing that a palm tree would not survive when planted in Westchester. It should be pointed out that a specific evergreen or shrub if planted in one zone colder than recommended will in many cases survive, but not necessarily thrive. Many trees or shrubs can be planted in colder zones provided they are sheltered from being fully exposed to the elements, specifically to wind.

Hardiness zones should be considered as a general guide as there are other factors that landscapers and home owners have to consider. Hill side exposures, and hilltop locations generally have better air-drainage than low lying frost pockets or hollows most common in northern Westchester and Putnam and northern Palisades Interstate Park area of Rockland where differences between valley and hilltop can be greater than 500 feet. However any exposures to the north can with cold temperatures and wind, result in wind burn and die back for many plant species.

The warmest zone (7a) lies in the urbanized part of Westchester that is closest to New York City and Long Island Sound and includes the Yonkers, Mount Vernon, New Rochelle, Mamaroneck and Rye area. This region rarely encounters winter temperatures colder than zero Fahrenheit.

The colder zone (6b) to the immediate north is based on temperatures at Scarsdale and Bedford Hills where over 70 years of 20th century records show average low winter low temperatures of zero and two below zero respectively. This zone includes all of the middle part of Westchester.

The coldest zone (6a) would include all areas in the Palisades Interstate Park region of Rockland, north of Route 35 in Westchester and all of Putnam County and is based on the 90 year Carmel record where the average coldest winter temperature is seven below zero.

All flora acclimated to zone 6 or lower can certainly be planted in either county. It can happen that you may know of plants of zone 7 that are growing happily in zone 6a. Local topographical and elevation conditions can create such situations. On the other hand 15 below zero has been recorded at Scarsdale and 25 below zero has been felt at Carmel (zone 4b). These extreme lows are rated as once in 25 years events. Under these highly variable conditions it is best to be conservative if you want your trees and shrubs to thrive.

Gardeners can also judge the relative growing season warmth by the average number of frost-free days at specific sites. Approximate 30 year averages for the period of 1950 to 1980 show that Scarsdale has 175 days, Dobbs Ferry has 205 days, Bedford Hills has 176 and Carmel has 154 such days.

FIGURE 7

JANUARY

The arrival of the new year and January brings the full force of winter upon lower Hudson Valley residents. All of the years coldest temperatures and harder forms of water now present themselves. By January nearly all of the local lakes and reservoirs have frozen over and ice skating and fishing are generally possible for the larger water bodies such as those of the Croton watershed..

January temperatures at Scarsdale average about 30 degrees Fahrenheit and 25 degrees at Carmel in Putnam County. At Central Park in New York City, the January average is about three degrees warmer than lower Westchester and Rockland.

Of greater importance than the average temperature is the fact that in both counties the high temperature of the day normally reaches a few degrees above freezing (See Tables 7, 8, 9). This period of a few hours is naturally longer in the south (See Figure 23). The economic consequences of this daily above-freezing period are substantial. The alternate daily freezing and unfreezing, (the freeze thaw cycle) of road surfaces and roof tops subjects them to the effects of the expansion and contraction of water as it changes from liquid to solid. Thus, a hairline crack on a road surface when filled with water will widen over a short time to a measurable crevice after daily cycles of freezing and unfreezing. This breakup process has been the undoing of many a local road and and maintenance under these conditions has to be an annual endeavor. Particular attention to proper road-water drainage is necessary in new road construction to avoid the worst of this freeze-unfreeze cycle. Normally there are thirteen to sixteen such days in January with the least in the south and most in Putnam.

There is a four degree difference in daily low temperatures between southern Westchester and Putnam (See Figure 24). The curve of the 22 and 23 degree isotherms shows the warming influence of the Hudson River, which is generally unfrozen in most years due to its salt content. During exceptionally cold Januarys, only three times in the last two decades, when the river does freeze over, 20th century iron-hulled ships are able to break through the ice on their trip up to Albany. Before the days of

*All weather is beautiful,
and full of powerful emotion-
The "icy blast" from the vast north,
the monotone
of grey and black and white
Trees seem to grow thinner,
and shrink into themselves
as do other objects*

Charles Burchfield - American painter

the iron hull and modern icebreakers, wooden ships remained in their slips till the end of the ice season. Ice fishing and the stage coaches on the Hudson River were common 18th and early 19th century winter sights on the frozen river north of Peekskill.

January daily high and low temperatures can show a wide range with some years soaring over 60 degrees, while others dropping to as low as 10 to 20 degrees below zero. The normal coldest January minimum in the south part of Westchester is five above zero, while in Putnam and northeast Westchester it is two below zero. Based on past 20th century records, one January in ten gives us nine below zero in the south and fifteen below zero in the north. The coldest recorded January temperature in Westchester and Putnam occurred on the 22nd in 1961 when 25 and 24 degrees below zero were recorded respectively at Shrub Oak and Carmel. In Rockland 16 below zero was registered at Suffern on that date, also its coldest January minimum.

Coldest Januarys of the past have been 1904, 1912, 1918, 1942, 1945, 1948, 1957, 1961, 1968, 1970, 1977, and 1982. The coldest of these at Carmel were in the years 1912 and 1918. During those cold months average temperatures were between 15 and 18 degrees. Some of the coldest spells were: January 4 - 6, 1904 twelve and seventeen below zero at Scarsdale and Bedford Hills; January 1 - 4, 1918 below zero in parts of all counties, as low as twelve below zero in the north; and January 21 - 30, 1961 a range of minimums from -1 to -25 below zero, with below zero minimums on eleven consecutive days in the north and five such days in the south. This was the longest recorded 20th century cold spell; January 8 -13, 1968 had zero and below minimums in Rockland, Putnam and northern Westchester.

The coldest individual January days were January 4th and 5th 1904 when the thermometer never rose above the zero point in Putnam. These two "Zero Days" while not recording the lowest temperatures of record, had the lowest overall average for the day.

January warmth is a modest phenomenon rarely lasting more than two days. When these days occur towards the end of the month, they are commonly known as the "January Thaw" which locally is a period of days when the thermometer rises above freezing during the night as well as daytime. The phenomenon does occur often enough as average daily temperatures from January 24th to the 27th are higher than those of the week before and after. Normally the coldest January temperatures occur between the 10th and the 16th.

The normal warmest January day is 56 degrees in the south and 50 degrees in the north with one January in ten peaking to 64 degrees in the south and to 60 degrees in the north (See Figure 23).

Some of the January warm spells of the past were: January 13 -16 1932 with 60 degree and higher maximums in both counties; January 3 -5, and 26, 27, 1950 with days of 60+ degree marks; and January 21 -25, 1906 with 60+ degree maxima in lower Westchester. The hottest January maximum temperature occurred on the 26th in 1950 when 73 degrees was recorded at Dobbs Ferry and Scarsdale.

Warm Januarys of the Carmel record were 1890, 1906, 1913, 1932, 1933, 1937, 1949, 1950, 1967, 1974 and 1990 ranging from 33 to 38 degrees. The hottest of these was 1932 with an average of 41 degrees at Scarsdale and 38 degrees at Carmel.

Precipitation in January can come as snow, sleet, freezing rain or rain. The least threatening of these unfortunately comes least often. Happily, forecasting for the greater New York City metropolitan region has improved to such an extent that the Hudson Valley portion of Westchester and Putnam are given equal coverage whenever threatening weather conditions are expected.

The normal five degree difference in temperature between Putnam in the north and lower Westchester in the south can be the difference between rain and snow, often with a mixture of sleet or freezing rain in between. Many January snowstorms in Putnam of a foot or so will show an inch or less just north of New York City. With the average temperature below the 32 degree mark in the south and a bit higher but near the freezing point in many urbanized places, temperature is the critical factor for snow depths (See Tables 7, 8, 9, 9a, 11, 12).

Normal January precipitation totals range from 3.3 to 3.8 inches. There are an average of twelve days with a minimum of of .01 inches of precipitation in both counties.

Earliest Westchester precipitation records dating back to 1868 reveal that 1891 had the wettest January with 9.71 inches at Bedford Hills and 9.06 inches at Croton Lake. In 1979, Putnam gave that county its greatest January total of 11.76 inches.

The driest January for both counties occurred in 1970 when less than one half inch fell at many rain gauge sites.

The heaviest precipitation periods usually come as rain since the atmosphere holds greater moisture at higher temperatures. Greatest 24 hour amounts have been between 4.5 and 5.0 inches and have occurred only once or twice in the last 100 years.

Snowfall during January is is a highly variable phenomenon. Nearly two-thirds of the Januarys have had the ground snow covered to a depth of five to ten inches. While monthly totals average from eight to ten inches, many individual days have seen greater amounts. In 1923, Scarsdale had a January total of 36 inches. About the same also fell that January in Carmel. Bedford Hills greatest January total was 28 inches in 1961.

The greatest single day of January snowfall came in Scarsdale in 1905 when 24 inches fell on the 25th. In recent years 12 - 17 inches fell over our three county region on January 20, 1961.

The Januarys of 1950 and 1967 recorded only traces of snow for the entire month for the least snowfall of the century to date.

In January one inch or more of snow can be expected three times during the month while a snowfall of four inches or greater can be expected once.

The prevailing winds during January are from the northwest and average 11 miles per hour at unobstructed areas. During daylight hours there is only 50% chance or 140 hours of sunshine during the average January.

FEBRUARY

In February, days grow longer—
But Winter's storms blow all the stronger.

FIGURE 8

FEBRUARY

With the arrival of February, one can sense the greater amount of daily light and see the more northerly position of the sunset on the horizon. Sunrise is more than half an hour earlier and sunset one half hour later than in early January. This extra hour of daylight is however, not enough to give us any sense of greater warmth. While the days have gradually become longer, the bitterness of winter with its attendant ice and snow is still the same.

The full moon of February was known as the "hunger moon" and the first week of the month is normally the coldest of the winter. Within Westchester, Putnam and Rockland most of what one can say of January's weather applies equally well to February.

A warm February, a bad hay crop;
A cold February, a good hay crop
old farmer lore

Although February has had the coldest days, it is not the coldest month of the year. Average daily temperatures after the 19th of the month rise rapidly so that by the last week of the month they are higher than any day in January. This is sufficient to raise the average temperature just enough to make February the second coldest of the year. The difference however, is small, about two degrees Fahrenheit and is statistically not significant. In many years the first five days of the month are the coldest of the winter.

Past records attest to the coldness of February. In Putnam and northern Westchester lows of zero degrees and below have occurred during the 20th century on every day of the month. In the south and in Rockland only four days during the last week have never felt below zero temperatures. In the north, the month has had as many as ten days with below zero minimums. These occurred in the years 1907, 1914, and 1934. During those months the weather station at Scarsdale had five such days. For consecutive days of below zero minimums, February 1934 with nine at Carmel has never been exceeded, although 1961 came close with six days in the first week. Lesser cold waves were recorded at Bedford Hills and Scarsdale in 1948 with three consecutive days of below zero minimums, with five noted at Carmel.

Based on past performance, the probabilities of below zero lows in February are such that one can expect below zero every year in Putnam and northern Westchester, once every three or four years in southern Westchester and in Rockland. A once in 20 year event of 20 below zero is expected in the north and ten below zero in the south.

The month of February 1934 was not only the coldest second month of the year, but the coldest of any winter month this century so far, not only for the lower Hudson valley but also for the entire northeastern United States. Within the two counties the mean temperature range was from thirteen degrees in the north to eighteen in the south. Other cold Februarys of bygone years, when average temperatures were lower than 20°F were 1888, 1895, 1904, 1905, 1914, 1923, 1961, and 1979. What is noteworthy is that there have been only two very cold Februarys in the second half of the 20th century.

During the cold month of February 1934, the ninth day stands out with seventeen, eighteen, nineteen and twenty below zero recorded at West Point, Scarsdale, Bedford Hills and Carmel respectively. At Scarsdale and Bedford Hills these lows mark the coldest ever at those official U.S. Weather Service stations. A colder temperature of 24 below, on another February day was recorded at Carmel in Putnam on the 28th of that month. At Yorktown Heights in northern Westchester, 26 below on February 16, 1943 marked its coldest February minimum.

In a normal February, there are eight days in the north and five in the south when the temperature does not rise above the freezing point of 32°F. There are thirteen to seventeen days in the month subject to the freeze- thaw cycle.

During the coldest week there is one chance in five that the low temperature of the day will be between 11 and 17 degrees in northern Westchester and Putnam.. There is one chance in three of the low being between 9 and 19 degrees. The odds are even that the daily low will be between 6 and 22. For the betting person, you can give three to one odds that the morning low will be between 0 and 27 degrees and ten to one odds that the low will be between 6 below zero and 33 degrees. On the high temperature side, in the north you can give ten to one odds that the daily high will not rise above 49 degrees that seven day period in February. For southern Westchester add 5.5 degrees to the above temperatures.

One does not think of February in terms of warmth, yet all weather is relative, and warmth has occurred in the past. In Putnam and northern Westchester there have been eighteen Februarys since 1888 averaging over the freezing point and over four degrees above normal (28°F). These were 1890, 1909, 1925, 1930, 1937, 1938, 1939, 1949, 1953, 1954, 1957, 1960, 1976, 1981, 1984, 1990, 1991, and 1997. The warmest of these were 1890, 1976, 1981, and 1984 when averages were about 35 degrees in Putnam and northern Westchester, and four degrees higher in the south.

The rarest of February days have been those when the maximum temperature has risen into the 70s. This is heat by February standards and has occurred only three times in the 20th century. It is an event that has a statistical probability of once every 25 years in most of Westchester and once in 80 years for Putnam. February peak heat for most parts of Westchester and Putnam came on the 16th of the month in 1954 when 73 and 74 degrees were recorded in Carmel, Bedford Hills and Suffern. Scarsdale's warmest day was February 15, 1949 when the thermometer registered a high of 74 degrees.

Some periods of extended February warmth were: February 19 - 27, 1930 - maximum temperatures in the 50s and 60s in all counties, February 19 - 23, 1943 - again three county temperatures in the 50s and 60s, February 13 - 16, 1949 -maximum temperatures from the 50s to the 70s in most parts of all counties, February 19-28, 1953 temperatures in the 50s and 60s throughout the three county region, February 15 - 28, 1954 - the longest spell of February heat with temperatures in all areas from the 50s to the low 70s, February 25 - 29 1976 - maximum temperatures in the 60s in all areas and the hottest Leap Year Day of record.

The culmination of the snow scene comes during February. The greatest depth of snow on the ground normally occurs during the second week of the month. This depth averages ten inches in the north and five inches in the south. Normal February snowfall is thirteen inches in Putnam and eleven at Scarsdale. Winter's greatest monthly snowfall totals have also come in February. In 1893, 47 inches was measured at Carmel and Scarsdale's greatest was 37 inches in 1907. Other snowy Februarys were 1934, 1947, 1957 and 1967, with over two feet measured. The average period of continuous snow cover lasts fifteen days in southern Westchester and twenty five days in Putnam. Most of these days come in February. In some years February has had little or no snowfall. In 1968 and 1981 only traces were recorded at most stations in the three counties.

Individual February days have seen snowfalls as great as 20 inches in Carmel, 22 inches at Bedford Hills and 24 inches at Scarsdale. These amounts came on February 10, 1969.

While a 19th century total precipitation (rain and snow) amount of thirteen inches was measured at White Plains in 1883, 20th century heaviest totals have been a more modest seven to eight inches. Wettest have come in the years of 1900, 1915, 1971, and 1972 (See Precipitation amounts in Appendices). As in the case of January, most of the precipitation in these wet months came as rain and not as snow. Average monthly precipitation is about 3.25 inches and is the least for any month of the year. Least monthly totals came in 1931 and 1968 when less than one inch fell. In 1863 as little as .15 inches fell at Croton Lake.

Heavy 24-hour precipitation amounts have ranged from 2.5 to 4.5 inches in different regions of the three counties, with a record 4.85 inches falling at Croton Lake in 1885.

FIGURE 9

MARCH

By the calendar March is a winter month. Climatewise it is considered spring as three other months in the year average colder. In the lower Hudson valley winter can easily be stretched to four months, since March by all objective and subjective observations acts feels and looks like the other winter months. While the deep frigid bitterness of late January and early February are gone, a good measure of coldness still remains. Single digit temperatures have visited all three counties and below zero lows in the north are not unknown.

The major difference between March and the other winter months is the greater amounts of daylight. The Vernal Equinox about the 21st, brings us equality of day and night for the for the first time since September, and this fact has important climate consequences.

Lion-like, March cometh in, hoarse, with tempestuous breath

William D. Howells

March weather over 100 years ago at one of the earliest Westchester county weather stations was not unlike that of the 20th century. The thirty year White Plains record in the latter part of the 19th century shows extreme daily temperatures ranging from 2 to 70 degrees Fahrenheit, a range close to that of the 20th century.

In Putnam County the average date of the last 16 degree temperature or below is on the 20th of March. By the end of the month there is less than a 25 percent chance of temperatures going below 24 degrees. Put another way, on March 6 the odds are eight to one that temperatures will drop to 16 degrees or below. By the end of the month these odds have changed to only one chance in ten of that happening (See Table 13).

In northern Westchester and Putnam, a normal March averages 37°F. A cold March would be one that averages freezing or below. Since 1888 there have been fourteen such months in the north. Included in those are the three coldest, with averages below 30°F. These were 1896, 1916, and 1960. In 1916, the coldest of these, minimum temperatures in southern Westchester were below freezing on all but the last five days.

The March freeze- thaw cycle has nine such days in the south and fifteen in Putnam.

The ice-out date for three lakes in northern Westchester and Putnam occurs about mid-month.

Some of the significant cold spells that have afflicted the two county area were: 1906 - Bedford Hills - minimums below ten degrees on the 24th and 25th; 1916- Bedford Hills(0°F), Scarsdale (3°F) and Carmel (-14°F) - a cold wave from the 15th to the 18th; 1923- Scarsdale and Bedford Hills - many single digit lows the last week of the month; 1943 - Carmel-below zero minimums from the 1st to 4th and single digit lows for six of seven days ending on the ninth; 1960 - Carmel - below zero lows on the 9th to the 12th.

The coldest March day of six station records came on the 19th in 1967 when the following minimums were registered Scarsdale - 3 below zero, Dobbs Ferry - 2 degrees, Westchester Airport - 6 below zero, Bedford Hills zero degrees (coldest day so late in season), Carmel - thirteen below zero (coldest day so late in season) and three below zero at Suffern.

At the other end of the thermometer is the warmth of the month, and while March is not noted for heat, as many as seven days in Westchester have seen high temperatures in the 80s. However, based on past records, one has to wait at least 20 years to see such a day, as that is its statistical return probability.

The warmest third months (greater than two standard deviations from the mean) were those of 1903, 1921, 1945 and 1946. For overall warmth, March 1945 stands out with four to eight days at different long-term weather stations in all three counties, setting record daily highs that stand to this day. There were only nine days with below freezing temperatures in most of Westchester. At the end of the month most of the days had highs in the seventies and there were six 80+ days during that period. At Bedford Hills 91°F was registered on the 29th, the hottest March day in Westchester history. Assuming no general climate warming, statistically such an event can be expected once in 200 years. In the following year, March warmth came during the first half of the month with nearly all the days in that period having maxima in the 60s and 70s.

But March is more than extremes of cold and heat. These extremes, while giving us a sense of the variability of March weather, do not give us a feel of what an average day is like. In a normal day during the first week of the month, there is a five degree difference (41 and 45 degrees) in the daily high temperature between Putnam and southern Westchester (See Tables 7 & 9). This average daily high temperature rises during the month till by the last week it is nine degrees higher. The normal daily high temperature usually occurs between noon and 2 PM. The normal daily low temperatures in the first week of the month in the north and south are 21.6

and 26.5 degrees. These increase by eight degrees during the course of the month. Normal daily low temperatures occur about dawn.

March snow is a common occurrence and within both counties measurable snow has fallen in the past on every day of the month. Total snowfall normally measures seven to nine inches, but none was reported at three sites in 1946 and only traces in 1995. At Yorktown the years 1973, 1979, and 1986 only had one-half an inch. On the other hand total amounts over 20 inches were measured at that location in 1967, 1984 and 1996. In 1956, Dobbs Ferry recorded 31 inches while Scarsdale measured a total of 39 inches in 1958. In 1967 all locations in both counties measured between two and two and one half feet.

Snow in March is not the same as in January (See Table 30). While it can be as treacherous on the roads, it does not have the staying power of a mid-winter storm and usually by mid-day, when temperatures normally rise to the mid 40s, the local roads rapidly become clear and only dirty water remains to splash on car windshields.

Some memorable 20th century snowy days have been: March 1- 2, 1914 with 10 - 18 inches countywide; March 7, 1941 - 7 - 9 inches in Putnam and northern Westchester; March 19, 1956 - 9 - 14 inches countywide; March 21, 1958 - 7 - 12 inches countywide; March 12, 1959 - 9 -12 inches countywide; March 4, 1960 - 12 - 26 inches all three counties; March 22, 1967- 12 inches most of Westchester; March 13, 1993- 10-17 inches all counties. There were three noteworthy identical March snowfall totals in the 19th century. 32 inches fell in 1868, 1875, and 1888 at White Plains.

With normal temperatures warmer than those of mid-winter, the moisture content is great enough to show the potential of heavier periods of precipitation. The number of individual days with two or more inches for March is more than twice that of February.

Total March precipitation is between 3.5 and 4.5 inches for all counties with most of the long-term weather stations showing average amounts about four inches. Total precipitation for Westchester and Putnam rain gauges has ranged from as little as less than one inch in 1910 and 1915 to as great as eleven inches in 1953.

While March has had many periods of sustained precipitation, heavy continuous rainfall over two inches has been generally confined to a 24 hour period. Twentieth century March precipitation in Westchester and Putnam, over three inches in one day, has occurred only three to five times at stations with records longer than 80 years.

For shorter time periods March 12,13 1953 at the Woodlands-Ardsley rain gauge had the heaviest short term rainfall in 3, 6 and 12 hours of 1.62, 2.52 and 3.58 inches.

FIGURE 10

APRIL

April in English literature is the time of the arrival of spring with flowers and new greenery. The English poets have long been in love with April as the embodiment of all of spring's best. One must caution English literature majors and foreign visitors unfamiliar to our counties that April in the northeastern U.S.A. bears no relation to the April of England.

Our April is at best a tease, an unfulfilled promise that is only occasionally realized. The blunt fact is that April in the lower Hudson valley is not a month for outdoor activities. The brown grass is still packed down from the past winter's snow burden and in many years in the early part of the month, snow still remains on north facing slopes of Putnam. During most of April's days, one is stuck indoors despite the yearning to move about comfortably outdoors, after five months of confinement.

Only the trees and other native vegetation understand the nature of April . The start of the unfurling of leaf buds usually coincides with the average date of the last frost in southern Westchester. This comes during the last week of the month, while in Putnam, not until the first week of May. Trees and shrubbery not native to this region such as the Magnolia are particularly susceptible to the great temperature variability and likelihood of damaging cold when flower and leaf buds are beginning to open.

By April 20th in Putnam there is still a ten to one chance that the temperature will drop to freezing or below. By April 28th these odds have dropped to four to one. By April 30th there is still a three to one chance of 32°F or below. At Yorktown Heights, April 30th is the average date of the last freeze (50 -50 chance). In Shrub Oak, this last freeze date is three days later. A normal April in Putnam still has six days with freezing or below minimums (See Table 13). While southern Westchester has an earlier average last frost date, the general temperature profile of the month is not much different, confirming a predominantly cold month averaging only six degrees warmer than November, certainly not one to pick and smell flowers as in "merry olde Englande." This all serves to make April a frustrating month for cooped-up gardeners, fishermen, golfers and parents with young children.

Past records give a bleak picture of April cold. All areas in our region have seen every day of the month with below freezing minimums. One of the longest cold spells came in 1904 when twelve consecutive days of lows 20 degrees and below occurred starting

April weather,
Rain and sunshine, both together

Old weather lore

on the thirteenth. Ten of these record lows have yet to be exceeded. In 1943 another cold period from the 4th to 16th had below freezing minimums and also set record cold marks in Yorktown and Bedford Hills that still stand. Four days of lows in the teens were recorded that month in Yorktown. Fourteen degrees has been recorded as late as the 16th of the month at Yorktown. In the south the latest of the season teen temperature cold was on the 11th in 1909 when 18 degrees was registered in Scarsdale. Long duration coldness is an exception in April rarely lasting more than two days.

April temperatures average about 48 degrees in Yorktown and Suffern, but during the coldest Aprils of the 20th century in the years 1907, 1943 and 1975 temperatures were about six degrees colder. The freeze-thaw cycle gives us two days in the south and four in Putnam.

In spite of all the coldness, there is a warm side of April. A surge of rapid warmth often comes during the third week of the month. The worst of the frigidity noted above fortunately occurs about dawn when most of us are still in bed. By mid-day there are can be many delightful hours. There is nothing more satisfying, after months of being homebound, to be able to remain outdoors without an overcoat and feel the April sun warmth for a while. In many Aprils, a walk around one's home or through a field or woods will reveal the early signs of the coming greenery - the first color of crocus, the first yellow of forsythia and daffodils, the tiny redness of the native soft maple flowers and the red cap of skunk cabbage. These are moments of rediscovered joy. On an occasional warm evening with temperatures lingering in the 50s or higher, the mating call of the swamp peeper frogs is a sound that one always associates with spring warmth.

The normal daily low temperatures for both counties range from 31 - 36 degrees in the early part of April to 43 - 47 degrees at the end of the month. The normal daily highs range from 52 - 56 at the beginning and 64 - 67 degrees at the end of the month (See Tables 7, 8, 9). Comfortable outdoor strolling without heavy clothes starts at about 50 to low 60 degree temperatures. For most of the month, a few short hours about mid-day can be considered as comfortable outdoors.

The hottest 20th century Aprils occurred in 1921 and 1941 with averages about 53 degrees in the north and 55 in the south. An April noteworthy for individual days of heat was 1976 when two days in the north and three in the south had highs of 90 degrees at Easter time (See Table 4). Other April days with 90 degree and higher marks came in 1915, 1927, 1942 and 1990. Maximums of 90 degrees and higher have a probability return period of once in 35 years in the south but only once in 80 years in Putnam.

April's fickle nature can be seen by comparing the year 1975 with that of 1976, when a very cold April was succeeded the following year by a very hot one

April precipitation also follows its pattern of great variability. While monthly normal amounts average just over four inches, daily rainfalls close to that amount have fallen on individual days during the month. Rain gauges in operation since early in the 20th century show that there is hardly a day in the month that has not had at least one or more inches of rain. One quarter of the days have had at least two inches of rainfall. In the north one or two days have had over three inches of rain and in the south three or four days in the 20th century. Normally eight days average at least one tenth of an inch.

Total precipitation has ranged from as little as one quarter inch at the Cross River rain gauge in 1923 to as great as 10.65 inches in. Bedford Hills in 1901. For nearly all stations, April of 1942 had the least total with just less than one inch.

For an individual day, April 5, 1984 at Dobbs Ferry stands as the greatest single day's amount with a deluge of 5.34 inches.

Along with many cold days comes the unexpected and unwanted snow. To those who may regard April snows in Westchester as a freakish occurrence, it may come as a surprise to learn that snow in most of the county is a regular event. One out of every three or four Aprils has measurable snow that averages between one and two inches. An April snowfall total as great as two feet was measured at White Plains in 1875 and one and one half feet was recorded as recently as 1997 in Yorktown Heights.

About one inch difference exists between April average snow amounts for Putnam and southern Westchester. While April snows rarely remain on the ground for more than a few hours, they have come in measurable depths as late as the third week of the month.

Other Snowy Aprils were 1984, 1907, 1915, 1944, and 1956 with totals over six inches.

Memorable April single day snowfalls have come on: April 13, 1875 in White Plains with 17 inches; April 12, 1894 at Bedford Hills with 20 inches; April 3, 1915 at three sites in Westchester 8 - 14 inches was reported; Scarsdale measured 4 inches on April 11, 1958. Most recently April 1, 1997 saw a storm with rain, then wet snow and wind that felled many a large tree and broke branches by the thousands in many parts of the lower Hudson valley. The snowfall amounts that day were 17 inches at Yorktown Heights, with amounts up to two feet reported at the higher elevations of Putnam County.

From all this, one can readily see that defining normal weather in April is a hopeless task with all weather phenomena conspiring to give us colder, hotter, wetter, drier and snowier - anything and everything but normal.

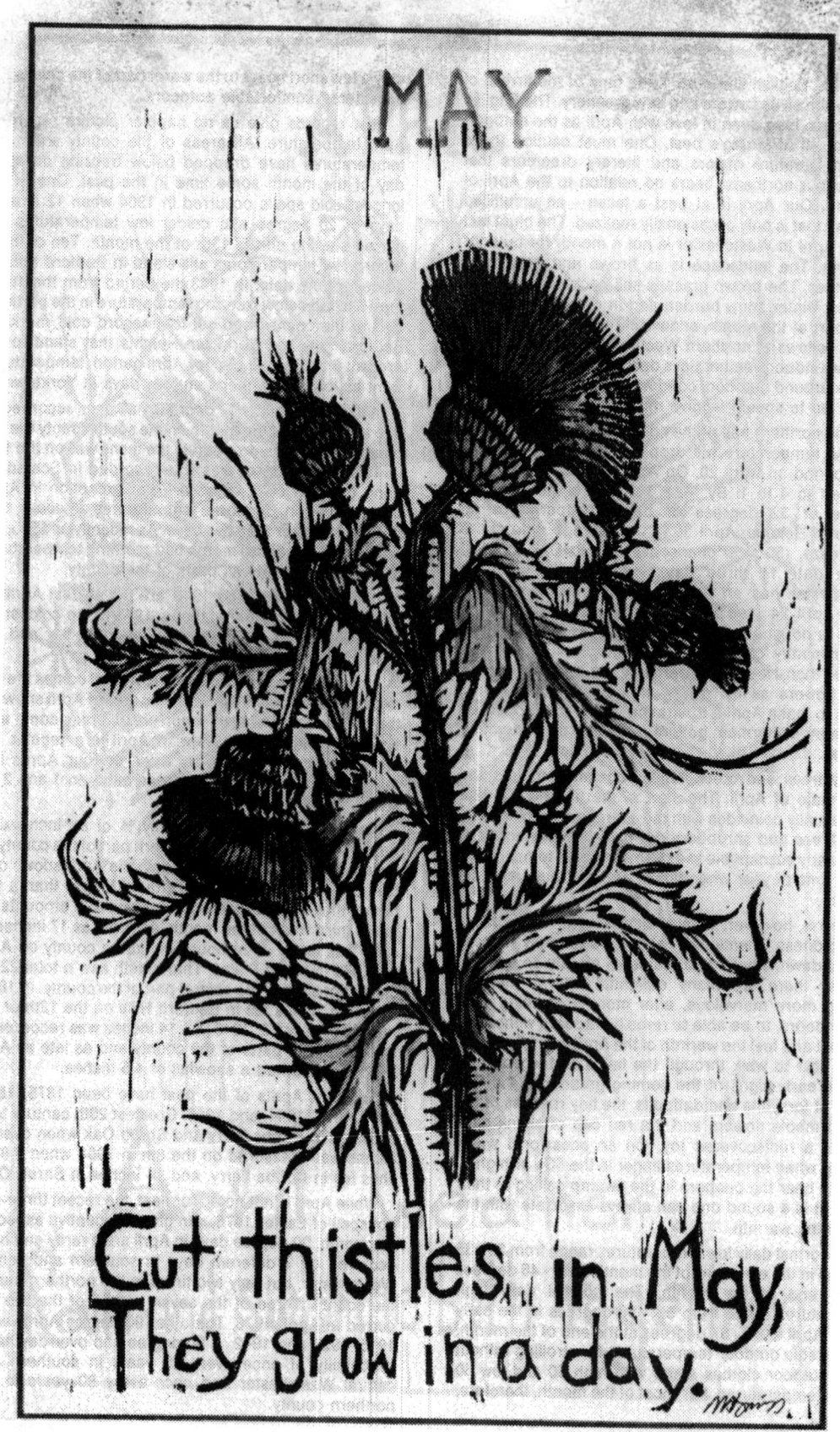

MAY

Cut thistles in May,
They grow in a day.

FIGURE 11

MAY

May is the month of new green, the "primavera," as spring is known in many romance language countries, and its arrival brings on in a short span of time one of nature's many wondrous changes - a color show. Within a few weeks, a bleak grey- brown open landscape turns into a riot of green; all shades of yellowish to bluish green emerge to screen our views of hills, lakes, roads and houses that were visible only days before. The local flowers of May, dogwoods, lilacs, azaleas and later rhododendrons are the accent colors to a basic theme of rapidly unfolding green.

As with an early snow in late fall, the small green leaves, so sensitive to temperature at this stage, provide an opportunity to see the effects of temperatures in the different regions of our three county study. The two colors, green and white are greatly dependant on temperature. In November, a small drop can turn a landscape from grey brown to snow covered white. In like manner, during early May, a small rise will transform a hillside from a faint, pale green to a deep Kelly green.

Since our area is divided into two climate zones and is influenced in the south by large bodies of water, the warmth of the New York City urbanization and lower elevation, the greening occurs earlier in that region. In some years a two week interval can pass between the flowering of dogwoods of southern Westchester and those of Putnam. Thus it is that temperature dictates the timing of our spring green, as May 6th is the average date of the last frost in Putnam, while it is two weeks earlier south of the waistline of Westchester (See Table 13).

By the 5th of May in northern Westchester and Putnam there is only one chance in three that temperatures will drop below freezing. By May 13th these odds become ten to one against seeing a below freezing mark, which fortunately occurs about dawn. For southern Westchester, the dates are about two weeks earlier.

A warm April can start the greenery sooner. However our native trees are cautious. Their bud unfolding relates to the amount of sunlight as well as the temperature and a cold early May will retard the leaf unfolding. These trees are the best monitor of spring climate. Their timetable has evolved over millions of years, whereas our temperature averages are based only on 100 years of data.

*That the green leaves came and
covered the high rock
That the lilacs came and bloomed,
like a blindness cleaned
Exclaiming bright sight,
as it was satisfied*

Wallace Stevens

While the southern or coastal division is essentially frost-free for all of May, below freezing temperatures were recorded as late as the 12th in 1907, when 28° F and 26°F were recorded at Mount Hope and Scarsdale. Past 20th century records show that Scarsdale has had below freezing minimums on eleven of first twelve days of the month. Further north at Bedford Hills, the latest below freezing low temperature came on the 26th, while in Putnam below freezing was reported as late as the last day of May. In Rockland, below freezing lows have been felt as late as the fourth week of the month. Consecutive days of below freeing minimums are rare, with none since 1900 at Mount Hope and Carmel. In 1961 and 1966 there were three non-consecutive days of below freezing minimums in the first two weeks of the month at Scarsdale. In the north, consecutive below freezing lows have occurred at Bedford Hills in 1920. At Yorktown Heights, there were two days in 1951, and three in 1947. Shrub Oak had three such days in 1955, and two in 1965 and 1966. The principal characteristic of the two coldest Mays of the century, 1917 and 1967 was not the days with below freezing marks but the many days with relatively low high temperatures. In 1917 there was only one below freezing minimum in Westchester, but also only one day with an 80 degree maximum. The same kind of temperature regime also occurred in 1967.

May snow is a true rarity in northern Westchester and Putnam. While traces have been reported even as late as the fourth week of the month, measurable snow amounts have been seen only twice in the 20th century. "Light snow" was reported in northeastern Westchester on May 16, 1834. Later that century, White Plains and Kensico on May 1, 1876 had about one inch. Most recently, Carmel and Yorktown Heights in the north measured one and two inches on May 9, 1977.

Typically, May in our region is an ideal outdoor month; ideal for gardening, fishing, golfing, hiking, and any work of an energetic kind. During the hottest part of the day, temperatures are usually in the high 60s or low 70s, perfect for those who want to work hard but still avoid sweating. On the exceptional day however, May can be hot enough for sweat even without work. After the first week, 90 degree days have been recorded in all three counties. During the first half of May in lower Westchester, extremes have been in the low 90s. In the second half of May there have been instances of highs in the mid 90s.

May heat waves with three or more consecutive days of 90+ degree high temperatures while infrequent are not unknown. Some of these were: 1896 Bedford Hills, 1903 and 1929 at Mount Hope just north of Yonkers, 1930 at Scarsdale. In the warmest months there have been at least two days with 90 degree maximums. The warmest Mays with average temperatures over 62°F in Putnam were 1889, 1896, 1903, 1911, 1918, 1944, 1975, and 1991.

Average rainfall differences in May within the three county region are small with only one half an inch between the wettest and driest rain gauge locations. Normal total rainfall for the month is just under 4 inches with about eight days having at least one tenth of an inch. Normal, however, is one of those numbers that is not seen often, as the high variability has given Westchester as little as one quarter inch and as great as 14 inches.

During the great drought of the mid 1960s, half a month would go by without rain, while other years have given us Mays with many continuous days of steady rainfall. The years 1902, 1903, 1939, 1955, 1964, 1965, 1986 and 1993 had periods of one to two weeks without rain. With rainfall so vital for plant growth in the spring, a drought in the latter part of May can have a severe impact on all vegetation.

During the wet months of 1868, 1946, 1948, 1968, 1978, 1984, and 1989, at least half the days of May had rain.

On May 29, 1968, between 3 and 5 inches of rain fell on all parts of the region and set county May records for six and twelve hours. In 1984, three consecutive days of two inch rains at the end of the month (28 - 30th) soaked nearly all of the region and provided the major amount in a month that totaled over ten inches. More recently on May 17, 1989 four to five inches fell, part of a wet month that totalled over eleven inches in four of five gauges. Those were the only two Mays of the 20th century with four digit amounts at the oldest county rain gauge in Yorktown.

A three inch 24 hour rain in May fortunately is a rare event with a return frequency of once every 50 years. Twenty four hour amounts over five inches have been measured at Carmel on May 19, 1900 and at Scarsdale on May 27, 1946. The degree of local flooding caused by heavy rains noted above is largely dependent on how saturated the ground is from previous rains.

Normally May in the lower Hudson valley has one day with a one inch rain, two or three days with about one-half an inch and a least six days with smaller amounts, making up a total of about four inches.

FIGURE 12

JUNE

June is nature's settling down time after a month of putting on the green. By early June the rush is over, the rapid unfolding, stem and leaf growth has ended and on many young trees new branch growth has reached over half the usual season's amount. June is the green interlude between the rush of May growth and the July drive of all vegetation toward podding and seeding. After some uncertainty of prolonged warmth in May, all doubt is gone by June. June is alive with the sounds of nature. At dawn many birds are already singing and those humans away from urbanized areas can be awakened at 5 AM, and have to close their windows or put a pillow over their head in order to get another hour or two of sleep. June also brings daytime insect activity to a near maximum.

Precipitation is the key factor in vegetation growth. A wet June will require at least a weekly lawn cutting and bring a surge of garden weeds. The day of weeding seems too often to coincide with rain, and in many years the weeds appear as healthy and as large as the garden crop.

Locally total June rainfall averages about four inches in most of the three county region, which is quite adequate for all vegetation. Like May however, June rainfall can show a wide range of amounts from one-quarter of an inch to over 15 inches (See Monthly Precipitation amounts in Appendices). Not only is the range of monthly totals very great, but individual days have seen amounts greater than what is normal for an entire month.

Nearly 4 inches of rain fell at Dobbs Ferry and Shrub Oak on June 1, 1952. At Carmel, 4.3 inches was recorded on the 16th in 1969. Rains from Tropical Storm Agnes in 1972 resulted in 5.5 inches on the 19th. Over 100 years ago at White Plains in 1884, 6.4 inches in one day came on the 25th of June. Based on statistical probability, a June rainfall of 4 inches or greater in 24 hours can be expected once in 100 years.

The wettest June weather in 1972 when new hourly, daily, weekly and monthly records were set the result of tropical storm "Agnes." The eleven day period from the 16th to the 26th deposited about eight inches of water in nearly all parts of Westchester and Rockland. Other rainy periods in June's weather history came at Bedford Hills when it rained from the 12th to the 25th; June 26 - 28, 1938,

The grim desolation of a remote forest on a bitterly cold night in winter is equal in beauty to that of a flower-starred meadow under a balmy June sun

Charles Burchfield - American artist

3.5 - 4.5 inches in both counties; June, 1968 when measurable amounts were recorded on half the days of the month; June 14 - 16, 1969 when 3 to 4.5 inches fell in both counties.

While vacationers, campers, golfers and other outdoor enthusiasts consider too much rain a tragedy, especially over a weekend, to those who work on the land, growing and caring for crops, drought is the greater evil. An outdoor event can always be rescheduled but the loss of vegetation is permanent.

Memorable dry Junes include 1863, 1873, 1885, 1913, 1949, 1954, 1966, 1971, 1988 and 1995. The worst effects of drought came in the mid 1960s when preceding and succeeding months were also very dry. Under those conditions many farms in the northeast were adversely affected. While very little of our region was farmed in those years, shrubbery, trees and gardens were severely affected.

In the normal weekly rainfall pattern, there is an 80% probability that .2 inches or more will fall in any week in June. There is a 55% probability that .6 inches or more will fall in any week in June. The odds are about one chance in four that 1.2 inches or more will fall in a June week and only one chance in ten that over two inches of rain will fall in any June week.

Except for one day at only one site, (32°F in Shrub Oak on June 18, 1958) temperatures have never registered freezing or below in June. There have been however, numerous days with minimums in the 30s at locations in Putnam and inland areas of northern Westchester. On four occasions in the 20th century lows in the 30s were recorded at Scarsdale. One as late as the 10th of the month. In 1907, Mount Hope reported a low of 38 degrees on the 13th. Other cold spells in June with minimums in the 30s have been June 21 - 23, 1940 in Yorktown Heights; June 5 - 8, 1945 in Yorktown Heights; June 14 - 16, 1958 at Shrub Oak. June 1958 had eight minimums in the 30s at Shrub Oak. That June along with those of 1903, 1912, 1916, 1927, 1947, and 1972 were the coldest. The probability of 30 degree minimums in June is one chance in four in the Hudson Valley climate division and only one chance in ten in the Coastal climate division.

At the other end of the temperature range, hot 90 temperatures in June can occur at any time of the month (See Table 4). While Putnam County has never recorded a 100 degree June temperature, there have been a scattering of such events in the latter part of the month. These were at West Point, Peekskill and Scarsdale in 1925; Mount Vernon and Peekskill in 1936; Bedford Hills in 1943 and 1945; West Point in1952; Scarsdale and Bedford Hills in 1953. A 100 degree temperature in June can be considered as a once in 25 year event in lower Westchester and a once in 50 year event in the Peekskill area.

The hottest Junes of record at Carmel with averages greater than 70°F have been 1892, 1925, and 1943. Those with averages about 69°F were 1949, 1957, 1976, 1984, and 1991. Most of these have had three or more consecutive days of 90+ high temperatures. Some of these heat waves were June 4 - 7, 1925 at Peekskill and Scarsdale, June 24 - 29, 1943 at Bedford Hills, June 25 - 27, 1952 at Scarsdale, June 12 - 14, 1956 at Bedford Hills and Peekskill, and June 13 - 20, 1957 in parts of all three counties.

Fortunately June heat waves are not frequent events and in Carmel, the month normally has only three nonconsecutive days with 90+ maximums, while Scarsdale normally has five such days. The normal daily high temperature in Rockland ranges from 80 to 84 degrees during the month and from 75 to 80 degrees in the northern Westchester and Putnam.

FIGURE 13

JULY

The height of the summer season comes with July. While some of the hottest days of a given summer may come in June or August, for long-term consistancy you can rely on the heat of July. Surprisingly, the hottest days of the summer do not coincide with the longest days of summer. The longest days of the year with the greatest possible sunshine are June 20, 21, 22. The hottest week of summer based on 100 year averages is the third week of July, nearly a full month after the summer solstice, the furthest north sunset or that point when the sun is directly overhead at the Tropic of Cancer (See Tables 7, 8, 9). Climatologists explain this discrepancy by noting that it takes two to three weeks of near maximum daylight to warm the land to the point of greatest heat.

That heat is what is longed for after many months of uncertainty. All our wanderlust dreams, our yearning for outdoor tennis and swimming, camping, golf and more assume reliable summer warmth.

In the lower Hudson valley, the long-term 20th century U.S. Weather Service Stations at Carmel/Yorktown Heights and West Point those formerly at Scarsdale and Bedford Hills show that the eleven days between July 16th and 26th are the warmest of the year. During this period the average daily high temperature is about 86 degrees at Scarsdale and 83 degrees at Carmel/ Yorktown Heights. If one wishes to escape or enjoy the worst or best of summer's heat this is the time to vacation. One should be cautioned that our great climate variability insures that peak heat in some summers can come in August. While this makes the following of climate patterns interesting to weather buffs, it can often frustrate the best made vacation plans.

Extreme July heat can often persist when three or more days of 90°+ maximums occur in a heat wave. Some of these have been; Mount Hope - July 15 - 19, 1900 and July 3 - 11, 1911; All three counties - July 8 - 11, 1936; Suffern & Bedford Hills- July 5 - 12, 1944; All counties - July 1949, three separate heat waves(14 to 19 days of 90°+ maxima); All counties - July 1955 (10 to 18 days of 90°+ maxima); All counties July 1 - 4, 1966. Included in some of these hot spells were 100 degree maxima. The most recent Westchester county 100°+ degree mark came on July 15, 1995 when Ardsley, West Point, Westchester Airport and Yorktown Heights registered those highs. Based on long term records 100°+ maximum temperatures can be expected once every seven years

Hot July brings cooling showers
Strawberries and gilly flowers
Weatherlore

in the south and every fifteen years in north Westchester and Putnam (See Table 15, 16). July 1999 recorded the hottest month of the Westchester/Putnam record with about half the days showing 90°+ maximums.

In a normal July, high daily temperatures range between 83 and 87 degrees and eight days can be expected to have 90+ degree maxima in Westchester. In Putnam daily highs are about 83 degrees with six 90°+ maxima the norm (See Figure 25).

The hottest Julys of record at Carmel/Yorktown Heights and West Point averaging over 74 degrees have been 1901, 1908, 1921, 1949, 1952, 1955, 1988, 1993, 1994, 1995 and 1999. The most recent of these is not only the hottest July of record, but also the hottest of any month (77.7°F) and (79.4°F).

Along with the peak warmth of the year comes an atmosphere that holds a greater amount of moisture. In July the average relative humidity is 70%, with a range of 90% relative humidity at sunrise to 50% at early afternoon.

Cold in July is associated with daily low temperatures in the 40s and mid-day highs below 65 degrees. An occasional low mark is quite bearable since it usually comes at dawn when few are out of bed. When two or more consecutive days with such temperatures occur, a summer vacation or outdoor activity can be ruined. July often produces an anomalous cooling in the second week of the month. In the north county (Westchester) three-day periods of July 40 degree minimums have occurred in 1940, 1943 and 1965. In 1954, Shrub Oak, the coldest Westchester location with a weather station had six days of lows in the 40s. In 86 years of records, Scarsdale has had 19 July days with lows in the high 40s, while Carmel has had at least twice that number with record lows in the 40s on every day of the month (See Table 6). Suffern with 60 years of records has had 25 July days with lows in the 40s.

In Westchester normal daily low temperatures range from 58 degrees in the north to 63 degrees in the south. In Putnam they average about 58 degrees (See Figure 26).

A temperature below 50 degrees in southern Westchester is a once in five year event in July, but can occur two out of every three years in Putnam county. Normal daily lows are 64 degrees in the south and 61 in the north. At Carmel, the coldest Julys of record, averaging less than 68 degrees were 1888,

1891, 1925, 1960, and 1962.

July rainfall is normally quite adequate for all vegetation. Averages in different pasts of the three counties including the Croton watershed range from 4 to 5 inches with about 4.5 the most central figure. The high variability of July rainfall as with the other warm season months, shows a range of monthly totals from less than one inch to over 13 inches. As with the other warm months of the year when the air is able to hold more moisture, individual days have had amounts fall in excess of what is normal for the entire month. A rainfall over four inches coming in one day can be expected in our region about once every 25 years.

Daily rainfall coming in from thunderstorms can be very spotty with over an inch at one site and none falling relatively close by. Lightning and hailstones can often accompany many of the severer storms.

While July in the years of 1933, 1936, 1954, 1955 and 1983 have given all three counties totals two or more inches less than normal, the three Julys in 1962, 1966 and 1968 had the most serious effects on vegetation as that occurred about or within the general great drought period of the mid 1960s. The drought in 1966 (totals of 1 - 1.5 inches) was also combined with intense heat to make the situation even worse.

The Julys of 1933, 1945, 1960, 1969, 1984 and 1996 were the wettest in different parts of both counties with amounts in excess of ten inches.

Individual July rainy periods have been: 1897 - over two inches on three separate days at Bedford Hills and Carmel; July 15 - 23, 1938 - over seven inches area wide with 14 days having rainfall; 1947 - 12 continuous days of small amounts of rain; 1960 - four days during the month with one inch or more including eight inches on the 30th at Bedford Hills (greatest 20th century July 24 hour amount); 1967 - 14 days with measurable rainfall; 1984 about five inches on the 6th and 7th; 1996 - four days with one or more inches of rainfall at Yorktown

The normal probabilities of weekly rain in July are far less spectacular. The chance of .2 inches falling is 90%; of .6 inches 60%; of 1.2 inches 22%; there is a one in eight chance of 2 or more inches, a one in twelve chance of 2.8 inches and only one chance in twenty of four or more inches.

Under the old barn wolf spiders weave a maze of nets to catch unwary flies. Good luck, spiders!

FIGURE 14

AUGUST

To city dwellers, August weather can be a copy of July. There is plenty of heat, with many of the same sultry hot humid days and comfortable night time temperatures. When one leaves the urbanized areas, however, and looks about carefully, one can sense and see a difference between the months. One subtle change is the light at midday. The sun's angle in the sky now is lower than it was in early July. By August we have also lost an hour and a half of daily sunlight. The sun is distinctly moving south in its setting on the western horizon. By the last week of August the first touch of autumn often reaches us in the form of a cold front, followed by a day or two of crystal clear days with chilly night temperatures. This is a touch that July never had.

August is harvest time for local gardeners. Tomatoes, cucumbers, squash and the longer root vegetables are ready for the table. Goldenrod and ragweed now cause their discomfort to many, late in the month. Hurricanes now make the news, potentially threatening our region.

The first chilly touch of fall comes with low temperatures in the 40s in the north. Occasionally such lows are felt in southern Westchester.

On rare occasions, minimums in the high 30s have been registered in the north in the latter part of the month. Some chilly periods have occurred during the last week of August in 1946, August 23 - 29, 1957, and in the middle of 1963. In 1964 there were twelve days with lows in the 40s and colder at Shrub Oak. The earliest coldest minimum (31°F) was recorded on the 25th in 1940 at Yorktown Heights. Such cold, a rarity in the north, is not seen in the south until September.

The coldest Augusts with average temperatures less than 67°F for the weather station with the longest complete record (Carmel/Yorktown Heights) were those of 1903, 1905, 1909, 1912, 1915, 1919, 1927, 1934, 1946, 1962, 1963, and 1964. The coldest of these with averages less than 65 F were 1903 and 1927.

In the Palisades Interstate Park, Putnam and northern Westchester, normal daily low temperatures range from 60 degrees at the beginning of the month to 55 at the end. In southern Westchester this temperature range is from 63 to 59 degrees.

Not that there is any lack of heat in August. It is an unusual August in the lower Hudson valley that

Fairest of the months! Ripe Summer's Queen, the Hey-day of the year With robes than gleam of sunny sheen, sweet August doth appear
R. Combe Miller

does not provide any 90 degree days. Normally there are five such days in the south and 3 in the north. While these hot days are usually distributed throughout the month, when they occur consecutively for three or more days, we have a heat wave. Some of the more noteworthy of these were: August 5 - 9, 1918 - highs in the high 90s in southern Westchester; August 10 - 17, 1944 - all days with maxima well over 90 including two 100 degree days; August 25 - 29, 1948 - mostly in high 90s with three 100+ degree days; August 25 - September 4, 1953 - high temperatures up to 104 degrees; August 1 - 7, 1955 - highs up to 101 degrees; August 12 - 22, 1959 - highs in low 90s in nearly all areas.; August 10 - 16, 1988 - one week of heat with high in mid 90s for most of the area.

One hundred degree maximum temperatures are not uncommon. In the 80 year Scarsdale records there have been eleven August days with highs over 100 degrees, up to 104. West Point at its warm location has registered twelve separate such August days in over 100 years of records. At the long term stations of Carmel, and Bedford Hills with over 90 years of daily records there have been five such days (See Table 4).

Hottest Augusts averaging about 73°F or higher at Carmel were 1937, 1939, 1944, 1955, 1959, 1980, and 1988. Normal August daily high temperatures range from 82 at the start to 77 degrees at the end of the month in the north and 85 at the start to 81 degrees at the end of the month in the south.

August precipitation can range in form from light drizzle to torrential downpours and include hailstones the size of marbles. On average, August is the wettest month of the year, just slightly wetter than July. Tropical storms with heavy rains, the remnants of hurricanes, have made August the wettest. However as little as one half an inch was measured in 1964 and as great a total as 17 inches in 1955 has been measured. Normal amounts for August in all three counties range from 4.3 to 4.8 inches.

The greatest one or more days of rainfall are associated with the byproducts of hurricanes. After reaching land, winds greater than 75 miles per hour drop to gale force or lower. However the heavy rainfall associated with the storm does not lessen and often can increase, as the storm is now moving less rapidly.

Four August hurricanes named Carol, Connie,

Diane and Doria have all left their precipitation marks on both our counties. Connie and Diane coming within one week of each other in 1955 caused major damage from flooding and washouts. The rainfall measured, approached record levels for hourly amounts up to 12 hours, and resulted in the second wettest month in Westchester weather history. In many areas of our region five to nine inches fell in two days from Connie alone. Tropical storm Carol, on the last day of the month, gave us three inches, while Doria in 1971 gave northern Westchester its wettest August day with 6.86 inches, a once in 100 year event. August 1933 had an eight day period with a six to eight inch total.

It is only after the erosive effects of such huge masses of water on our countryside that we realize how rapidly a landscape can change. We get lulled into a sense of security over many years and come to believe that nature's more devastating effects will not touch us. After all, earthquakes almost never affect us, tidal waves up the Hudson River are a rarity and tornadoes are seen perhaps once in a lifetime here. But for those who live or work in valleys and those with homes on the sides of unprotected hills, any moderate rainfall of long duration or combined with high intensity can subject many to flash floods and washouts. Any 24 hour rainfall over two inches is a matter of concern, and when prolonged, raises the potential for disaster. The ground quickly becomes saturated, sloping hillsides become a sheet of running water and low areas turn into ponds and lakes where none previously existed. Trees can get uprooted, roads and homes flooded, depending on the topography of their location. While it is unlikely that most of us will see such pluvial events more than once or twice, we should all be aware that such potential exists in our local climate. Heavy August total rainfall amounts over ten inches have occurred in our two counties in 1875, 1901, 1915, 1933, 1937, 1942, 1945, 1955, 1974.

The flip side of flood is drought. Drought is a slower process but is devastating in its own way to vegetation and to the non-irrigated farmland of the northeast. (See Diaries). A two month drought started in the last week of August 1908. In the year before, August had less than half the normal amount with no rain between the 7th and 16th. In 1944 less than one half inch fell during the first two weeks of the month. In terms of prolonged effect, the drought of August 1964 was the worst, coming after months of extended dryness. No rain fell in lower Westchester the first eleven days, and what came after was less than one half inch. In Putnam and northern Westchester the total for that month was greater but still less than half of what is normal. August totals, less than one inch, have come in the years 1899, 1953, 1964, 1968, and 1981.

Normally August precipitation provides one or two rains over one inch, three or four with amounts of one half inch, and smaller amounts up to a quarter of an inch. This is adequate and still leaves us with enough sunshine.

SEPTEMBER

The garden bounty fills basket and barrow as we hurry to harvest our winter vegetables before the frost can claim them.

FIGURE 15

SEPTEMBER

September is beautifully described by Hal Borland, former New York Times editorial page naturalist. September he says, "Is the year at the turn, a young mother sending her children off to school and wondering if she can catch up with the unfinished tasks of Summer. It is Autumn at hand and Summer reluctant to leave, it is hot days and cool nights, hurricanes and flood. September is the bright gleam of goldenrod and the purple and lavender of fence row asters. September is fog at dawn over river valleys and lakes and the creep of scarlet on the tupelos, Virginia creeper and among the swamp maples. It is the late phlox like a flame in the garden and zinnias in bold color."

September blow soft,
till fruits in the loft
Old English Motto

All along the stone walls of many abandoned farms of Putnam are the ragweeds, pigweeds, milkweeds, burdock, thistles and sumac grown to full height to join the spectacle of the oncoming autumn.

In September, days are shortening as fast as they were lengthening in March. Even by the autumnal equinox, with the sun setting directly west and moving quickly south, the summer's warmth still lingers with normal daily high temperatures in the mid 70s. The month can almost be considered as summer since it only averages three to five degrees cooler than June. By the calendar and the sky summer ends on the 21st of the month. Climatologically, however, summer ends about the 8th of the month, when the last of the warmest 91 days of the year occurs. Over the years September in the lower Hudson valley has proved to be summer like, and were it not for school opening, youngsters would still be swimming into the second week, as 80+ degree daily highs are common in all parts of our region, even to the equinox (See Tables 7, 8, 9).

Summer-like extremes of heat are not unknown in our two counties, with highs into the high 90s early in the month. It is rare however to find more than two such consecutive days. In southern Westchester two 90 degree days are normal for September, while northward only one can be expected during the month.

In 1906 Mount Hope registered two days of 90+ maxima in the second and third week of the month. In 1929 there were three consecutive days of 90+ heat in the first week of the month at Mount Vernon, Scarsdale and Bedford Hills. In 1931 Bedford Hills registered four 90+ days after the 9th of the month. In 1941, Ossining and Bedford Hills reported three consecutive days of such highs as late as the 24th. September 1946 saw three consecutive days of such heat at Carmel starting on the 18th. In 1953 a continuation of a late August heat wave gave both counties five scorching days with highs soaring to 100+ degrees on the second of the month at Dobbs Ferry, Westchester Airport, Scarsdale, and Bedford Hills, the only time such a high has been reached in September. In 1961 the first six days of September had highs hovering about the 90 degree mark for all of our area.

Hottest Septembers averaging near 66 degrees and higher, dating back to 1888 at Carmel were 1891, 1915, 1921, 1959, 1968, 1971, and 1983.

Gardeners south of the waistline of Westchester can take comfort in knowing that their garden will probably never feel a frost in September. Freezing and below has only occurred there six times in the 20th century, the last of which was in 1957 at Scarsdale.

In Rockland and West Point below freezing has not occurred before the fourth week of the month. Increased urbanization make it highly unlikely that such low temperatures will recur. North of the waistline in the Hudson Valley Climate Division the climate shows a very different picture. From mid-month on, extreme lows have been registered on nearly every day at four U.S. Weather stations. The warming influence of Long Island Sound and the Hudson River are key factors as Peekskill has had only four days in September with freezing or below, while Yorktown Heights and Carmel inland have had twelve such days. A reminder of the cold to come often occurs in the second week of the month, the week when climatological summer ends.

During September, the average daily temperature drops eight degrees, from 70 degrees in the south and from 66 degrees in the north.

There have been eight cold Septembers in Putnam that have averaged between 59 and 60 degrees, the most recent of which was 1988. Five Septembers were even colder. These occurred in 1893, 1917, 1918, 1924, and 1963.

One has to include the effects of tropical storms when discussing September rains. While only six such storms have reached Westchester and Putnam in the last 60 years, these have left severe impacts on our landscape as well as on our imagination, so that this month is always associated with the "hurricane season" in the minds of all weather watchers. The addition of nicknames and accurate television coverage of these tropical storms on the entire east coast has heightened public awareness of their impact. Remember in September- Edna (1954), Donna (1969), Eloise (1975) and Floyd (1999).

As in August, all significant rainfall amounts from one to 24 hours and from one to ten days are connected with these tropical storms. Except for the 1938, 1944 and 1960 hurricanes where there was extensive wind damage, most of the adverse effects have come from the heavy rainfall. The wettest and most destructive by far in our lower Hudson valley came from the deluge (9 - 11 inches) on September 17, 1999, with the greatest recorded one day rainfall for all months. The wettest Septembers with totals over ten inches were 1882, 1907, 1934, 1938, 1944, 1975 and 1999 (See Table 21).

But for tropical storm precipitation, September would be one of the driest months of the year. These heavy rain events make September the third wettest of the year. The 112 year Carmel/Yorktown Heights precipitation record shows thirteen days with 24 hour amounts greater than three inches giving a September flood probability of once every eight years.

The oldest Westchester rain gauges at Kensico Dam and at Croton Lake show September in the years 1881, 1884, 1885, 1914, 1941 and 1948 as having less than one inch of rainfall (See Appendices H & P). For a region of relatively high humidity, to have as little as one inch of rain in an entire month requires a combination of dry continental air and a pattern of air flow or stagnation that will continuously maintain itself. To achieve this in the northeast part of this country is quite a meteorological feat in an area where atmospheric conditions are so changeable. However, these patterns were in place to produce drought conditions in 1914, 1941 and 1948 when September totals less than one half inch fell throughout our region.

FIGURE 16

OCTOBER

October in the lower Hudson valley can be characterized by one word - "change." For visitors unfamiliar with our region which segues from urban to suburban to near rural, October can be a startling month. Subjectively, being outdoors for most people will change from comfortable at the beginning to discomfort at the end.

After five months of a green landscape, the transition to a bare landscape begins in October. Most Octobers begin with predominantly green scenery in the first week. During the second week, the trees in Palisades Interstate Park, northern Westchester and Putnam start their change to all other colors of the spectrum. Normally, by mid month all of the wooded areas are a riot of colored splendor. Words fail to describe a perfect October sunny day with the leaf color at it peak. By the third week, too quickly, many of these painted leaves begin to fall and in most years by the end of the last week nearly all trees except for the oaks and an occasional sugar maple are denuded. This rapid change from a fully green vista to a naked horizon in one month gives one a keener sense of nature's changes.

October daylight is the equivalent of what it was the previous March and is dwindling rapidly. Along with the diminishing light is the normal eleven degree drop in average temperature during the month. The only month during the year that shows a greater change in temperature is April.

The significant climate event in October is the coming of the first freezing and below temperatures (See Table 13). Past history shows that this event can come a early as the first week or as late as the last week of October. Normally October 7th and 16th are the first frost dates in the north and in the south. While the variability of climate in our region will often result in a change of these dates, gardeners should take these norms seriously.

Local topography and bodies of water can greatly influence the day of the first killing frost. Even a small lake with its stored reservoir of heat can keep frost from appearing within a few hundred yards of its shores. Long Island Sound, the Hudson River and the Croton reservoir network of lakes delay the appearance of frost near their shores. The first frost or killing frost (below 30°F) will usually come on a clear still night soon after the passage of a cold front.

The progression of freezing and below

*The chill is on from near and far
In all the months that have an R*

unknown source

minimum temperatures for Putnam and northern Westchester expressed in terms of odds is as follows - September 20 - a 1 in 10 chance; September 28 - a 1 in 4 chance; October 1 - a 1 in 3 chance; October 7 - a 1 in 2 chance (even odds); October 13 - a 2 in 3 chance; October 16 - a 3 in 4 chance; and October 24 - a 9 in 10 chance. For southern Westchester the above probabilities are later by nine days. Extreme minimum temperatures in the 20s are rare at Mount Vernon, Dobbs Ferry and Ossining reflecting their locations near the warmer New York City and the major bodies of nearby water.

In a normal October there are only three days with below freezing minimums in the south, and six in the north. Normal daily low temperatures about mid-October are 43 degrees in the north and 46 in the south. At Shrub Oak in northern Westchester, long known as the "ice box" of the county, lows into the teens have been recorded on a dozen October mornings.

Coldest Octobers at Carmel, averaging about 45 degrees occurred in the years 1888, 1895, 1907 and 1925. Along with below freezing temperatures has come that October rarity- snow. Twentieth century snowfalls have been limited to eight Octobers with measurable amounts up to three inches in four events. The earliest Westchester snowfall came on October 4, 1987 at Yorktown Heights when one eighth of an inch was measured. At that location six inches was recorded on October 10, 1979. Putnam has reported at least six 20th century Octobers with measurable snowfalls.

By October, the fires of summer heat are gone, although extreme highs in the 80s can occur through the end of the month, in both counties, giving an occasional touch of summer. A rare 90+ degree maximum has even been felt on five October days in the 20th century in the years 1908, 1939, 1941, 1950, and 1959 at five U.S. Weather Service Cooperative stations. The hottest Octobers of the 20th century with averages equal or greater than 57 degrees at West Point and Carmel/Yorktown Heights have been 1920, 1947, 1949, 1954, 1971, and 1990.

Total precipitation during October averages about 3.5 inches for all counties, a distinct drop from the previous four warmest months of the year. October is also the month with the greatest number of clear days, caused by high pressure cells stalled over the mid-Appalachian mountains.

As little as one eighth of an inch fell in October 1924 at the Cross River rain gauge in the Croton watershed, while 16 inches total was measured in 1955. That year had the only 20th century October with over ten inches.

Heaviest amounts in hourly and daily categories came during the great October 1955 storm from the 14th to the 17th when amounts of six to eight inches were measured in the area. Individual days at some locations had amounts of 4 inches. An October rainfall of three inches or greater can be expected once every 20 years.

Fortunately, the normal October precipitation regime is far from those flood producing extremes. There is a 50% probability of .6 inches of rain falling in one week, a 25% probability of 1.2 inches in one week, and only one chance in ten of more than two inches falling in the same period.

FIGURE 17

NOVEMBER

Brown is the predominant November landscape color for the northern parts of our three county region. By the end of the first week the last golden leaves of the sugar maples have dropped to the ground. Only the oaks and beeches hold on to their leaves, now shades of brown. The wind, for the first time since early April can at times be heard from within a house. The open starkness of the countryside is in vivid contrast to the landscape of the previous six months. Now the land becomes visible again and the terrain, contour, crest, ridge and escarpment become the dominant earth features.

The climate of a region is difficult to determine by only knowing the average temperature and precipitation. An improvement is made by adding a knowledge of the probabilities of temperature occurrence. For low temperatures, in northern Westchester, Putnam and the Palisades Interstate Park region there is a two in three chance that temperatures will drop to 24 degrees or below by November 19. By November 13 these odds increase to three out of four. By November 21, the odds are ten to one that 24 degrees or below will be reached. By November 25, 16 degrees or lower can come one out of four chances. For the Coastal Division of southern Westchester add ten to fourteen days to those noted above. In November there are normally between four and ten days when temperatures are below freezing about dawn, but rise above freezing during the day.

The above method of describing November's low temperature regime helps, but is still not wholly satisfactory since the lows cited generally occur only in the early morning and thus are not typical.

November can also be described by citing the number of days that the temperature drops below freezing or goes above 60 degrees. Thus a warm month would have fewer of the former and a cold month fewer of the latter. One would indicate an uncomfortable day while the other would be a comfortable outdoor time. In the north, November normally has 18 days with below freezing minimums and six with above 60 maximums. In the south there are twelve and nine such days respectively.

In a cold November such as 1933, Carmel had 19 days with below freezing minimums and only 2

If there's ice in November that will bear a duck

There'll be nothing after but sludge and muck

old time climatology

with 60 degrees or above. Scarsdale that month had nine days below freezing and four of 60 and higher.

In the warm November of 1948, Carmel had ten days of below freezing minimums and thirteen with maximums of 60+ degrees. At Scarsdale that month there were seven of the former and fifteen of the latter.

A contributing temperature factor to the cold November of 1933 was the cold spell from the 15th to the 17th when all counties had lows in the teens. In 1936 the month gave the region five to seven days of lows in the teens or below and in 1951 from eight to twelve days saw minimums in the teens or colder. In that latter month Shrub Oak recorded such lows in nine of its last eleven days.

Normal daily low temperatures during November run from 41 to 31 degrees in the south and 37 to 27 degrees in the north. Temperatures below ten degrees can be expected once in 12 years in the north and once in 25 years in the south.

Most cold Novembers with averages about 36 degrees and below at Carmel and West Point occurred early in the 20th century in the years 1901, 1903, 1904, 1911, 1917, 1933 and 1936 (See Appendices A, F).

Warmest Novembers have followed the pattern mentioned above with few below freezing minimums and many warm days with highs over 60 degrees. Maximum temperatures of 70+ have been recorded in the area through the third week of the month and even extreme maximum temperatures in the 80s were registered in the first days of the month at four weather stations in 1950 (the only time in the 20th century). A 75 degree day and higher is a once in six year November event in Scarsdale but only has a frequency of every 40 years in Carmel. Warmest Novembers with monthly averages about 46 and higher at Carmel/Yorktown Heights were 1902, 1931, 1948, 1963, 1975, 1979, 1990, and 1994.

As one can see, there is no single best method to evaluate temperatures of any given month. One certainly cannot rely on one's memory. A single cold weather experience can color one's perception of an entire month. Within our region the natural climate variability can also insure that a cold week be followed by a hot spell.

November snow can also color one's memory. Snow is a regular aspect of November climate with one to two inches normal for the area generally coming in the last week of the month. Snowfalls earlier, like those of April have little staying power and are usually gone within a day. Single storm amounts as great as eleven inches have been measured even in southern Westchester (Thanksgiving Day, 1938 at Scarsdale). Of the 20th century November snows, 1938 and 1968 appear to have the greatest total amounts with 18 and 11 inches respectively. In 1882 a total accumulation of 22 inches was measured at White Plains. Except for November 1995 there has been no November snow in the 1990s.

Precipitation in November averages between 4 and 4.5 inches at the many rain gauge sites in the three counties. Extreme totals range from as little as a trace at Bedford Hills in 1917 to as great as ten inches at the Kensico dam in 1972. Individual days have seen amounts as great as 5 inches. The wettest November was 1972 with totals of eight to ten inches throughout the counties. Rainless periods up to three weeks in length have occurred in 1904, 1917, 1949, 1960, and 1976. The driest occurred in 1917 and 1976.

DECEMBER

The first snow of winter
swirls silent in the night
The stoveside season
has begun.

FIGURE 18

DECEMBER

December is the start of winter, both astronomically and climatologically. While the shortest day of the year, the winter solstice does not come till the 4th week of the month, the earliest sunset comes at the end of the first week. December is the third coldest month of the year, marking it as a winter month. Although it is the warmest of the winter months it has the necessary ingredient to produce the crowning product of winter, namely snow. Cold is that ingredient, and the rapidly falling daily average temperature provides us with enough after the first week (See Tables 7, 8, 9). In the Coastal climate division of Westchester, the average daily temperature by the second week is in the low 30s. By early December the sun is now at its earliest sunset and also is at its lowest point above the horizon. This lower or flatter angle together with the least amount of daylight of the year provides the coldness at the start of the winter season. The last two days of November and first few in December often produce a sharply colder week rather than a gradual drop in temperature.

By mid December, normal daily low temperatures are in the high teens in the north and in the low 20s in the south. In a typical December there are two days of zero and below minimums in the north and none in the south. Below freezing lows can be expected 28 days of the month in the north and 25 days in the south. Normally December temperatures rise above freezing and slip below freezing on fifteen days in Putnam, and on ten such freeze- thaw days in southern Westchester.

Really cold winter temperatures are always associated with zero Fahrenheit. In Putnam and northern Westchester, extreme below zero minimums have come as early as the 4th day of the month, but not until the 3rd week in the south.

"Below zero" is a familiar term to all of us that endure winter in the northeastern part of the United States. When one hears the term mentioned in a weather report or forecast, we know that extreme cold is the subject.

During the second coldest December of the century in 1917 there were four days with zero and below minimums in the south and seven in the north. In 1950, there were two such days at Scarsdale and three at Shrub Oak. In 1958 and 1960, December dealt five days of below zero lows to Shrub Oak but none in the south. In 1962 and 1963 there were three days of below zero low in the north and one in the south. The coldest of December cold waves was the last three days of 1917

What freezings have I felt,
what dark days seen,
What old December's bareness everywhere!
Sonnet 97
William Shakespeare

when not only did the temperature drop below zero (-19°F), sixteen below at West Point, but it never rose above zero for three consecutive days at Carmel. Coldest Decembers at Carmel with averages below 23 degrees were 1903, 1904, 1917, and 1989.

Warm Decembers have no zero lows, fewer below freezing days, numerous days with highs in the 50s or higher and of course, less snow. While 36 degrees in the north and 41 in the south are the normal highs about the middle of the month, extremes in the 60s have occurred in the past at nine temperature monitoring stations. A most recent warm spell was that of December 4th to 6th 1982, when highs as great as the mid 60s were registered at Yorktown Heights, Dobbs Ferry, Scarsdale and Westchester Airport.

The warmest Decembers at West Point and Carmel/ Yorktown with averages over 36 degrees were 1891, 1923, 1931, 1982, 1990 and 1998.

Total precipitation during December averages just under four inches, but can range from as little as one-half an inch (1955) to as great as 9 - 10 inches (1973). In months with above normal precipitation most of it has come as rain rather than snow. In those wet months the temperatures are usually warmer. Individual days of rainfalls totaling three inches or more are rare and have occurred about once at each long-term rain gauge. Nineteenth century records at White Plains however, show two December days measuring over four inches.

Snow in December or in any winter month is an "iffy" business. In order to get any snow, weather conditions have to fall within certain narrow ranges. Temperature, air moisture, and barometric pressure have to be just right. In order to get heavy snow these conditions have to persist, something that is even harder to obtain in nature. Thus heavy snows of nine inches or greater can be expected only every other year, while a two foot snowfall is a once in 30 year event. (See Table 30).

Normal total snowfall for December is 8.2 inches at Scarsdale and 9.4 inches at Carmel and in the lower Hudson valley has ranged from just a trace in 1953, 1954 and 1965 to 30 inches in 1947. A 19th century December total of 32 inches was measured in White Plains in 1876. In the north the average date of the first one inch snowfall is December 1. The majority of December snowfalls are quite small (about one inch) and the chances for rain to fall are greater than for snow in most of the month.

WEATHER PHENOMENA

THE ZERO DAYS OF WINTER

There is a mystique surrounding the zero degree temperature mark. It has become a benchmark for the epitome of coldness. By itself, it is a barrier to human outdoor activity and when combined with wind, creates a "wind chill" that will drive the hardiest to seek shelter. The term Wind Chill is the subjective evaluation of the combination of a given low temperature with a given wind speed. With or without the wind, zero and below create outdoor conditions where only fools or heroes venture forth.

When considering the zero degree point, one has to specify the temperature scale or system used. The zero degree point on the Celsius/Centigrade scale is quite different from the zero on the Fahrenheit scale. Worldwide, the United States is the only country that still measures temperature on the Fahrenheit scale. There are good reasons for the United States to convert to the metric system.

However in the case of temperature, the Fahrenheit scale is a better one as it can measure temperature to a closer accuracy by a factor nearly double that of the Centigrade scale.

Zero on the Centigrade scale is 32 Fahrenheit degrees warmer than Fahrenheit zero and so will never convey the same thermal impact. If conversion to the centigrade system is ever made, zero Fahrenheit will become -17°C, an easily forgettable number that will never have the impact of our own 0°F. If such a change is soon made, old-timers may joke that 21st century winters without 0°F can never have the same "zing and wallop" that the 20th century ones did.

In an examination of the zero cold shown below, one should note that other than January, our normally coldest month there have been no cold spells, with zero or below lasting more than one day in the other winter months for the last two decades of the 20th century.

Within our three county region, zero temperatures almost define winter. Zero (F) degree daily minimum temperatures have occurred as early as the first week of December and have been recorded as late as the third week of March, almost at the Vernal Equinox. It may be comforting to note that these coldest minimum temperatures usually come with little or no air movement and generally happen about dawn when few of us are outdoors. (See Table 6)

Some of the more memorable cold spells or cold waves that have persisted for two or more consecutive days are given by month as follows:

DECEMBER

1835 - Below zero (-22°) was recorded at Poughkeepsie on the 16th of the month.

Late 19th century White Plains temperature records show individual days of zero or below in 1880, 1882, 1883, 1884, the earliest of these reported on December 4, 1882.

1914 - Below zero marks were set at Scarsdale, Bedford Hills and Carmel on the 26th and 27th.

1917 - In the coldest spell of the 20th century on the last three days of the month there were three "zero days" at Carmel (-19°F) when the temperature did not rise above zero. West Point set its coldest December low of sixteen below zero. At Mount Vernon, Scarsdale, Bedford Hills, and Carmel below zero minimums lasted for seven days into January 1918.

1919 - Below zero minimums were recorded at West Point, Mount Hope and Bedford Hills on the 18th.

1933 - There were three days of zero cold, including one "zero day" at Carmel. Four stations and West Point reported below zero lows on two days beginning the 29th.

1942 - Six consecutive days of below zero minimums were recorded at Carmel beginning on the 17th. Bedford Hills and West Point registered three below zero lows in this period.

1948 - A three day cold spell came to Yorktown Heights and two days at Carmel beginning on Christmas day

1950 - December 27th and 28th brought below zero low cold at Shrub Oak and Carmel

1955 - Only Putnam experienced this short two day cold snap of below zero lows on the first day of astronomical winter.

1958 - In a month with five zero and below lows, there were only two such days back to back at Suffern, Shrub Oak and Carmel

1960 - Two cold spells came to Carmel and one to Shrub Oak and Suffern, the earliest on the 23rd.

1980 - This was a Christmas day cold snap at Dobbs Ferry, Scarsdale, Westchester Airport, Carmel and Yorktown Heights. There were two consecutive below zero days at Suffern.

JANUARY

1821 - Surges of below zero cold as low as fourteen below from the 16th to the 26th following a cold November and December froze the Hudson River as far south as Tribeca (triangle below Canal Street) in New York City opposite Jersey City permitting crossings there. At the western end of Long Island Sound, it was solid ice from New Rochelle across to Long Island.

1835 - Standard thermometers at the New York State Regents Academy in North Salem registered a sunrise reading of 31 below zero on the fifth of the month in a below zero week.

1852 - Severe near zero and below cold for the latter part of the month at New York City froze the East River so that it could be crossed on foot for many on the 20th.

1857 - On the 18th of the month the temperature did not rise above 2 above zero in New York City in this coldest January of record. Manhattan Island was icebound for a few days.

1859 - White Plains on the 10th had a zero day with a high of 10 below zero.

1866 - Records reveal White Plains on January 8 reporting 20 below zero, with 15 below in New York City.

1899 - There was a two day cold spell at the start of the year, Bedford Hills recording -17° F

1904 - Five and two day long spells of below zero minimums were recorded at Carmel (-15°F) and Bedford Hills (-17°F) the longest beginning on January 2. Carmel had three consecutive "zero days" - with highs of each day below zero.

1914 - A cold wave across New York State on the 13-14th produced another zero day at Carmel

Below zero lows were recorded at Mount Hope, Scarsdale, Bedford Hills and West Point.

1918 - See December 1917

1925 - Two cold spells came in the fourth week of the month in all but southern Westchester.

1935 - Three to five days of the last week of the month had below zero minimums areawide.

1945 - Cold wave conditions brought two below zero periods to Carmel and one to Bedford Hills.

1948 - Of the six days with below zero minimums in the latter part of the month at Scarsdale, three were consecutive. At Carmel, there were twelve such days with two three day spells of consecutive below zero lows. At Shrub Oak with ten such days, 21 below zero was registered on the 19th.

1957 - In northern Westchester, Putnam and Rockland there were six consecutive days with below zero lows beginning on the 14th of the month. Shrub Oak recorded nine days with below zero minimums and a low of -23° F on the 18th.

1961 - The longest 20th century cold wave in the north began on the 20th of the month and lasted through the first week of February. Record marks as low as 24 and 25 below zero were set on the 22nd at Carmel and Shrub Oak respectively. In the south, four continuous days of below zero minimums were reported at three government weather stations. At Suffern sixteen below zero was its coldest of record.

1964 - A two day (15,16), cold spell in the north gave below zero lows at Carmel and Shrub Oak

1968 - Four to six consecutive days of zero and below minimum readings were reported at all Weather Service Cooperative stations starting on the 10th. Peekskill had five such days.

1976 - Two below zero cold spells were registered at Carmel and Yorktown Heights

1977 - At Dobbs Ferry, Scarsdale and Westchester Airport, a two day cold spell began on the 17th

In the north county and Putnam there were three such days.

1981 - Yorktown Heights endured four consecutive days with below zero lows starting on the 11th

1994 - Three consecutive days of below zero minimums were recorded at Westchester Airport, Ardsley and Yorktown Heights beginning on the 19th. Low readings of -12°F and -15°F were registered readings at Peekskill, Yorktown Heights and West Point on the 27th.

1996 - Yorktown Heights registered a two day cold wave with 6 below zero on the 6th and 7th.

FEBRUARY

1813 - "Early that month the cold was so severe that people had no trouble crossing the river on two days and the ice was sufficiently well packed to permit of loaded sleighs crossing from the Jersey shore to this city."

1836 - Below zero lows during the first week froze the Hudson and East Rivers at New York City permitting hundreds to cross the ice at all hours on the 6th. The western end of Long Island Sound was frozen for 50 days and the ice barrier at Throg's Neck not broken till the 9th of March.

1861 - On the 8th, nine below zero was reported in New York City. It was certainly ten degrees colder in Putnam County.

1875 - "Between the 9th and the 13th many were able to cross the Hudson at New York City."

1907 - During this month there were three 2 day cold waves at Bedford Hills and Scarsdale and two 3 day and one four day spell of below zero minimums at Carmel (-23°F).

1914 - Mount Hope and Scarsdale reported two cold spells of three and two day duration. Below zero minimums were registered at West Point on three days.

1916 - Two periods of 2 days of below zero readings characterized the month at nearly all six reporting weather stations.

1918 - Below zero cold came on three successive days to Mount Vernon and Scarsdale and one day longer in the north.

1923 - A three day cold wave with consecutive lows of below zero only reported at Carmel Starting on the 18th.

1934 - In this coldest of 20th century months, southern Westchester experienced one 3 day period of below zero daily lows, while at Carmel there were eight continuous days of such cold with the coldest mark of 24 below zero coming on the last day of the month. There were seven days of below zero minimums at West Point.

1943 - In this war year there were no weather stations reporting from southern Westchester. Sing Sing prison reported two consecutive days of below zero lows. At Yorktown Heights and Carmel there were five such days, with lows during the week of the 15th of 26 and 21 below zero respectively. At West Point there were three days.

1948 - In the first two weeks of this month there were eight days with below zero minima at Yorktown Heights (-18°F) and Carmel (-17°F). There were five in Peekskill, Scarsdale and Bedford Hills. The lowest at West Point was nine below zero.

1950 - An end of the month cold spell came to Peekskill, Shrub Oak and Carmel with zero and below for three straight days.

1958 - Five days of below zero lows came from the 9th to the 19th at Carmel and Shrub Oak.

1961 - A continuation of the longest 20th century spell of below zero saw eight more such days at Carmel and Shrub Oak (-21°F). In the south, there were only two back to back below zero days in the first week of February. The coldest in the south was 7 below zero at Westchester Airport. At Suffern, ten below zero was registered on the 2nd.

1979 - In this coldest February since 1934, there were five to seven days mid-month with below zero low marks in southern Westchester (-11°F) and six days of continuous below zero lows at Carmel (-14°F) and Yorktown Heights. Lows between five and nine below zero were registered at Suffern and West Point.

MARCH

1906 - 2 below zero on the 24th of the month was the latest in the season below zero mark of the 20th century at Carmel.

1916 - 14 below zero at Carmel on the 18th is the coldest March low recorded in the 20th century

1943 - Two zero and below days occurred at Carmel in the first third of the month. Zero recorded at Suffern on the 9th.

1948 - Single day zero and below minima at West Point, Scarsdale, Bedford Hills and Carmel on the 6th.

1960 - A four day cold wave reported for Shrub Oak with the lowest recorded of 9 below zero. Cold began on the 9th.

1967 - For weather stations with less than 50 years of records in the latter part of the 20th century this was the latest in the season (March 19) below zero mark. Shrub Oak (-13°F), Carmel (-10°F), Yorktown Heights (-20°F), Westchester Airport (-60°F), Dobbs Ferry (-20°F), Peekskill (-20°F), Bedford Hills (0°F), Scarsdale (-30°F), Suffern.(-4°F), and West Point (0°F).

Heat Waves

A heat wave is defined as three or more consecutive days when maximum temperatures rise to 90 degrees or higher. Ninety degree heat on separate days is a regular event in a typical summer. Six to eight days are the expected normal number of 90+ days in July while August normally gives us from two to four. In our lower Hudson Valley, periods of consecutive days of such heat are unusual, and should not be expected every summer. In the last half century however, there has been an increase in the numbers of such events during the summer months. Early September has also given us occasional heat waves particularly before the 8th of the month, the last date of summer climatologically speaking, as the warmest 91 days of the year end on that date. The most likely cause of the greater number of such hot weather events is the increased urbanization that has occurred in all parts of our two county region. (See Tables 3 & 4)

What makes such weather oppressive is not so much the heat itself but the humidity that in our northeastern U.S.A. is usually over 50% in summer. It is this combination of air moisture with high temperatures that drives as many of us as possible indoors to air-conditioned refuges.

The following are nearly all of the significant 20th century heat waves that have visited our region.

JUNE

1925 - The first seven days of June had maxima of 90+ at Scarsdale, there were six such days at Mount Hope and five at Bedford Hills and Carmel. Scarsdale, Peekskill and West Point recorded highs of 100+ during this period.

1934 - Five consecutive days of heat began on the 29th of the month. Record highs were registered at the official weather service stations at Scarsdale, Bedford Hills and Mount Vernon, the latter having a peak high of 101° in this period. Carmel with a high of 89 in the middle of its 90+ spell and thus by definition did not have a heat wave, three consecutive days (Small consolation to those who sweltered in those pre air-conditioner times).

1943 - There were two heat waves at Scarsdale, Bedford Hills and Carmel, with thirteen days of 90+ maxima at Bedford Hills and West Point during this unusually hot month.

1949 - There were four consecutive days of 90+ at Dobbs Ferry, Westchester Airport, Bedford Hills and Carmel.

1950 - Beginning on the 27th , there were four days of 90+ at Dobbs Ferry and Scarsdale.

1952 - 100 degree marks were set at Scarsdale, Bedford Hills and West Point during a month with two heat waves. One heat wave was noted at Dobbs Ferry and Carmel.

1956 - Heat waves of three to six day duration were recorded at Shrub Oak (3), Carmel (4), Dobbs Ferry, Bedford Hills (5), Scarsdale (6) and Suffern (5).

1957 - There were seven consecutive days of 90+ maxima beginning on the 14th at Suffern, Scarsdale and Shrub Oak and six days at Dobbs Ferry, Bedford Hills and Carmel.

Nighttime low temperatures were in the mid 60s.

1983 - There was a mid month heat wave at Scarsdale, Dobbs Ferry and West Point.

1984 - A four to seven day long heat wave occurred

at Westchester Airport (4), Dobbs Ferry, Yorktown Heights (5), Scarsdale (7), West Point (7) in the second week on the month.

1991 - End of the month heat wave came at Dobbs Ferry, and Scarsdale.

JULY

1900 - The last of five days of 90+ heat at Mount Hope - southern Westchester came on the 19th.

1901 - A start of the month heat wave at Mount Hope and Bedford Hills with 100+ one day each.

1930 - There were two heat waves at Scarsdale (seven consecutive days) and Bedford Hills; 100+ were recorded at Mount Vernon, West Point and Scarsdale.

1933 - Four hot days in July and two in August produced 100+ maxima at Mount Vernon, West Point, Scarsdale (three days peaking at 103°) and Carmel. Nighttime lows were in the 70s.

1936 - Three consecutive days of 100+ were recorded at Bedford Hills and West Point. Scarsdale Mount Vernon and Carmel had five consecutive days of 90+ including two with 100+. Scarsdale recorded the hottest of 105 degrees

1940 - Five to six consecutive days peaking in the mid 90s at Mount Vernon, Scarsdale, Bedford Hills, Carmel and West Point. Newspaper reported 103° at Peekskill during this 25th to 29th period.

1944 - Two heat waves of seven and three day duration oppressed the lower Hudson Valley.

1949 - During this hot month there were heat waves on three occasions lasting from three to five days at Dobbs Ferry, Scarsdale, Bedford Hills, Yorktown Heights and Carmel.

1952 - Twice during the month six day long heat waves struck Scarsdale and Bedford Hills.

There were nineteen days with 90+ maximums at West Point.

1955 - Shorter length heat waves were registered at Dobbs Ferry, Shrub Oak and Carmel. In one of the hottest Julys, all five local government cooperative weather stations except Westchester Airport reported about half the days of the month recording 90+ maximum temperatures, resulting in numerous heat wave periods. West Point registered 23 days with 90+ highs, three of which were over 100 degrees.

1964 - A four day heat wave ended on July 3 with 90+ maxima at Dobbs Ferry, Scarsdale, Bedford Hills, and Carmel.

1966 - Ten to fifteen days of 90+ maxima gave the month at least two heat waves in both counties; longest consecutive days of 90+ was eight at Scarsdale with 100+ marks registered at Dobbs Ferry, Scarsdale, Bedford Hills, Suffern and West Point.

1980 - There was extended 90+ heat for about ten days at Scarsdale, Dobbs Ferry and West Point centering on the third week of the month. The thermometer soared to 104 on the 21st at Dobbs Ferry during this period.

Ordinary heat waves were also noted at Westchester Airport, Yorktown Heights and Carmel.

1983 - Seven and ten day heat waves were recorded at Dobbs Ferry and Scarsdale during the Second and third week of the month. Four and five day such heat spells were registered at Yorktown Heights and Westchester Airport. West Point had 19 days with 90+ highs.

1988 - There were three heat waves at Dobbs Ferry and West Point, one nine and one five day period of consecutive 90+ highs at Scarsdale, and two short heat waves at Yorktown Heights and Suffern.

1993 - A seven day heat wave inflicted Ardsley, Westchester Airport and West Point beginning on the 7th of the month. Five such days happened at the weather station in Yorktown Heights and Suffern.

1995 - For the third year July produced heat wave conditions in southern Westchester, again at the official stations at Ardsley, Westchester Airport and West Point. One hundred degree peaks were recorded there and at Yorktown Heights on the 15th.

1999 - The hottest month of record at two official sites. 90+ maxima on half the days, 77.7°F at Yorktown Heights, and 77.2°F at Westchester Airport

AUGUST

1900 - A four day heat wave came to Mount Hope in the south county in the second week of the month. Temperature peaked at 101 during this period.

1917 - Four days of 90+ maxima at Mount Hope, Mount Vernon, Scarsdale and Bedford Hills ended on August 2.

1918 - Mount Vernon and Scarsdale registered 101 and 104 degree maxima during a four day heat wave in the second week of the month.

1928 - Nine days of 90+ maxima at Mount Vernon and Scarsdale resulted in one heat wave at each weather station site. West Point had eight such days.

1930 - There were eight consecutive days of 90+ highs at Scarsdale, Bedford Hills and West Point beginning on the 2nd of the month. Mount Vernon and Carmel had four day heat waves.

1931 - Bedford Hills, Scarsdale and West Point had five and six day heat waves in the first week of the month. A high of 105 degrees was reached at West Point on the 7th.

1935 - Mid month heat wave came to Carmel, Bedford Hills, Scarsdale and West Point.

1936 - Early in the month heat waves occurred at Mt. Vernon, Scarsdale, Carmel and Bedford Hills.

1937 - Scattered 90+ highs numbering from five to nine days throughout the region resulted in one three or four day heat wave.

1938 - This August began with a heat waves at Scarsdale, Carmel and West Point.

1939 - Carmel with sixteen days of 90+ maxima had two heat waves of seven and eight day duration.

Scarsdale had one six day heat wave.

1943 - Heat wave starting on the first at Carmel, Bedford Hills, Scarsdale and West Point

1944 - Torrid 100+ days occurred at Scarsdale, (4) and Bedford Hills (2) as part of a three and eight day 90+ highs at the former site and three separate heat waves at the latter. Suffern had eight consecutive days of such heat.

1947 - Four and three day heat waves came to Scarsdale, Bedford Hills, and Carmel. Ossining had one. At West Point there were five and four day heat waves.

1948 - A five day heat wave in the last week of the month produced 100+ degree maxima at Dobbs Ferry, Bedford Hills and West Point.

1949 - During the second week of the month there were five day heat waves at Dobbs Ferry, Bedford Hills, Carmel (100), Scarsdale (100), and West Point (103).

1953 - Seven consecutive days of 90+ highs were registered at five of seven cooperative weather stations in the three county region.

1955 - In this hottest August of record at most stations, about one third of the days of the month had 90+ highs. Seven day heat waves at the start of the month were recorded at all seven station sites except Ossining.

1959 - There were at least nine days with 90+ maxima at the seven station network of temperature recording sites with two heat waves at most locations. Sixteen days at West Point were 90+.

1970 - Highs in the low 90s for consecutive four to five days were recorded at five stations about mid month.

1973 - The last four days of August and first four of September gave the region mid 90s heat in all three counties.

1980 - Six, five and three day heat wave occurred at Scarsdale, Dobbs Ferry and Carmel respectively in the last week of the month. Suffern had three heat waves.

1983 - Near heat wave conditions were at Dobbs Ferry and Westchester Airport in the first week but ten consecutive 90+ days at Scarsdale and three heat waves at West Point.

1988 - Yorktown Heights recorded a four day heat wave in mid month, while to the south in this period the 90+ heat persisted for seven days at Dobbs Ferry and five days at Westchester Airport. Twelve days at Suffern had 90+ maxima.

FALL HEAT

1884 - From the Peekskill Democrat, September 13, "The oldest inhabitant, that re-lie-able individual does not remember as continuous a spell of hot weather as humanity has suffered from for the past eight days. During that time, the thermometer has reached 90 degrees each day and the suffering has been terrible and the rate of mortality has increased as evidenced by our death rate this week. In Peekskill, the foundries all shut off Tuesday, Wednesday and Thursday. The hot spell has been general throughout the country."

1915 - In mid September there were near heat wave conditions with 85+ highs and a few 90 degree peaks at Mount Hope, Mount Vernon, Scarsdale, Bedford Hills and West Point.

1929 - Heat wave conditions the first four days of September at Mount Vernon, Carmel, West Point and Scarsdale with the latter site registering 102° on the 3rd.

1931 - From the 9th to the 13th heat wave conditions prevailed at Scarsdale and Bedford Hills.

1953 - Super four day heat early in September, with all weather stations except Shrub Oak recording 100+ on the 2nd. Bedford Hills and Carmel peaked at 103°. There were three consecutive days of 100+ at West Point.

1961 - During the first week of September four to six days had 90+ maxima except Shrub Oak.

1970 - A post equinox hot spell occurred with near heat wave duration in mid and southern areas.

1983 - Heat wave conditions prevailed at the end of the first week of September at Scarsdale, Dobbs Ferry and Westchester Airport, the latter site registering 98° twice, the second time on the 11th , its hottest mark so late in the season. There were seven days of 90+ highs in the first two weeks at West Point.

Individual days of 90+ maximum temperatures have been recorded as late in the season as October, principally in the first week of the month. Twentieth century examples are as follows: 90 on October 17, 1908 at Bedford Hills; 90+ on October 2, 1927 at Bedford Hills, Scarsdale and West Point; 90+ on October 10, 1939 at Carmel, Bedford Hills, Scarsdale and West Point; 90+ on October 5, 1941 at Bedford Hills(97), Yorktown Heights, Peekskill, Carmel, Scarsdale, Mount Vernon, Ossining, Suffern and West Point; 90 on October 10, 1949 at Scarsdale.

November has given the lower Hudson Valley only one early in the month taste of 80+ maximum daily temperatures. That occurred on November 1-2, 1950 when highs between 80 and 84 degrees were registered at five official weather stations.

In the dwindling days before the Winter Solstice, 20th century 70+ degree highs have been registered locally on a few occasions in December. These were on December 10, 1946 at Scarsdale; December 5, 1982 at Dobbs Ferry, Westchester Airport, and Scarsdale, and most recently on December 7, 1998 when high marks up to the mid 70s were registered at Yorktown Heights, Peekskill, and Ardsley. At Suffern a 70 degree mark was set on the 10th in 1946. West Point has recorded three 70+ December highs, the most recent of which came on the 8th in 1998.

SPRING HEAT

In the 20th century, the earliest days of the year with daytime high temperatures giving a taste of the steady warmth to come have occurred about mid March. In 1910 and 1921 Scarsdale registered 80+ highs in the fourth week of the month. Carmel and Bedford Hills reached highs of 80 on March 22, 1938. In the warmest March of the 20th century, 1945, 80+ maxima were recorded up to six separate days in the latter part of the month at Peekskill, Yorktown Heights (88), Bedford Hills, Carmel, Scarsdale and Suffern. In the last week of March 1989, 80+ highs were registered at Westchester Airport, Dobbs Ferry and Yorktown Heights. On March 13, 1990, highs over 80 degrees were recorded at Ardsley, Westchester Airport, Scarsdale and West Point. Most recently in 1998, during the three last days of March, 80+ maxima were recorded at Yorktown Heights (86), Ardsley, Suffern and West Point.

The latter half of April has sprinkled our counties with a few 90+ days of summer-like heat including one heat wave. As far back as 1896 West Point had a heat wave as early as the 16th. In 1915, Bedford Hills recorded five days of 90+ maxima in the fourth week of the month. In 1942, both Bedford Hills and Scarsdale hit over 90 on the last day of the month. The only April days of 90+ highs in Putnam county came as a heat wave beginning on the 17th of the month in 1976 along with West Point. Bedford Hills and Scarsdale also had three consecutive days of 90+, while Yorktown Heights had two that month. Two consecutive days of 90+ high temperatures were recorded in 1990 at Ardsley, Yorktown Heights and Suffern in the last week on the month.

While May in our area has had numerous days of 90+ maximum daily temperatures, and even a good number of two successive days of 90 degree heat, there have been only a few heat waves with at least three consecutive days of such heat. As far back in time as 1896, Bedford Hills and West Point recorded a three day heat wave beginning on the 9th. In 1930 Bedford Hills again reported four straight days of 90+, while Mount Vernon

and Scarsdale had three near the end of the month. The following year was a near repeat as Mount Vernon, Scarsdale, Bedford Hills and West Point starting on the 28th of the month hit 90+ highs. In 1959, a surprise four days of 90+ maxima were reported at Shrub Oak and West Point but none for the other three Westchester stations in operation. In 1962, Bedford Hills and Shrub Oak set 90+ marks for three days starting on the 18th. Three other stations that month came up one day shy of a certified heat wave. An end of the month heat wave in May 1987 was recorded at West Point, Peekskill, Westchester Airport and Dobbs Ferry. The most recent May hot period came from the 19th to the 21st in 1996 when West Point, Suffern, Ardsley, Yorktown Heights and Westchester Airport had 90+ high temperatures.

ANNUAL HEAT

Consensus among nearly all the climatologists of the world has it that global warming is a real phenomena. The global record shows that the six warmest years have all occurred in the 1990s. This record also shows that the average surface air temperature of the globe has warmed one degree Fahrenheit since the middle of the 19th century. The warmest eight years, averaging over 51 degrees in the Carmel/ Yorktown Heights 111 year record have been 1898, 1900, 1949, 1973, 1990, 1991, and 1998 (the warmest). The West Point record for the same period shows the years averaging over 51 degrees to be 1913, 1921, 1931, 1938, 1949, 1952, 1953, 1973, 1990, and 1991(the warmest).

It has been estimated that 265 billion tons of carbon have been released into the atmosphere since 1751. Half of these emissions have occurred since the mid 1970s, with the greatest amount in 1996. Additionally research (see Gribbin) has shown that the period of 1990 through 2010 is part of a long term solar cycle giving warmer than normal temperatures. The reader can judge the seriousness of these facts and speculate on the implications of the progressive warming.

FLOODS

Periodic flooding along any of the streams flowing through Westchester, Rockland and Putnam is a regular episodic event (See Figure 28). Along the twelve miles of the Bronx River that lie within Westchester, the sixteen miles of the Saw Mill River and fourteen miles of Peekskill Hollow Creek, any heavy short period or continuous moderate amount of precipitation will cause these streams to overflow their banks. Based on past experience, in certain places along their banks one can almost predict where future flooding will occur. Even our majestic Hudson River that normally is only affected by tides of about one foot, can cause floods along our western shore when a severe coastal storm coincides with a high astronomical (spring) tide. The frequency of flooding has not changed over the last two centuries. What has changed is the steady encroachment of man made structures on previously pristine waterways and their wetland accompaniment. Roads, factories, stores and homes now occupy many of the lowlands that were the flood plains of these streams. In some areas of southern Westchester closest to New York City 65% of the land has an impervious cover. It is mankind that is the intruder, not the water. Additionally, with the removal of much of the native vegetation and replacement with pavement in the immediate watershed region of these and other local streams, the speed of runoff from even a moderate amount of rain is increased. This can often result in flash flood situations downstream.

Since 1974, about $50 million in private sector flood losses have occurred in Westchester and 47 separate areas on the parkway system alone have been identified by the county as flood prone. In 1981 the U.S. Corps of Engineers judged that structural flood control measures on Westchester streams would be economically unjustifiable. Three parkways, the Saw Mill River, the Bronx River and the Hutchinson closely parallel their namesake streams. Designed for scenic drives some 60 years ago, these parkways are in most part located on the flood plain of the streams, only one or two yards in many places above the stream surface. With increasing urban and suburban land cover, heavy rains can cause flooding from minutes to a few hours, often before necessary barricades can be erected to stop traffic from entering the flooded areas.

The tropical storm of mid September 1999 in Putnam and northern Westchester at least, showed the inadequacy of the highway culvert system. Designed to handle a 7 inch amount in 24 hours (incorrectly reckoned as the 100 year storm) many culverts spilled over from the 9 - 11 inches and washed out blacktop and fill over the drain pipes (See Table 21 and Figure 29).

Westchester county has installed Automated Flood Warning System river gauges on the three above mentioned streams plus the Mamaroneck River, Blind Brook and the Beaver Swamp Brook.

Unfortunately, these systems only detect when water reaches a certain level and cannot differentiate between rainfall events that just exceed the warning threshold from those that exceed by several feet.

In 1982, in collaboration with the National Weather Service, an ALERT system was set up, consisting of 15 precipitation gauges, 9 river gauges, 1 temperature gauge, a radio repeater and two base stations. While this system can do little to prevent floods it does reduce the risk of flood related deaths and allow for timely action for property saving and protection.

Normal monthly precipitation in our region ranges from 3.5 inches in winter to 4.5 inches in the warmer months. When these amounts or greater fall within one to three days, flooding is certain to result. In winter, flooding can also come when even moderate rain falls on top of melting snow. Late twentieth century records kept for at least 50 years for five local weather stations show that a one day rainfall of two inches is an annual event and 3.5 inches and greater occurs every three years. Flooding is therefore a regular aspect of our environment. To lessen the destructive effects by natural means should be our focus and goal.

The following are some major rainfall events of the past 60 years that have produced significant flooding within Westchester and Putnam, principally along the waterways mentioned above.

1938 - "The Great Hurricane" of September 19 - 21 dropped 9 to 10 inches of rain in all areas.

1944 - Torrential rains from September 12 - 15 produced 6 to 10 inches. Scarsdale had 5 inches in 24 hours.

1953 - March 13, heavy rains falling on melting snow caused local flooding; 3 inches or more fell in less than 12 hours; 3.52" at Westchester Airport, 4.07" at Scarsdale and 4.46" at Dobbs Ferry.

1955 - Hurricanes "Connie" and "Diane" from August (11 - 20) produced ten to fourteen inches, the wettest such period of the 20th century. Carmel measured 14 inches in this period. At Scarsdale, 9.6 inches was measured up to the 14th and was followed by 3.3 inches. Four to six inches was measured area wide from the 17th to the 20th. Extensive flooding was reported from all local streams.

October 14 - 17 1955 produced rainfalls of eight to eleven inches at seven rain gauges in Westchester, the wettest such October period dating back to 1860 in the Croton Watershed.

1968 - May 28,29 "Flooding of highways and villages" in all three counties from rainfall such as 5.55" at Dobbs Ferry, 5.00" at Scarsdale, 6.30" at Suffern,. 4.94" at Westchester Airport, and 3.50" at Yorktown Heights.

1969 - March 24,25, Flooding from local streams, 2.75" at Suffern, 2.25" at Dobbs Ferry, 2.72" at Scarsdale and 2.82" at Westchester Airport.

June 15,16 , 2.5 to 5.5 inches of rain flooded roads, parking lots and basements in lower Westchester; Carmel

FIGURE 19: FLOODING FROM PEEKSKILL HOLLOW BROOK (PUTNAM VALLEY) 6-11 INCH 24 HOUR RAINFALL, AUGUST 6, 1990

and Shrub Oak measured 5.56" and 5.61".

1971 - August 27, Hurricane "Doria" filled five rain gauges to 6"-7" resulting in the inundation of highways, streets and low lying areas in the lower Hudson valley.

September 11-14, over 7 inches of rain in this period caused widespread flood damage to property in Westchester and in Haverstraw and Nyack.

1972 - June 16 - 19 Hurricane Agnes, Saw Mill, Bronx River and Taconic Parkways closed from 6 to 8 inches rainfall that fell mostly in the southern third of Westchester. At Dobbs Ferry and Westchester Airport 5.69" and 5.40" fell on the 19th. Commuter trains were halted by mud slides. In Greenburgh 300 cars in a parking lot were submerged to a depth of five feet. Property damage was about 2 million dollars in White Plains and Yonkers. October 6,7, Up to three inches of rain in southern Westchester inundated highways and city streets in this third wettest 24 hour October rain at Dobbs Ferry in 55 years.

1973 - February 1, 2, local flooding in Westchester from 2.5 to 3.5 inches rain. Rainfalls greater than three inches set one day records for February at Carmel, Yorktown Heights and Dobbs Ferry.

1980 - April 9,10, Up to 4.8 inches of rain (Dobbs Ferry's 2nd wettest two day April total) caused the county's normally docile streams to become swift torrents and flooding from these closed the Taconic Parkway at Mount Pleasant, the Saw Mill Parkway from Yonkers to Elmsford and the Bronx River Parkway from Yonkers to White Plains. One death was attributed to this event.

1990 - August 5 - 15, two events of three to four inches of rainfall in this period resulted in the Saw Mill and Hutchinson Parkways closed on two occasions. Five to six inches in northern Westchester and Putnam caused flooding of homes at Lake Secor.

1991 - March 2, 3, 4, flooding of Saw Mill and Bronx River Parkways.

August 19,20, 3.3 to 5.5 inches rain; Putnam County flooding reported.

1992 - December 11,12, nor'easter, 2 to 3 inches snow and rain (2.5" - 3.6") plus a high astronomical tide resulted in Hudson River flooding of Annsville Creek Route 6 traffic circle, just north of Peekskill and the Croton on Hudson Railroad Station parking lot.

1996 - April 16, Flooding of the Bronx River at Bronxville from over three inches of rain.

May 11, Torrential rain flooded Saw Mill Parkway in Chappaqua

1998 - March 9, Flooding of Bronx River covere Parkway near Palmer Road at Bronxville at Nanuet 2.3ð inches was measured.

1999 - September 16, 17, Within and outside the Croton watershed, hundreds of culverts spilled over and washed away blacktop and road beds overlying and along side these drain pipes of state, county and town roads, when 8 - 11 inches fell for the wettest one and two day amounts of the 20th century. (See Figure 30). The month was the wettest at six rain gauge sites. Eight inches in one day at West Point was the heaviest of the 20th century.

DROUGHT

Drought is an important climate phenomenon despite the fact that it is not a sudden weather event such as a snow storm or hurricane. It can take weeks or even months before drought becomes noticeable to the average person even during the growing season. During the non-growing season of winter, drought is almost a non-event. With most Westchester, Rockland and Putnam residents uninvolved with gardening and with no commercial farming in both counties other than a few orchards in the north, our first notice of drought comes from a look at our Croton watershed reservoirs. A drop in the water level of a few yards and a reminder of shortage by the New York City Department of Water Supply is enough to alert even the least observant person. Since nearly all of our domestic water comes from this source, its supply should be of concern to all.

Drought becomes a serious matter when it occurs at the start of the growing season in May and June when all vegetation is neediest. Water consumption by humans is also greater during the warmest months of the year.

With the population increase in the greater New York City metropolitan area and with only a finite supply of good water from the Catskill, Delaware and Croton watersheds, this valuable resource needs to be conserved and treated with loving care. Precipitation can vary from season to season as well as from year to year. The Croton precipitation record dating back in time to 1860 shows drought conditions in the early 1870s, a seven year growing season drought beginning about 1908, and the severest drought of record from 1963 to 1966 (See Figure 30). These four years of the 1960s gave the entire northeast its greatest drought since records began and resulted in the driest decade of the 20th century. The decade following was the wettest of the century. This kind of precipitation variability makes consumption difficult to predict. In view of this, a program of strict conservation at all times should be a must for the 21st century.

Some of the more noteworthy precipitation 20th century deficit periods for the years warmest eight months in the Hudson Valley Climate Division have been:

April - 1942, the third driest April in climate division, about one quarter of normal 1963, the fourth driest, about half of normal 1966, half the normal April in Westchester

April 1968, little or no rain the middle two weeks of the month

May 1903, less than one half inch for Westchester 1964, one third to one half the normal rain, driest of record at Tarrytown 1965, about one third of normal for May.

June 1913, one quarter the normal amount in Putnam and Northern Westchester

June 1965, driest June, one quarter of an inch total in county after the 3rd of the month

1966, second driest June, driest June at Amawalk, one tenth of an inch after the 10th of the month.

July 1965, driest July in Hudson Valley Climate Division

1966, third driest July, less than a third normal for month, driest at Amawalk, Bedford Hills, Croton Falls, Croton Lake, Peekskill and Titicus

1968, no rain for first two weeks of month, driest July at Cross River, Kensico Reservoir, Ossining, Tarrytown and Westchester Airport

1999, two consecutive months (June & July) with half of normal rainfall

August 1964, dry August, about one third of normal, driest at Dobbs Ferry, Scarsdale, and Westchester Airport

1970, no rain middle two weeks of month

September 1914, less than one half inch for month, driest at Titicus

1964, driest September, no rain the first two weeks, driest at Westchester Airport

1965, second driest September in climate division

October 1924, less than one half inch for month in Croton watershed, driest at Titicus

1963, third driest October, no rain for three weeks, driest at Scarsdale

1965, driest October in climate division

November 1917, half of normal in Croton watershed

1920, driest at Amawalk, Cross River, Croton Falls, and Titicus

1964, driest November in division, first rain of month on the 17th.

THUNDERSTORMS, HAIL AND TORNADOES

Thunderstorms are the most common of the potentially damaging and life-threatening weather phenomena. They develop when warm, moist air rises rapidly in the atmosphere. With ascent into the cooler air aloft, condensation or cloud formation results. With further ascent the moist air cools and condenses and ice crystals form to become the nucleus for rain droplets. When these drops become heavy enough they fall to become rain. The associated lightning is the dangerous element of thunderstorms. The discharge of lightning through the air is the result of an electric charge difference between the negative storm cloud and the positive ground. The lightning bolt which can last a fraction of a second and is only about the width of a pencil is extremely powerful and dangerous.

In the United States there is a wide range of the number of thunderstorms that normally occur in a given region in a year. Along the coast of California, only five occur in a normal year, while in the Tampa area of Florida there are as many as 100. In our Westchester Putnam region there are normally 25 to 30 such events each year, and while most of them happen in the warmest months they have occurred in every month of the year.

Preventative avoidance action should be taken when the first thunder is heard from an approaching storm. Remove yourself from open, clear areas, stay away from large trees and bodies of water and retreat to the safety of a car or house.

On occasion, during some of the severer thunderstorms when rapid updrafts of moist air rise to greater heights, the droplets freeze and fall as ice particles. The size of these hail particles depends on the number of trips the hailstone makes into the below freezing higher reaches of the atmosphere where additional layers of ice are added. Golf ball sized hailstones have been reported in some storms in our counties. Normally one or two days each year have hail associated with thunderstorms in our area. Hail is a warm season weather phenomenon and should not be confused with sleet that only occurs in the winter.

While tornadoes are rarely experienced here, they are not unknown. In many cases destructive winds associated with severe thunderstorms have been attributed to tornadoes. In general, a narrow path of such destruction has to be identified in order for the damage to be attributed to a tornado. Trees that are downed in the same direction are not necessarily from a tornado. Unlike in the mid-west where tornadoes can often been seen with their characteristic funnel, here such a sight is nearly always hidden in the low clouds of the storm or blocked from view by hills or vegetation. Over the last two hundred years, there have been perhaps a dozen tornadoes impacting our three counties. One of the most recent of these documented events happened at Lake Mahopac on July 29, 1971 when a path of destruction moved northeastward through the village. While there was no loss of life, five homes and two business structures had major damage and numerous trees were twisted off above ground or toppled. A funnel cloud was observed.

Most recently, a documented tornado occurred at Continental Village, just north of Peekskill on June 2, 2000. By National Weather Service standards it was a type F-1 with winds between 110 and110 miles per hour. While cars and homes were severely damaged no deaths resulted. According to the National Weather Service, since 1960, eight tornadoes have been recorded in Westchester.

CALENDAR OF EXTREMES
MAJOR TWENTIETH CENTURY YEARLY WEATHER EVENTS

1901 April 21, over 3.5" rainfall, July 2, 97°F & 102°F at Carmel & Bedford Hills

1902 Second hottest November of record at Carmel (46.5 degrees)

1903 Warmest Spring of the century; Driest May and coldest August at Bedford Hills; Over 10 inches of rainfall in June at Bedford Hills and Carmel; Oct. 8, 5.5" rain at Bedford Hills

1904 Coldest year of record & coldest January at Carmel, with zero days on the 4th and 5th; Killing frost on 9/22

1905 January 25, twenty two inches of snow at Scarsdale

1906 Single digit lows on March 24 & 25 at Bedford Hills

1907 West Point coldest Spring & Fall of century - 28°F on May 6.

1908 Only one inch of rain in September, driest since 1889

1909 Christmas day snowstorm - 14" and 12" at Scarsdale and Carmel

1910 At Bedford Hills 99°F on July 9, the hottest countywide

1911 July 7 - 13, Heat wave; Hottest 4th of July with 102°F and 104°F at Bedford Hills and West Point

1912 Coldest January; Driest June since 1890 statewide; Pre Christmas snowstorm, 20" at Scarsdale

1913 Agricultural drought from June through August

1914 Single digit lows for half of February; March 1,2 snowstorm with near hurricane force winds left over one foot of snow countywide, 18" at Scarsdale

1915 April 3,4 Spring storm, with over one foot of snow at Scarsdale, Coldest summer at West Point

1916 Coldest March of record at West Point,Carmel, Bedford Hills and Scarsdale; Coldest Spring at Carmel

1917 Coldest May at West Point; Coldest Fall at Carmel; December 29 - 31 Zero days at Carmel

1918 Coldest 20th Century Winter (1917-18); Coldest New Year's Day -9 & -12°F at Scarsdale and Carmel

1919 Second warmest February since 1891; Meager snow season since January, 7 - 14 inches

1920 February 4 - 6 Ice, sleet and snow with 14 - 16 inches at Scarsdale and Carmel

1921 Second warmest April and warmest September of record at Carmel; Warmest Spring at West Point

1922 January had five below zero lows at Carmel; May was the warmest in the state at Mount Hope

1923 Warmest December of record at Carmel and Scarsdale

1924 Coldest September at Bedford Hills and Scarsdale

1925 Warmest June at Scarsdale with a seven day heat wave

1926 Three feet of snow on ground at Scarsdale in February, Coldest Spring

1927 Coldest June and August at West Point; Coldest August at Scarsdale and Carmel,(coldest Summer)

1928 Coldest September at West Point; Until this year, driest December with 1 - 1.5" of precipitation area wide

1929 July - start of three year period of below normal precipitation

1930 Early May heat wave with highs in the 90s at Scarsdale and Bedford Hills

1931 Warmest Fall at West Point; November hot spell in the fourth week with Westchester highs in the 70s

1932 January warm spell at start of third week with 60+ highs, Warmest winter of 20th century (1931-32)

1933 Early heat wave (June 7 - 9) with seven days of 90+ highs that month at Scarsdale

1934 In February there were 9 consecutive days of below zero lows at Carmel in this coldest month of record in the three county region; On the 28th of that month 24 below zero was registered at Carmel

1935 January 22 -24, Snowstorm with 12" at Scarsdale

1936 Five day heat wave in July with highs over 100 on at least two days at four stations

1937 Early July six day heat wave

1938 The Great Long Island - New England Hurricane with over 10 inches of rain in all counties and severe wind and rain damage; second wettest September

1939 Growing season drought with one-third normal precipitation in May and July

1940 February, Valentine's Day storm with 4 - 8 inches of wind blown snow; March 4 glaze and ice storm

1941 Warmest April of record at Bedford Hills and Carmel with 80°F highs in third week

1942 Solstice cold spell, December 17 - 23 with below zero lows at Carmel

1943 Cold wave in third week of February, -21°F the coldest low at Carmel

1944 September Hurricane with six inches rainfall in all counties

1945 80+ degree highs on St Patrick's Day; Warmest March at Scarsdale and Bedford Hills

1946 Warmest March at West Point and Carmel; Warmest Autumn of record at Carmel

1947 December post Christmas snowstorm, the greatest in Westchester and Putnam, 20" in 6 hours at White Plains

1948 Late August Heat Wave with highs up to 104°F

1949 Second hottest July of record with some maxima as great as 100 degrees

1950 The Great November Wind Storm with sustained winds over 50mph and gusts over 70 mph

1951 Two to three inches rain on November 7th storm

1952 A hot July with half the days with highs of 90+ in Westchester

1953 January 8 -11 Ice Storm, ice 2 - 3 inches thick, 75

power lines broken in Westchester, no power for 72 hrs

1954 Heavy rains from hurricanes Carol (2-3") in August and Edna (4-5") in September

1955 Hurricanes Connie and Diane left 6-9" and 4-8" of rain and resulted in the wettest 20th century August

1956 Heavy March Snow left 13-18" for our three county area

1957 Below zero lows in third week of January for Rockland, Putnam and northern Westchester

1958 Shrub Oak registered a low of freezing on the 18th of June

1959 No extraordinary weather events in this year; 6-9" of snow on December 22

1960 Tropical Storm Brenda in July (3-8" rain); In September Donna with 50 mph winds and 4-5" rain caused much damage. Coldest March at Suffern

1961 Late January, early February fifteen day cold wave with below zero lows in north and single digits in south; Hurricane Esther in September disrupted power and communication in all counties

1962 Heat wave in third week of May in three counties; Start of four year drought

1963 Drought conditions with precipitation 9 - 15 inches below normal for year; Coldest Aug. & Sept at Suffern

1964 Driest year since 1860 at Croton Lake; most gauges about 15 inches below normal

1965 Only one month during the year with above normal precipitation in the lower Hudson Valley

1966 July heat wave in first week with highs 100+ in southern Westchester; Drought not as severe as last 3 years. Second hottest summer at West Point

1967 Sixteen inches of snow in all areas in first week of February

1968 Cold second week of January with below zero lows on six days

1969 February 9,10 one to two feet of snow

1970 March 30 - ten inches of snow on Easter Sunday

1971 Warmest October at West Point; Tropical Storm Doria gave 5 - 8 inches of rain in all counties

1972 Following heavy rains (6+ inches) in the third week of June, tropical storm Agnes gave 2-3 inches more

1973 Wettest December at Westchester Airport, Yorktown and Carmel with over 9 inches

1974 November 1, 79°F warmest Yorktown November date

1975 April 2 - 5 storm with high winds up to 60 mph; Warmest November of record at Scarsdale

1976 93 degree high temperature on April 18 in Yorktown was the hottest maximum of the year

1977 May 9, latest measurable snowfall (2") in northern Westchester and Putnam; Bedford Hills station closed

1978 One of the five coldest years of the century; Maximum of 41°F at Carmel in February was lowest of record

1979 Over ten inches precipitation in January - wettest of record in north; September, damage from storm David

1980 Growing season drought; Christmas Day minimums below zero in north

1981 A drought year with most stations 10 inches below normal; three months with less than one inch

1982 April 6, Spring Blizzard with up to one foot of snow

1983 February 10-12, Megalopolis snowstorm with 18" to 24" area wide; Wettest April & December at West Point

1984 April 5,6, Heavy two day rains up to 5 inches in Putnam; Carmel temperature station closed after 96 years

1985 Fourth week of September ex-hurricane Gloria left 3-4 inches of rain areawide

1986 One inch of snow on April 23 in northern Westchester and Putnam

1987 October 4, earliest measurable snowfall in northern Westchester and Putnam (.12 to 1.0 inch)

1988 Driest June of the century in northern Westchester (.47")

1989 Coldest December of the 20th century, ice breakers had to free 40 ships on Hudson River

1990 August heavy rains (about 10 inches) caused flooding at Lake Secor in Putnam and southern parkways

1991 Warmest May of century; Tropical storm Bob left 4-5 inches of rain leaving many Putnam roads flooded

1992 February drought warning for New York City watersheds; One foot of snow from December northeaster

1993 Great super storm of March giving lowest barometer reading at White Plains of 28.38 inches and 10-18 inches of snow; April flooding of Saw Mill and Bronx Parkways. Driest May at West Point

1994 January, snowy - 15 - 24 inches and cold - 6 degrees below normal

1995 Eight consecutive days of above freezing minimums in Yorktown in January

1996 April snows of 6 inches on the 8th and 10th

1997 17 - 24 inches of snow on April 1, greatest single fall so late in season, electricity outages for 1 - 3 days

1998 Eight consecutive days in January with above freezing in Yorktown; Warmest February, December and Year in the Carmel/Yorktown Heights record dating back to 1888

1999 July was the hottest month of record; Hottest summer of record at Yorktown; September 17 - wettest day in Putnam and Northern Westchester and West Point with 8 -11 inches of rain, four rain gauge stations recorded their wettest month.

2000 Earliest Heat Wave in northern Westchester (May 7-9 at Yorktown Heights)

DAILY CALENDAR OF EXTREMES

JANUARY

1   1877   White Plains, 14 inches of snow, greatest for New Year's Day

2   1876   White Plains, 66 degrees, hottest late 19th century January day

3   1999   Ardsley and Westchester Airport, 4.10 & 3.47 inches of rain in 24 hours, greatest January amount

4   1835   North Salem, 31 below zero in a cold week of the 3rd to 10th

5   1993   Yorktown Heights, 60 degrees

6   1905   Bedford Hills, 2.28 inches precipitation, Croton Lake - 3.53 inches,

     1885   Yonkers, 5.35 inches precipitation in 19 hours

7   1907   Scarsdale, 64 degrees

8   1866   White Plains, 20 below zero, coldest late 19th century day

     1874   White Plains, 5.5 inches precipitation, wettest January day in all counties

9   1953   Parts of Westchester, ice storm, ice up to 2 inches thick

     1884   Croton Lake, 4.97 inches precipitation

10   1859   White Plains, a zero day during which the highest temperature was 10 below zero

11   1968   Shrub Oak, midpoint of 5 days of below zero minimums

12   1912   Bedford Hills, 12 below zero, 3rd coldest January day of record

13   1964   Scarsdale & Shrub Oak,. 12 inches of snow

     1912   West Point, 15 below zero, coldest January minimum

14   1932   West Point , 71 degrees, hottest January maximum

15   1831   Westchester County, 2 to 3 feet of snow on ground after "Great Snowstorm"

16   1879   White Plains, 10 inches of snow

17   1957   All three counties, fourth consecutive day of below zero minimums

18   1954   Putnam and N. Westchester, below zero minimums

19   1936   Carmel, 14 inches snow

     1973   Suffern, 64 degrees, hottest January maximum

20   1961   Dobbs Ferry, 17.3 inches snow, heaviest for January at that station

           Shrub Oak, 16 inches of snow

21   1974   Larchmont, .57 inches precipitation, greatest in 1 hour

22   1961   Suffern -16°F, Shrub Oak -25°F, Carmel -24°F coldest January minimums at those stations

23   1935   Scarsdale, 12 inches of snow

24   1966   Bedford Hills, 14 inches of snow

25   1961   Shrub Oak, fifth day of below zero minimums

26   1950   Dobbs Ferry & Scarsdale, 73 degree maxima, hottest January day

27   1994   Yorktown Heights, 15 below zero minimum

28   1943   Larchmont, 2.07 inches precipitation, greatest in 12 hours

29   1973   Carmel, 13 inches snowfall

30   1961   Shrub Oak, the 10th consecutive day of below zero minimums

31   1878   White Plains, 2.90 inches precipitation

DAILY CALENDAR OF EXTREMES

FEBRUARY

1	1882	White Plains, 14 inches of snow
2	1973	Northern Westchester, Local flooding following snow, warmth and rain
		Yorktown Heights & Suffern, 3.33 & 3.00 inches precipitation (wettest February day)
3	1961	Shrub Oak, 14th consecutive day of below zero minimums (-21°F on 2nd)
		All three counties, 12 - 19 inches snow from 2nd to 5th
4	1960	Dobbs Ferry, 27 inches of snowfall in last 2 days
5	1882	White Plains, 15 inches snowfall
6	1855	White Plains, temperature 1.5 degrees below zero at 3 PM
7	1941	Yorktown Heights, 2.82 inches precipitation
		Sparkill, 2.29 inches in 12 hours
8	1965	Shrub Oak, .42 inches precipitation greatest 1 hour amount
9	1934	Scarsdale, Bedford Hills, & West Point -18°F & -19°F, -17°F, coldest February minimums
10	1885	Southern Westchester, 6.78 inches precipitation in 11 hours
	1969	All counties, 16 to 22 inches snowfall, 1000 cars abandoned at Tappan Zee bridge
11	1948	Putnam and northern Westchester, Last of 5 consecutive days of below zero minimums
12	1959	Scarsdale, 11.6 inches snowfall
	1881	Croton Lake, 3.65 inches precipitation
13	1950	Scarsdale, 4.20 inches precipitation, greatest in 12 hours
14	1899	Carmel, 20 inches snowfall
15	1949	Scarsdale, 74 degree maximum, highest so early in the season
16	1943	Yorktown Heights, 26 degrees below zero, coldest 3 county February minimum
	1885	Croton Lake, 4.85 inches precipitation, wettest day
		Southern Westchester, 5.35 inches in 8 hours
17	1958	Westchester County 3 day snowstorm ending AM, 1 -2 feet of snow
18	1943	Yorktown Heights, last of 4 day cold spell, warmest minimum (-1°F)
19	1971	Westchester County warm spell to end of month, minimums nearly all above freezing
20	1920	Scarsdale, 20 inches of snow
21	1975	Three county warm spell, 9 degrees above normal
22	1974	Mohansic Lake unfrozen one month before normal date
	1893	Carmel, 19 inches of snowfall
23	1874	White Plains, 68 degrees, warmest late 19th century February maximum
24	1985	Dobbs Ferry & Scarsdale, 75 degrees, warmest February date
25	1956	Westchester Airport, 28.95" barometer reading, 75 mph winds
	1916	Southern Westchester, 6.50 inches of rain
26	1888	White Plains, 2.13 inches precipitation
27	1940	Yorktown Heights, 4 below zero minimum
28	1954	Three counties, final day of 13 day longest hot spell, highs in 60s
29	1976	All three counties, hottest Leap Year day, highs to mid 60s

DAILY CALENDAR OF EXTREMES

MARCH

1	1900	Carmel, 2.58 inches rainfall, 5th wettest March day
2	1914	Scarsdale & Carmel, 18 and 10 inches of snowfall
3	1868	White Plains, 24 inches snowfall
	1971	All county coast storm with high winds, sleet and ice
4	1960	Bedford Hills, (17"), Dobbs Ferry (27"), & Scarsdale, (18"), greatest March snowstorm
5	1948	Bedford Hills, 4 below zero minimum
6	1967	Dobbs Ferry, 3.23 inches rainfall, greatest 2 day total
7	1911	West Point, 10 below zero, coldest March minimum
	1941	Carmel, 9 inches snowfall
8	1875	White Plains, 12 inches snowfall
9	1943	Yorktown Heights, 4 below zero, coldest day so late in season
10	1943	Carmel & Yorktown Heights, near zero minimums 6 of 7 last days
11	1901	Carmel, 2.53 inches of rainfall, greatest for that date
12	1960	Shrub Oak, 4th consecutive day of below zero minimums
	1959	All counties, 9 to 12 inches snowfall
13	1953	Woodlands-Ardsley, 3.58" rainfall in 12 hours, local flooding
	1913	Yonkers, 5.85 inches of rain
14	1888	White Plains, "Blizzard of 88," 26 inches snowfall in 2 days
	1993	Westchester Airport (15"), & Carmel (17") snowfall
15	1912	Scarsdale, 2.75 inches rainfall
16	1945	Carmel, 84 degree maximum, hottest day so early in season
17	1955	Tarrytown, 3 died when 50 mph gusts sank tugboat on Hudson River
18	1916	Carmel, 14 below zero minimum, coldest March day in Putnam County
19	1967	Suffern (-4°F), Westchester Airport (-6°F), Scarsdale (-3°F), Dobbs Ferry (-2°F) the only March below zero minimums for these stations
	1956	All counties, up to 19 inches of snow, traffic paralyzed due to high wind drifting
20	1945	Scarsdale & Yorktown Heights, 82 & 84 degrees, hottest maximum so early in season
21	1958	Westchester, 13 - 22 inches snow at 5 official U.S. Cooperative Weather Stations
22	1967	Westchester County, about 12 inches of snowfall
	1980	Yorktown Heights (4.60"), Carmel (3.68"), greatest March 24 hour rainfall
23	1934	Carmel, 7 degrees minimum temperature
24	1906	Carmel, 2 below zero, coldest low mark so early in the season
25	1969	Dobbs Ferry, 2.19 inches rainfall, 8th wettest March day
26	1945	Carmel, 85 degree maximum, hottest March mark
	1876	White Plains, 6.1 inches rain, greatest March amount
27	1890	Croton Lake, 3.00 inches rainfall
28	1932	Bedford Hills, 2.20 inches rainfall
29	1945	Scarsdale (88°F) & Bedford Hills (91°F), hottest maxima for March
	1970	Putnam & Westchester, Easter Sunday snowstorm, 9 - 12 inches
30	1998	Suffern - 87°, Ardsley - 86°, Westchester AP- 82°, Yorktown Hts 1W - 86°, hottest March maxima
	1951	West Point & Westchester Airport, 4.40 & 3.79 inches rainfall, wettest 20th century day
31	1923	Three county end of month 4 day cold wave, (8 to 25 degrees)
	1987	Yorktown Heights, 2.95 inches, 2nd wettest March day

DAILY CALENDAR OF EXTREMES

APRIL

1 1997 Yorktown Heights, 17 inches snowfall, greatest amount so late in season
   1923 West Point (12°F), Carmel (6°F), Bedford Hills (7°F), & Scarsdale (10°F), coldest April minimums
2 1968 Three county drought of three week duration with only one-quarter inch of rainfall
3 1915 Scarsdale, 14 inches of snow, greatest April amount
   1970 Countywide severe storm, 25 - 50 mph winds, 2 - 3 inches rainfall in 2 days
4 1876 White Plains, 3.10 inches rainfall, wettest 19th century April amount
   1954 Suffern, 12 degrees, coldest April minimum
5 1984 Dobbs Ferry (5.34") and Westchester Airport (4.46") wettest April day
6 1982 Dobbs Ferry, 9.7 inches snowfall
7 1991 Yorktown Heights, 87°F, hottest day so early in season
8 1871 White Plains, 84°F, hottest April day, late 19th century
   1940 Spring Valley, 2.20 inches rain in 6 hours
9 1901 Bedford Hills, seventh consecutive day of rain, 4.41 inches
10 1972 Carmel, daily minimum temperatures below freezing since beginning of month
11 1907 Carmel, 14 inches of snow
12 1894 Bedford Hills, 20 inches snow, greatest county 24 hour April amount
13 1875 White Plains, 17 inches snowfall, greatest late 19th century April amount
14 1945 Yorktown Heights, 85°F, 6th consecutive day of record highs
15 1942 Scarsdale, last day of rain that month, driest 20th century April also at Croton Lake
16 1966 Three county drought, less than one-quarter inch since start of month
17 1963 Bedford Hills, first measurable rain of month, all counties drought,
18 1976 3 county "Great Easter Heat wave" maximums in low 90s, hottest April day & 17th to 19th
   West Point, 96 degrees, hottest April maximum of century
19 1966 Scarsdale, 1.55 inches rainfall in 3 hours
20 1904 Bedford Hills, 13 degree minimum, 4th consecutive day of record breaking cold
21 1941 Carmel, 89°F, 3rd consecutive day with maximums in high 80s
22 1901 Croton Lake (4.65") and Bedford Hills (4.50") 2 day rainfall total
23 1904 Bedford Hills, 18 degree minimum, coldest so late in season
24 1967 Southern Westchester, 4.5 inches snowfall, latest heaviest snowfall
25 1868 White Plains, 4 inches snowfall
26 1972 Three counties, 7th consecutive day of 30 degree minimums
27 1915 Bedford Hills, 96°F, hottest of three day heat wave
28 1947 Dobbs Ferry, 31 degree minimum, last below freezing temperature
   1990 Suffern, 91 degrees, hottest April maximum
29 1885 White Plains, 2.85 inches rainfall
30 1909 Carmel, 4 inches snowfall

DAILY CALENDAR OF EXTREMES

MAY

1   1876   Kensico Reservoir and White Plains, 1 inch snowfall

      1867   White Plains, 29 degree minimum, coldest May day in last third of 19th century

2   1963   Dobbs Ferry, trace of snow

3   1911   Mount Hope, 34 degrees, Bedford Hills, trace of snow

4   1941   Yorktown Heights, 27 degree minimum,

5   1871   Croton Lake, 3.55 inches rainfall

6   1967   Dobbs Ferry, Scarsdale, & Shrub Oak, traces of snow

7   1930   Scarsdale & Bedford Hills, 3rd consecutive day of 90+ maximums

      1967   Peekskill & Yorktown Heights, record cold, with minimums in high 20s

8   1886   White Plains, 2.33 inches of rain

9   1977   Cortlandt, Carmel, Somers, Yorktown, & North Salem, 1 - 3 inches of snow, greatest 20th century May snowfall

10   1947   Carmel (24°F) & Yorktown Heights (23°F), record coldest May day

      1996   White Plains , severe thunderstorm with hailstones (3/4 inch diameter)

11   1966   Areawide cold since beginning of month, with some below freezing lows, vegetation and birds suffered

12   1907   Scarsdale, 26 degree low, coldest May day

13   1964   Three counties, no rain since beginning of the month

14   1951   West Point, & Suffern 31 degrees, latest below freezing minimum

15   1900   Mount Hope, 94 degree maximum

16   1939   Scarsdale, 3rd consecutive day with minimums in mid 30s

17   1967   Countywide cold wave for previous two weeks, coldest May of previous 50 years

18   1955   Shrub Oak, 28 degree minimum

19   1962   Dobbs Ferry, 96 degree high

           Shrub Oak, 94 degree high, hottest May maximum

      1966   Larchmont, 1.40 inches rainfall in two hours

20   1996   Suffern (96°F), Ardsley (97°F), Westchester Airport (95°F), & Yorktown Heights (94°F), hottest May day of record for all four stations

      1998   Cold Spring, severe thunderstorm with hail stones up to 1.75 inches in diameter

21   1939   Putnam & Northern Westchester, first rain after ten dry days

22   1907   Mount Hope (32°F) and Scarsdale (36°F), minimums

23   1962   Three county dry spell for past two weeks

24   1964   Bedford Hills, 100 degree maximum, hottest May day for both counties

      1921   Bedford Hills, 24 degree minimum, coldest May day

25   1955   Shrub Oak, first rain after only one quarter inch that month

26   1946   Woodlands-Ardsley, 2.40 inches rainfall in three hours

27   1946   All counties, 3 - 7 inches in two days

           Scarsdale, 5.80 inches, greatest May 24 hour total

      1961   Westchester Airport, trace of snow

28   1949   Yorktown Heights, 34 degree minimum, first of three days with lows in 30s

      1984   West Point, 3.98 inches rain, greatest one day May amount

29   1968   Woodlands - Ardsley, 4.82 inches rain in 12 hours

           Dobbs Ferry, 5.44 inches rain, greatest May 24 hour total

30   1969   Westchester Airport, 96 degree high, hottest May maximum

      1931   Bedford Hills, heat wave, 3rd day of 90+ highs

31   1938   Scarsdale, 99 degree maximum, hottest May high

      1939   Carmel, 97 degree maximum, hottest May high

DAILY CALENDAR OF EXTREMES

JUNE

1 1918 Mount Vernon, 92 degree high
2 1969 Hastings-on-Hudson, severe thunderstorms, lightning and over 1 inch of rain caused damage to homes

    2000 Peekskill area tornado caused damage to homes, cars with many trees downed
3 1971 Bedford Hills, .43 inches of rain, heaviest single rainfall in month with only 1.29 inches
4 1910 Scarsdale, 38 degree minimum, coldest June date
5 1925 Peekskill, 102 degree high, hottest June date

         Scarsdale, 100 degree high, hottest June date
6 1945 Peekskill (35°F), Bedford Hills (38°F), & Yorktown Heights (34°F), coldest June dates
7 1925 All counties end of five day 90+ degree heat wave
8 1956 Ossining, 36 degree minimum, coldest June date
9 1933 Mount Vernon, 96 degree high mark
10 1957 Shrub Oak, 30 degree minimum, coldest Westchester minimum

     1881 White Plains, 3.15 inches rainfall
11 1914 Mount Hope, 98 degree high, 3rd hottest date
12 1954 All counties only one tenth of an inch rainfall since end of month
13 1957 All counties start of week long heat wave (90+ maxima)
14 1956 Scarsdale, 97 degree maximum during 4 day county heat wave
15 1969 Southern Westchester flooding, with 2 - 4 inches rainfall countywide

         White Plains-Maplemoor & Carmel, (1.8 & 3.2 inches) in 3 hours
16 1969 Dobbs Ferry (3.34 inches) & Carmel (4.30 inches), last of 3 days of heavy rain
17 1960 Shrub Oak, greatest 1 and 3 hour rainfalls, 1.5 & 2.0 inches
18 1871 Croton Lake, 4.86 inches rainfall, greatest 19th century amount

     1908 West Point, 39 degrees, coldest June minimum
19 1972 County flooding closed Saw Mill, Taconic & Bronx Parkways, 3.4 - 5.6 inches rainfall; greatest 12 hour amounts (3.7 - 5.2 inches) at the Scarsdale, White Plains - Maple Moor and Woodlands-Ardsley recording rain gauges
20 1972 All counties, 3 - 5 inches rain from Tropical Storm Agnes over five days
21 1945 Larchmont, and Spring Valley greatest 1, 2, and 3 hour rains, 1.50 to 2.16 inches
22 1958 Shrub Oak, six days of 3rd week with record lows in the 30s
23 1941 Ossining, 94 degree maximum temperature
24 1949 Bedford Hills and Dobbs Ferry, 94 degree maxima in 4 day heat wave
25 1943 Yorktown Heights (96°F) & Bedford Hills (100°F) hottest June maxima
26 1952 Suffern, Scarsdale, & West Point 101, 100 & 102 degree maxima, hottest June date

     1884 Yonkers, 6.58 inches rainfall in 17 hours
27 1950 Shrub Oak, 100 degree maximum, hottest June date
28 1966 Southern Westchester, no rain for past 18 days
29 1965 Three counties, only one tenth inch of rain in last two weeks

     1934 Mount Vernon, 101 degree high mark, hottest June day
30 1963 Putnam and Westchester, only one half inch rain in last two weeks

DAILY CALENDAR OF EXTREMES

JULY

1	1943	Yorktown Heights, start of three day cool spell, minimum in low 40s
2	1897	Carmel, 5.03 inches rainfall, greatest 24 hour July amount
3	1966	Suffern, Dobbs Ferry, Carmel, & Scarsdale, highs of 100+ degrees
4	1949	Lower Westchester wind and dust storm, (50 mph), downed trees & power lines
	1973	Yorktown Heights & Carmel, 2.5 inches rain in 3 hours
5	1955	Dobbs Ferry, 100 degree maximum
6	1875	White Plains, 5.9 inches rainfall, heaviest late 19th century July 1 day amount
7	1865	White Plains, 91 degrees, hottest July maximum in 1862 - 1891 period
8	1909	Mount Hope, 43 degree minimum, coldest July date
9	1936	Bedford Hills & Scarsdale, 105 degree maximum, hottest county high, start of 3 days with 100+ highs at Bedford Hills, 104 & 103 degrees at West Point & Carmel
10	1936	Mount Vernon, 103 degree high, hottest July date
11	1945	Yorktown Heights, 38 degree minimum, coldest July date for Putnam & Westchester
	1995	Kent Cliffs, golf ball sized hail stones covered the ground at Route 301
12	1937	Peekskill & Bedford Hills, past week of maximums 90 to 100 degrees
13	1944	Yorktown Heights, last day of week of 90+ maximum temperatures
14	1966	All three counties, end of 3 week heat wave with highs from 85 to 102 degrees
	1948	Ossining, 4.5 inches rainfall
15	1995	Ardsley, Westchester Airport & Yorktown Heights, 100+ maximums
	1966	Countywide drought with only one third inch of rain in past 4 weeks
16	1968	All counties, only one-tenth inch rain in previous 18 days
17	1945	White Plains-Maple Moor, 1.37 inches rain in 1 hour
18	1953	Carmel, Dobbs Ferry, Scarsdale, 100+ degree maxima
19	1900	Mount Hope, last of 5 consecutive days of 90+ maxima (101 degrees on the 17th)
20	1923	Scarsdale, 100 degree maximum, 95 degrees at Carmel
	1965	Shrub Oak, first of three consecutive days with minimums in low 40s
21	1930	Mount Vernon, 100 degree maximum temperature
22	1946	Croton Lake, start of 3 day total of 7.21 inches rainfall
23	1945	Suffern, 6.27 inches of rain, greatest July single day amount, Spring Valley -3.71" in 6 hours
	1955	Ossining, 99 degree maximum, hottest July date
	1938	Scarsdale, 5.61 inches rainfall
24	1952	All counties, last of 13 consecutive days with 90+ maxima
25	1963	Shrub Oak, start of five day heat wave (90+ maxima)
26	1942	Scarsdale, 5.30 inches rainfall
27	1889	Yonkers, 21.73 inches rainfall in last five days of month
	1942	Larchmont, 5.86 inches rain in 3 hours
28	1922	Bedford Hills, 3 inches rainfall
29	1971	Mahopac, mini-tornado caused building and boat damage in and near village
30	1960	Bedford Hills, 8 inches of rain, greatest 20th century single day's amount
	1877	Croton Lake, 4 inches of rain, greatest 19th century amount
31	1933	Scarsdale, 103 degree maximum, 4 consecutive days of 90+ maxima

DAILY CALENDAR OF EXTREMES

AUGUST

1 1812 Harrison, & Rye, tornado "tearing up trees, barns, fences and some houses"
2 1963 Chappaqua, 1.2 inches rainfall
3 1975 Westchester Airport & Yorktown Heights, last of 3 day heat wave
4 1915 Scarsdale, 5 inches rainfall, 3rd heaviest 24 hour August rainfall
   1903 Southern Westchester, 6.35 inches rain in 12 hours
5 1970 All three counties, no rainfall from this date to the 17th
6 1957 Shrub Oak, 38 degree minimum in a cold first week of month
7 1918 Mount Vernon (101°F), Scarsdale & West Point (104°F), hottest August maxima
   1986 Pleasantville, 4.41 inches of torrential rain and local flooding
8 1955 All three counties, last day of 90+ maxima since start of month
9 1969 Chappaqua, rain on 22 of last 23 days
10 1944 Westchester, start of 8 day heat wave, temps to mid and high 90s
11 1971 Rye, short and narrow tornado, trees and limbs ravaged
12 1944 Suffern & Yorktown Heights, 100 & 101 degree maximum, hottest August date
   Bedford Hills, 102 degree maximum
13 1875 Croton Lake, 4.85 inches rainfall, wettest August date
   1877 White Plains, 3.6 inches rainfall, wettest 19th century amount for August
14 1955 Scarsdale, 9+ inches rain from Hurricane "Connie," 4.08 inches in 12 hours, 3 day total areawide
      was 5 - 9 inches
   West Point, 4.87 inches in 24 hours
15 1953 Westchester, no rain after this date through the end of the month
   1959 Chappaqua, 92 degree maximum, start of heat wave
16 1909 Scarsdale, 5.5 inches rainfall, greatest August amount
   1968 Yorktown Heights, 2.4 inches of rain in 3 hours
17 1952 Peekskill, (5.19 inches) & Shrub Oak (6.64 inches) rainfall
18 1879 White Plains, 3.9 inches rainfall, wettest August date (1862 - 1891)
   Croton Lake, 2.0 inches
19 1955 Yorktown Heights, 6.66 inches rainfall in 2 days from Hurricane "Diane," Heaviest 1, 2, 3, & 6 hour
      amounts (up to 3.4 inches) at Scarsdale,
   White Plains-Maplemoor, and Woodlands-Ardsley
20 1950 Shrub Oak, 6 inches rainfall, greatest August downpour
21 1964 Southern Westchester, less than one-quarter inch rain to date this month
   1888 Southern Westchester, 6.37 inches rainfall in 16 hours
22 1933 Scarsdale, 3.3 inches rainfall
23 1937 Carmel, 3.38 inches rainfall, and Scarsdale, 3.86 inches rainfall
24 1953 Westchester, start of 12 consecutive days of 90+ degree maxima
25 1940 Scarsdale, (40°F), Bedford Hills (38°F), Yorktown Heights (31°F),
   Suffern (34°F), coldest August minimums
26 1948 Dobbs Ferry (102°F), Peekskill (102°F), Bedford Hills (104°F), hottest August maxima
27 1971 All counties, Hurricane "Doria" deposited about 6 inches rainfall
   1948 Carmel, 102 degree maximum, hottest August day
28 1948 Ossining, 100 degree maximum, hottest August day
   1971 Pleasantville (5.9") and Yorktown Heights (6.86"), wettest August day
29 1908 Mount Hope, 41 degree minimum, coldest August day
   1982 Dobbs Ferry, (44°F), and Westchester Airport (41°F), coldest August minimums
30 1948 All counties, last day of 5 day heat wave
31 1954 Westchester Airport, 3.57 inches rainfall from Hurricane "Carol"
   1867 White Plains, 43 degree minimum, coldest 19th century August minimum

DAILY CALENDAR OF EXTREMES

SEPTEMBER

1 1953 Ossining (100°F) & Peekskill (99°F), hottest September maxima
2 1953 Suffern, West Point, Carmel, Bedford Hills, Dobbs Ferry, Westchester Airport, Scarsdale, 100+ degree maxima for all 7 sites, hottest for all and only September day to break 100 degree mark
3 1974 Westchester Airport, 5.01 inches rainfall, wettest September day
4 1929 Mount Vernon, last of 4 days with maxima in mid 90s
  1868 White Plains, 5.25 inches rainfall
5 1878 White Plains had 4.70 inches rainfall
6 1972 Mid-point of dry spell in three counties
7 1962 Putnam & Westchester, 2 day cold spell, minimums from 34 to 48 degrees
8 1914 Areawide 15 day drought began, driest September at Bedford Hills
9 1862 White Plains, 91 degree maximum, 2nd hottest September day (1862-1891)
  1931 Southern Westchester, first of 5 consecutive days of 90+ maxima
10 1930 Scarsdale & Bedford Hills, start of 14 and 16 consecutive days of 80+ maxima
11 1954 Shrub Oak, Hurricane "Edna" gave 4.3 inches rain in 6 hours, West Point (4.56 inches), Dobbs Ferry, (4.84 inches) & Westchester Airport (4.93 inches) in 24 hours
12 1960 Peekskill, up to 5 inches rain in 2 days from Hurricane "Donna," West Point, 4.76 inches; 40 to 60 mph gusts in Yorktown Heights
13 1964 All three counties, mid-point of 4 week drought
14 1944 Scarsdale, & Sparkill 4.88 & 3.75 inches rain in 6 hours; 6 inches in 24 hours in Yonkers
  1952 Countywide, no rainfall since 3rd of the month
15 1904 Yonkers, 5.65 inches of rain in 24 hours
  1944 Lower Hudson valley, "Great Hurricane of 1944," last of three days of 6 to 10 inches rain total
16 1915 Mount Vernon, 91 degree maximum, hottest so late in season
17 1999 Croton Watershed' wettest day of 20th century - 9 - 11 inches from Tropical Storm "Floyd"
18 1968 Areawide warm spell, 8 consecutive days of 80+ maxima, longest so late in season
19 1894 Yonkers, 7.59 inches rainfall in 24 hours
  1938 Westchester & Putnam, "Great Hurricane," high winds and torrential rain (9-10 inches) in 3 days, 6.55 inches in Yonkers in 24 hours
20 1938 Carmel, 6.04 inches, 8.94 inches in 3 day period; Croton Lake 8.05 inches in 3 days
21 1961 New Rochelle, "Hurricane Esther," 40 - 60 mph gusts, power lines down, 1.5 inches rain area wide
  1962 Suffern, 31 degrees, earliest in season below freezing date
22 1904 Mount Hope & Scarsdale, 29 degree minimum, coldest September date
23 1975 Both counties, start of "Hurricane Eloise" 5 day period with totals of 9 - 10 inches rainfall
24 1970 Westchester Airport & Scarsdale, 94 degree maximum, hottest in county so late in season
25 1963 All counties cold spell, Dobbs Ferry and Shrub Oak, 39 and 26 degree minimums
26 1975 Larchmont, 3.76 inches rain in 6 hours, White Plains-Maplemoor, 3.3 inches in 3 hours Yorktown Heights, 4.13 inches in 24 hours
27 1947 Peekskill & Yorktown Heights, 29 & 24 degree minimums, coldest September day
28 1947 Bedford Hills (28°F), Dobbs Ferry (33°F), coldest September date
29 1958 Shrub Oak, 26 degree minimum, coldest recorded in New York State that month
  1963 Shrub Oak, 3.0 inches in 24 hours, greatest in New York State that month
30 1884 Yonkers, 6.10 inches rainfall in 24 hours

DAILY CALENDAR OF EXTREMES

OCTOBER

1 1884 White Plains, 85 degree maximum
2 1927 Mount Vernon, 89 degree maximum
3 1877 Croton Lake and southern Westchester, 6.0 and 5.3 inches rainfall respectively
4 1987 Yorktown Heights, .12 inches snow, earliest Westchester measureable snow
   1964 Westchester and Putnam, no rainfall for next 13 days
5 1941 Suffern, West Point, Peekskill, Bedford Hills, Carmel, Yorktown Heights, Ossining, Scarsdale, all stations with 90+ maxima, for hottest October date
6 1903 Bedford Hills, start of 4 day storm measuring 5.6 inches
7 1946 Westchester, last day of 4 day hot spell, high in mid 80s
8 1924 Putnam, last day of rain for entire month
9 1877 White Plains, 9.7 inches, greatest 19th century 24 hour October amount
10 1979 Yorktown Heights, 6 inches of snowfall
    1949 Scarsdale, 90 degree maximum
11 1898 Bedford Hills, 27 degree minimum, last of 3 days with lows in 20s
12 1949 Westchester, last of 5 days of 80+ maximums
13 1906 Mount Hope, 26 degree minimum, coldest so early in the season
14 1876 White Plains, 3 inches of snow, earliest 19th century snowfall of record
15 1955 Woodlands-Ardsley, 3.61 inches rain in 6 hours
    1943 Ossining, start of 3 days of rainfall totaling 6.3 inches
16 1955 Croton Falls, 8.4 inches rain in 24 hours, greatest October amount
17 1955 Westchester & Putnam, last of 4 day storm, with rain amounts 8 -11 inches
18 1972 All counties, 4 day cold spell with minimums in high 20s
19 1972 Yorktown Heights, Carmel, Dobbs Ferry & Westchester Airport, snowfall amounts up to 2.5 inches
    1952 Dobbs Ferry, 1.1 inches snowfall, greatest amount so early in season
20 1909 Mount Hope, 22 degree minimum, coldest so early in season
21 1972 Westchester Airport, 24 degree minimum, coldest October date
22 1940 Yorktown Heights, 16 degree minimum, coldest October date last day of week long lows below freezing
    1995 West Point, 4.50 inches rain, greatest single day October amount
23 1964 Putnam, mid-point of 6 day cold wave with lows in high 20s
24 1969 Shrub Oak, 16 degree minimum, coldest October mark
25 1960 Scarsdale & Dobbs Ferry, traces of snow
26 1962 Westchester Airport & Scarsdale, 2 and 4 inches of snowfall
27 1963 All three counties, drought conditions, no rain for past 3 weeks
28 1936 Peekskill (22°F), Carmel (16°F), & Bedford Hills (16°F), coldest October minimums
29 1904 Mount Hope, 22 degrees, 2nd day in row in low 20s
30 1925 Bedford Hills, trace of snow
31 1925 Westchester, below freezing minimums for last 4 days
    1897 West Point, 20 degrees, coldest October minimum

DAILY CALENDAR OF EXTREMES

NOVEMBER

1   1950   Dobbs Ferry (82°F), Bedford Hills (83°F), Scarsdale (84°F), hottest November date

2   1950   Suffern, West Point & Carmel, 81 degree maxima, only and last of 80+ in November

3   1958   Scarsdale & Yorktown Heights, 2.5 & 1 inch of snowfall

4   1923   All three counties, last of three days with minimums in 20s

5   1895   Bedford Hills, 3.29 inches rain

6   1963   Scarsdale, start of two day 3.69 inch rainfall

     1951   Larchmont, 2.64 inches rain in 2 hours

7   1879   White Plains, 3 inches snowfall

     1953   Westchester and Putnam, 2 - 6 inches snowfall

8   1977   Westchester Airport & Dobbs Ferry, 4.95 & 5.25 inches rainfall, wettest November day

9   1972   Yorktown Heights, 1.3 inches rain in 3 hours; Woodlands-Ardsley, 2.7 inches in 6 hours

     1947   Yorktown Heights, 3.47 inches rain, wettest November day; Sparkill- 3 inches in 12 hours

10   1975   Westchester Airport, last of 3 days with highs in low 70s

11   1947   White Plains-Maple Moor, 2.98 inches rain in 12 hours

12   1968   Northern Westchester, 4 - 8 inches snowfall

13   1960   Cross River, no rainfall for almost the remainder of the month

14   1904   Mount Hope, no precipitation for next 12 days

15   1928   Mount Vernon, Mount Hope & Scarsdale, 65 - 70 degree highs in 4 day warm spell

16   1969   Yorktown Heights, rain every day but 2 since start of month

17   1933   All three counties, lows in teens for last 3 days

     1964   Westchester, temporary end of 10 week drought

     1903   Carmel, 3.07 inches rain, greatest November amount

18   1968   Yorktown Heights, rain on all but four days since start of month

     1924   Carmel, 8 degree minimum, earliest single digit temperature of the three counties

19   1955   Westchester and Putnam, 3 inches snowfall

20   1917   Westchester, no precipitation for last three weeks

21   1931   All three counties, start of 4 day warm spell, highs in low 70s

22   1967   Shrub Oak, last of 9 consecutive days with below freezing temperatures

23   1888   Carmel, 8 degree minimum, earliest and lowest 19th century mark

24   1956   Shrub Oak, 9 degree minimum, coldest November date

     1989   Ardsley, 12 degree minimum, coldest November date

25   1950   Countywide, gale force winds with 1 - 2 inches rainfall

     1971   Putnam & N. Westchester, 3 - 5 inches snow, none in south

26   1938   West Point & Scarsdale (8°F), Carmel (5°F) minimums, coldest November date

           Thanksgiving Day snowstorm, 6 and 10 inches of snow at Bedford Hills & Scarsdale

27   1882   White Plains, 10 inches snowfall, heaviest November day for 1873 to 1891 period

     1932   Peekskill, 8 degree minimum, coldest November date

28   1889   White Plains, 5.0 inches rainfall, heaviest 19th century November date

           Croton Lake, 2.5 inches rainfall

29   1955   Ossining, 17 degree minimum, coldest November date

30   1875   White Plains, 8 degree minimum, coldest November date late 19th century

     1958   Suffern, 9 degrees, coldest November minimum

DAILY CALENDAR OF EXTREMES

DECEMBER

1   1962   Shrub Oak (68°F), hottest maximum December date

2   1960   Westchester and Putnam, no precipitation for next nine days

3   1962   Shrub Oak, 3rd day with high temperatures over 60 degrees

4   1982   Dobbs Ferry, Scarsdale & Westchester Airport, 70 degree maxima, hottest December highs

      1940   Carmel, 2 below zero minimum, earliest 20th century recorded in both counties

5   1955   Croton watershed, only one-third inch precipitation in remainder of the month

6   1879   White Plains, 4.45 inches rainfall, wettest December date

7   1998   Yorktown Heights, (73°F), hottest December maximum, 60+ degrees for 7 of last 9 days

      1932   Mount Vernon, 60+ degree highs for four of last six days

8   1906   Mount Hope, 8 degree minimum, zero low at Carmel

9   1928   Westchester, no precipitation for next seven days Carmel, 68 degree maximum, hottest December date

10   1958   Westchester, less than one-quarter inch precipitation to end of month

      1878   White Plains, 4.1 inches rainfall

      1968   Lake Mohansic frozen over about one week earlier than normal

11   1952   White Plains-Maplemoor, 1.3 inches rain in 6 hours

      1966   Westchester, last of four days with highs about 60 degrees

12   1960   All counties, major snowstorm, 16 - 19 inches

13   1915   Carmel, 18 inches of snowfall, over 12 inches in Westchester

      1941   Spring Valley & Larchmont, 2.20 & 2.75 inches rain in 12 hours

            Croton Lake & Scarsdale (3.16 inches), Bedford Hills (3.22 inches),

            Yorktown Heights (3.29 inches) greatest December 1 day amounts

14   1922   Bedford Hills, 15 inches snowfall

15   1901   Mount Hope, 70 degree maximum, warmest December date

16   1950   Scarsdale, 2.04 inches rainfall in 6 hours

      1917   Carmel, 16 below zero minimum, coldest so early in season

17   1942   Yorktown Heights, 15 below zero minimum, 3 of 4 next days with below zero mins

18   1917   Mount Vernon, 4 below zero, 2nd day with below zero

19   1971   Yorktown Heights, normal temperatures after nearly one week of warmth

      1895   Bedford Hills, 60 degree maximum

20   1884   White Plains, 5 below zero minimum, coldest December date late 19th century

      1874   White Plains, 13 inches snowfall

21   1973   Yorktown Heights, 2.6 inches in 12 hours

            White Plains-Maplemoor, 2.1 inches in 12 hours

      1942   Suffern & Peekskill, 10 &14 below zero, coldest December low mark

            Yorktown Heights, 21 below zero minimum, coldest December date

22   1955   Shrub Oak, 12 below zero minimum, Westchester Airport, 3 below zero minimum

23   1966   Westchester & Putnam, 7 to 14 inches of snow

      1967   Both counties, warm temperatures for last 2 weeks, some highs in 60s

24   1945   Yorktown Heights, 3rd consecutive day with below zero minimums

25   1948   Yorktown Heights, start of 3 consecutive days of below zero minimums,

            2 straight days in most of Westchester

26   1943   All counties, first precipitation since December 7

      1958   Shrub Oak, last of 4 below zero days this month

27   1872   White Plains, about 22 inches of snow

      1947   All counties, greatest 20th century snowstorm, 25 - 30 inches

28   1969   Carmel & Yorktown Heights, about 1 foot of snowfall

29   1917   Area-wide, start of most severe 3 day cold wave of 20th century (-13° - -19°F)

30   2000   All 3 counties, 12"-16" snowfall

31   1962   Pleasantville, 2.81 inches rainfall, greatest December amount

ALL ABOUT TEMPERATURE

As we have seen, there are important factors that affect the daily high and low temperature of any specific site. Elevation, urbanization, distance from water bodies, thermometer location and even the time of the reading of the thermometer all contribute to make each thermometer location have its own unique temperature profile. Consequently, there are rarely any two sites that will produce exactly the same monthly average temperature. At the present time there are only four currently operating weather stations with at least 35 years of record in our three county region. The temperature isotherms shown in Figures 23-26 and the other tables shown below are the product of these stations and of the discontinued ones. Differences in averages can be attributed to all of the above factors. Despite these differences, a reasonably accurate profile of the temperature of our counties has been determined and can be used while noting the precautions above. The tables and figures below show nearly all aspects of temperature in different time frames.

The newest monthly averages or normals for the thirty year period ending in 2000 (see Tables 1 and 2a), reveal that for each of the first few months there has been a significant increase in monthly and seasonal temperatures over the currently used 1961-1990 normal or average (see Table 1, 2). How much of this increase can be attributed to greater urbanization as opposed to global warming is uncertain.

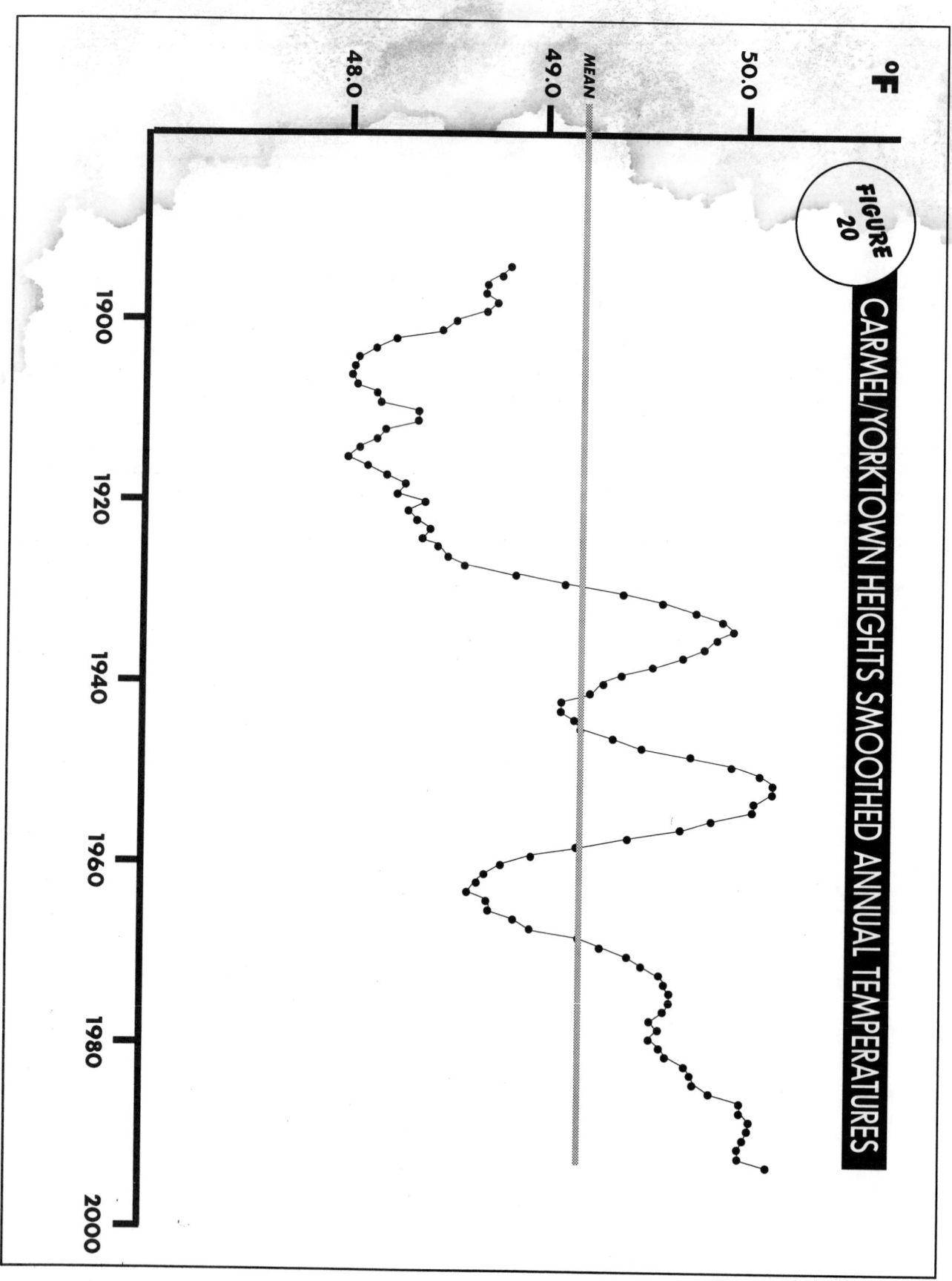

CARMEL/YORKTOWN HEIGHTS SMOOTHED ANNUAL TEMPERATURES

FIGURE 20

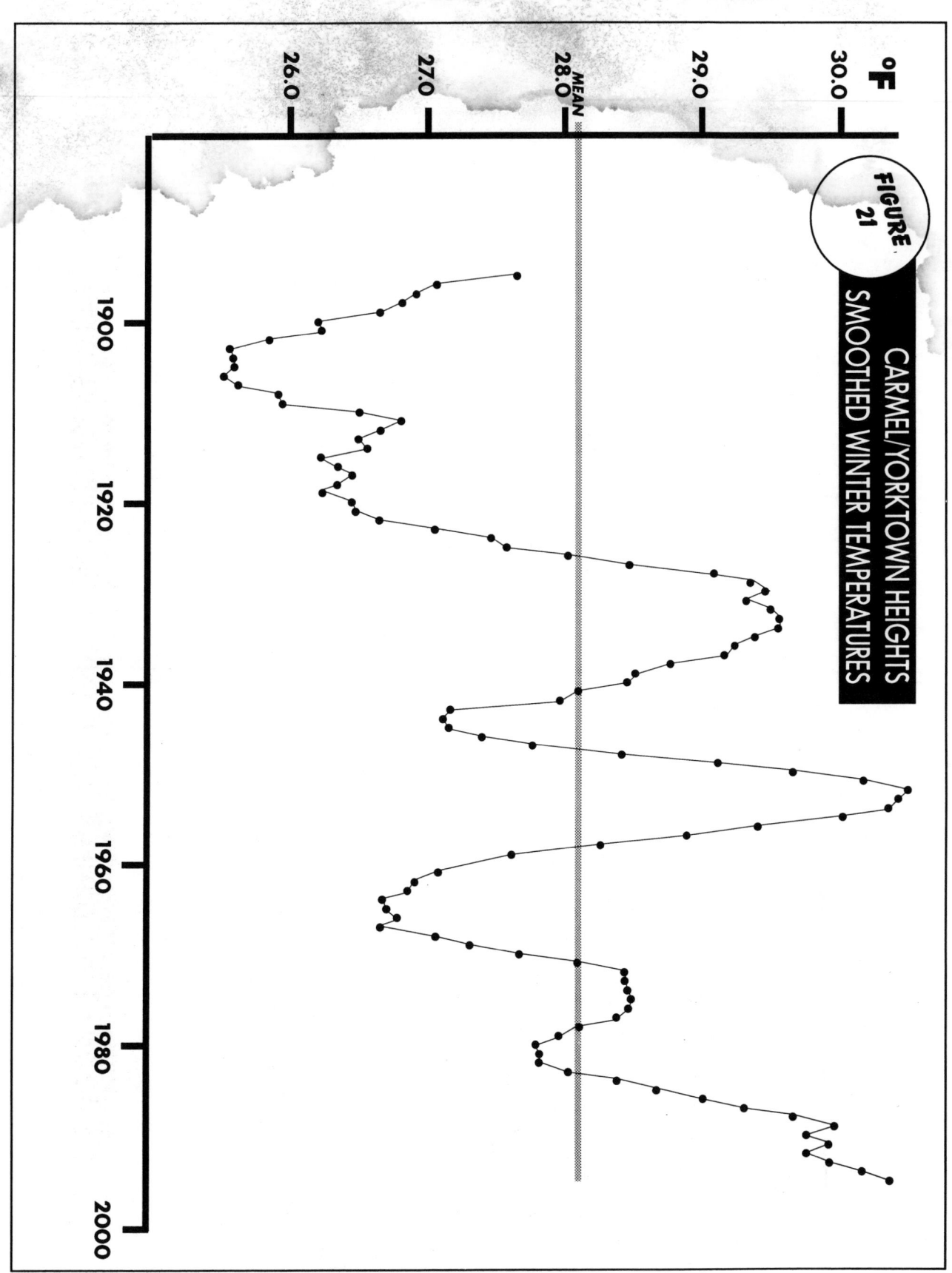

FIGURE 21

CARMEL/YORKTOWN HEIGHTS
SMOOTHED WINTER TEMPERATURES

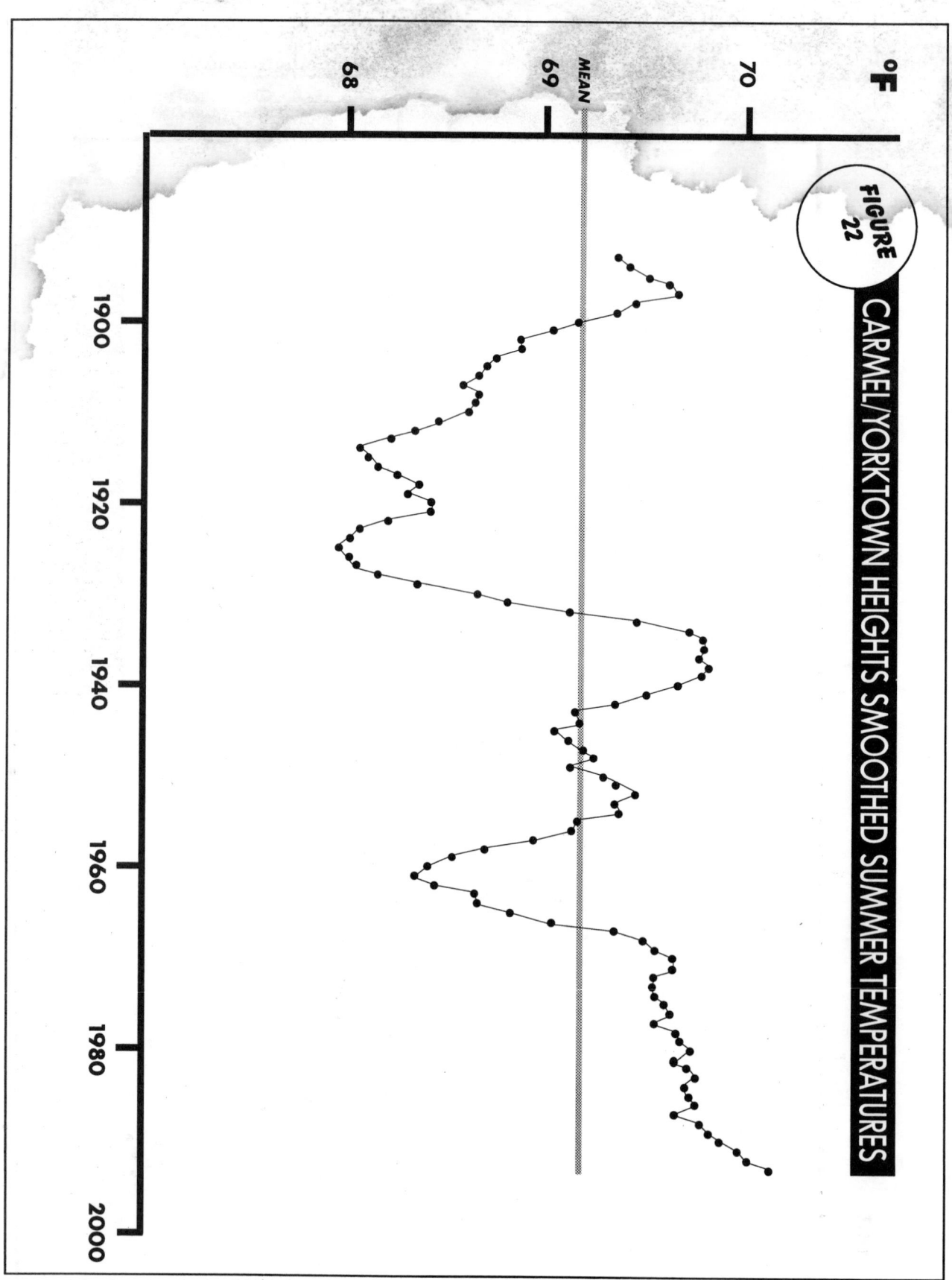

°F

FIGURE 22

CARMEL/YORKTOWN HEIGHTS SMOOTHED SUMMER TEMPERATURES

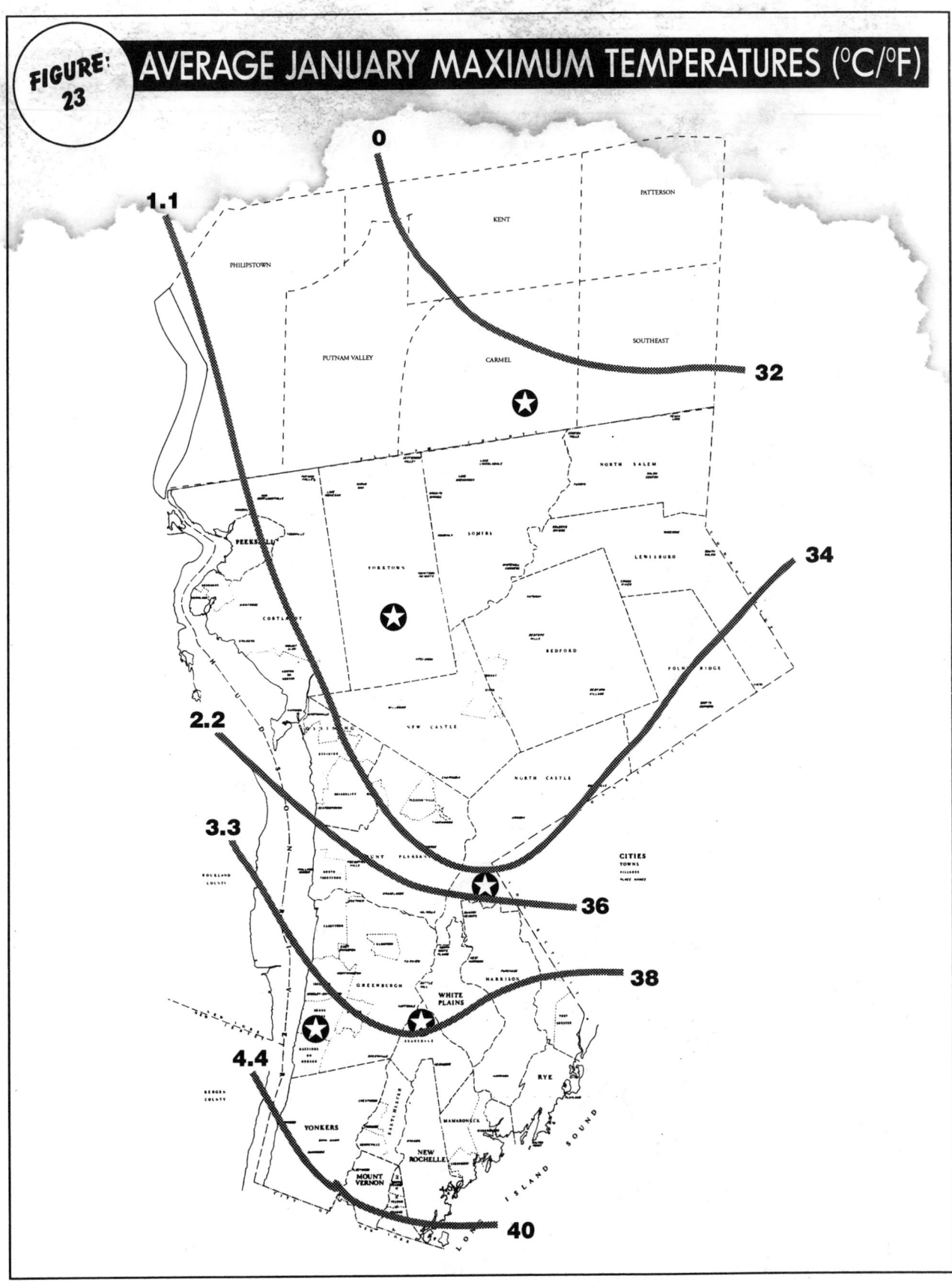

AVERAGE JANUARY MAXIMUM TEMPERATURES (°C/°F)

FIGURE: 23

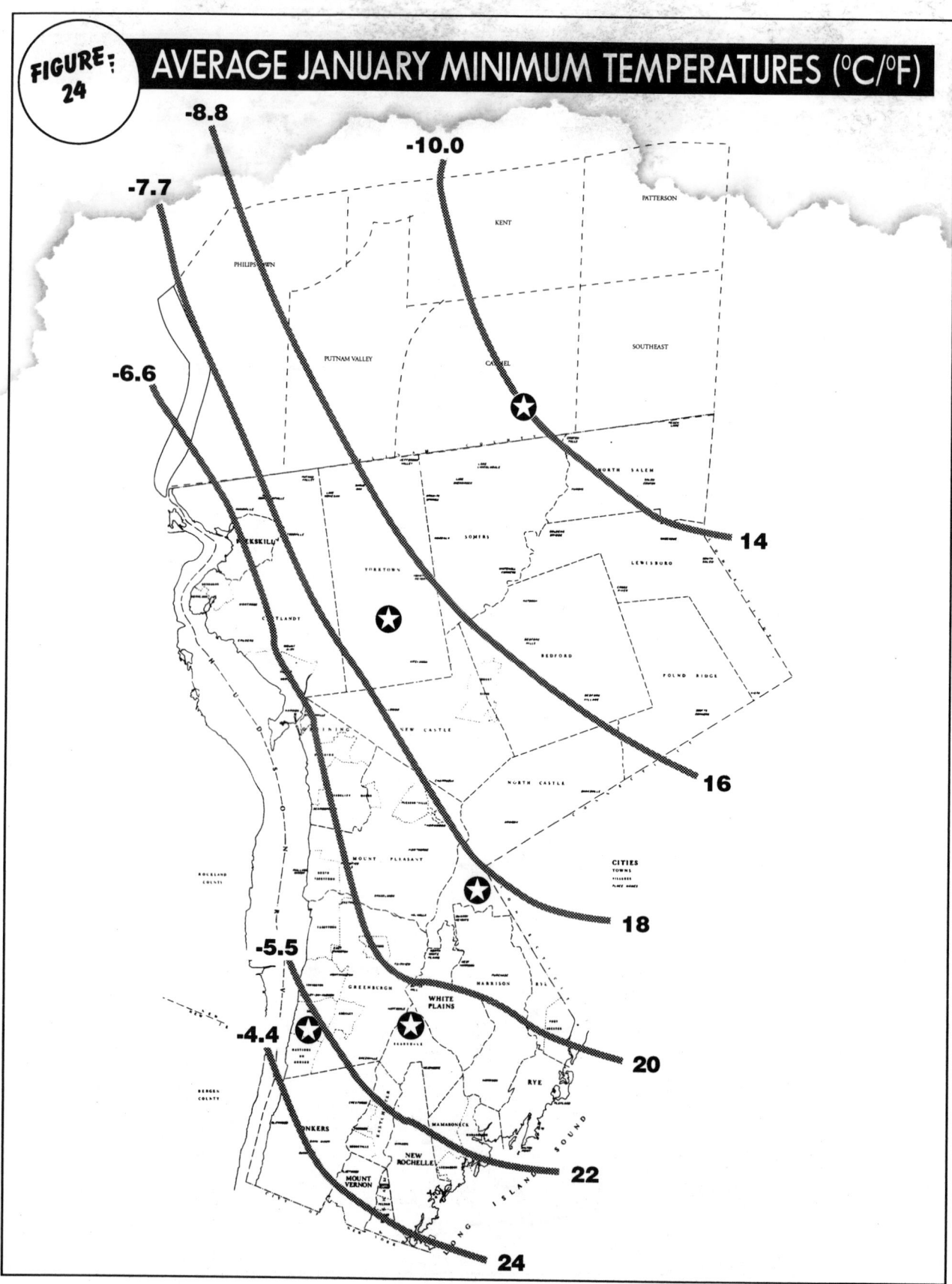

FIGURE: 24

AVERAGE JANUARY MINIMUM TEMPERATURES (°C/°F)

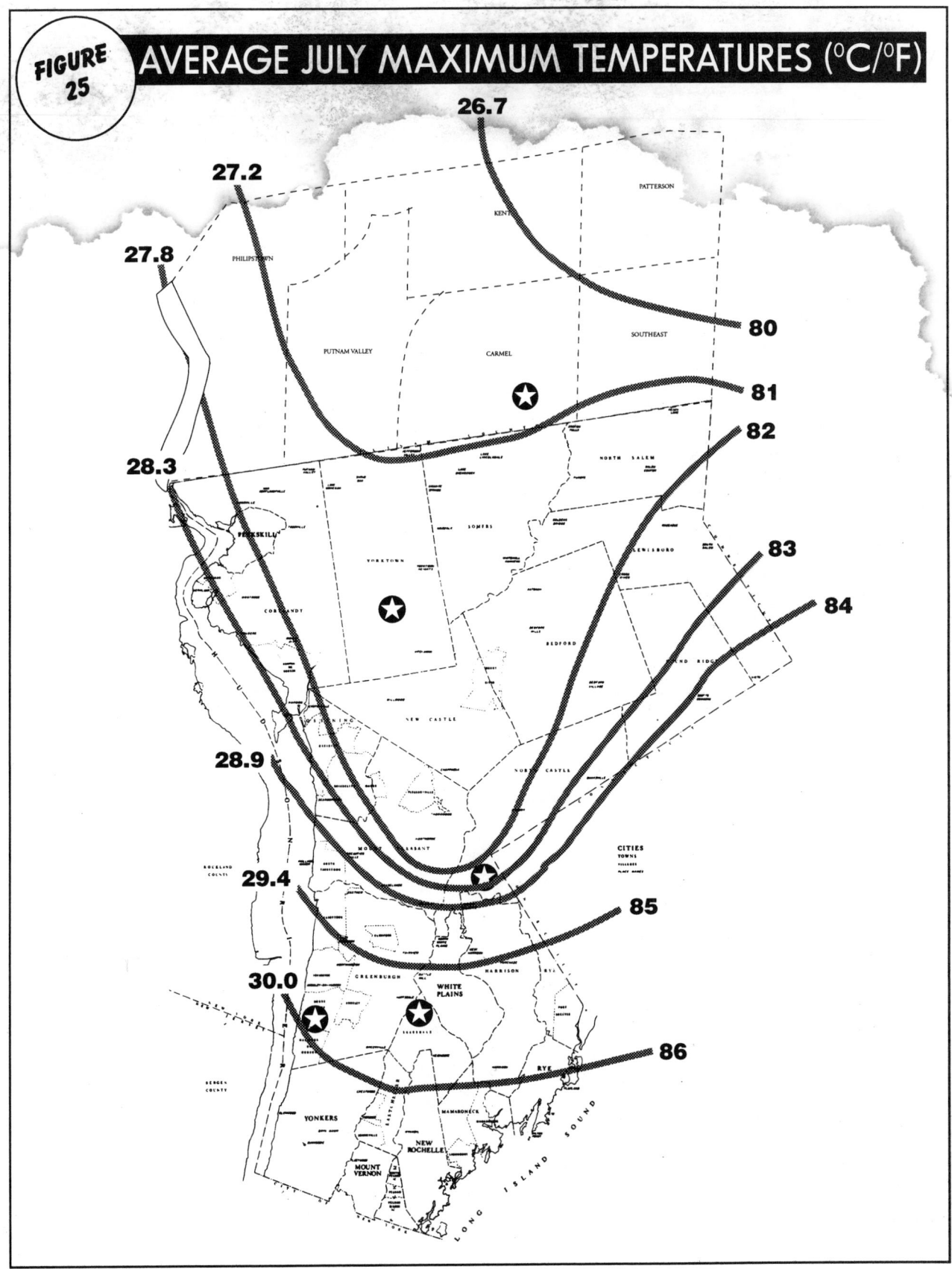

FIGURE 25 AVERAGE JULY MAXIMUM TEMPERATURES (°C/°F)

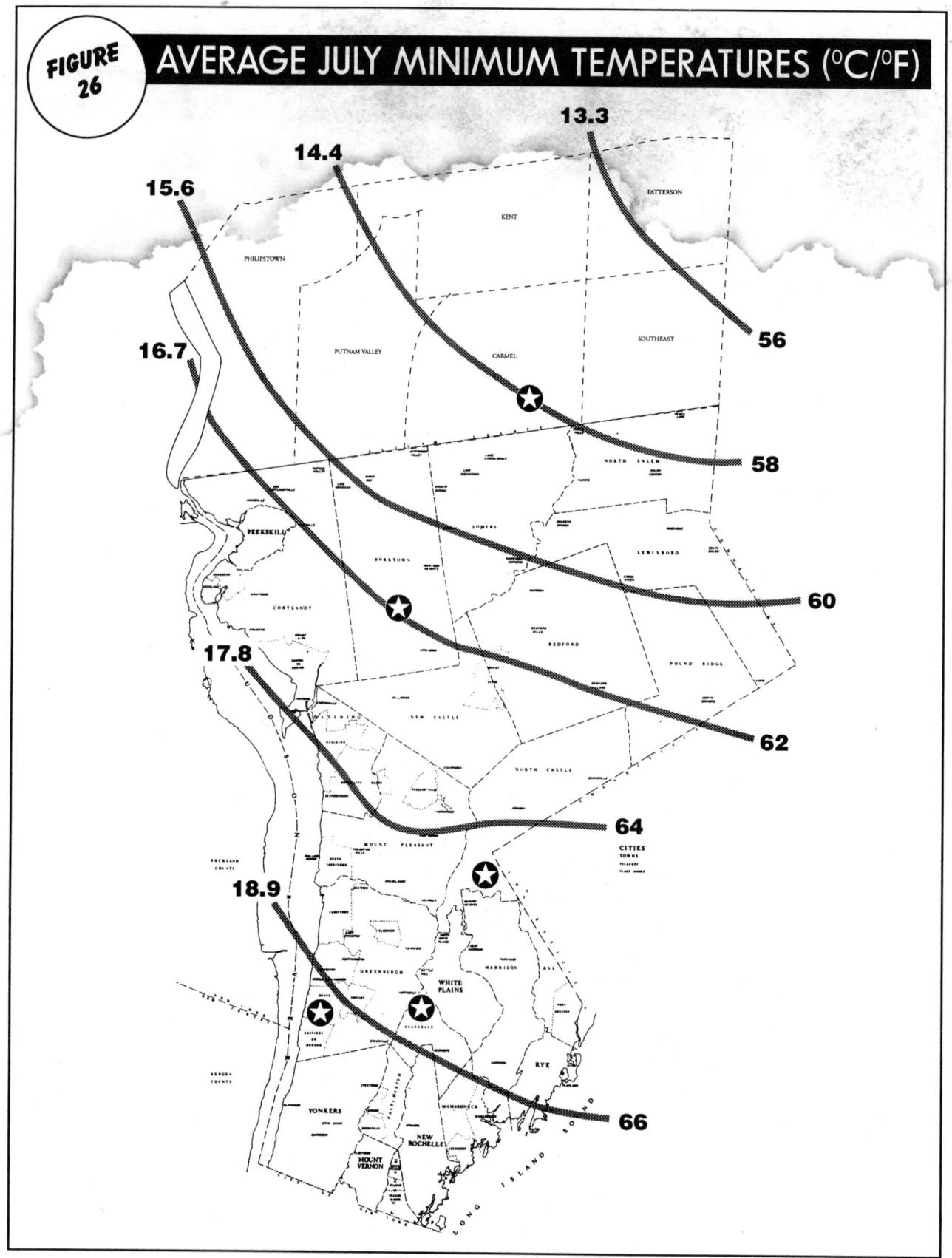

FIGURE 26

AVERAGE JULY MINIMUM TEMPERATURES (°C/°F)

TABLE 1

CORRECTED AVERAGE TEMPERATURES (° F)
1961 - 1990
1971 - 2000

	Jan	Feb	Mar	Apr	May	June	July	Aug	Sep	Oct	Nov	Dec	Annual
DOBBS FERRY													
	29.0	30.7	40.2	50.5	60.5	69.6	74.6	73.2	65.6	55.0	44.8	34.0	52.31
	29.0	30.8	39.0	49.3	59.5	68.7	74.0	72.4	64.7	53.6	44.6	34.5	51.68*

*Station moved in 1989

	Jan	Feb	Mar	Apr	May	June	July	Aug	Sep	Oct	Nov	Dec	Annual
SCARSDALE													
	28.7	31.5	39.9	50.2	60.4	69.1	74.2	72.5	65.2	54.3	44.8	33.6	51.99

Station closed in 1990

	Jan	Feb	Mar	Apr	May	June	July	Aug	Sep	Oct	Nov	Dec	Annual
WESTCHESTER AIRPORT													
	27.2	29.4	38.4	48.7	59.0	67.9	73.3	71.9	64.3	53.5	43.6	32.4	50.81
	28.3	30.7	38.9	48.9	59.1	67.9	73.3	71.8	63.9	53.0	43.7	33.7	51.10
PEEKSKILL													
	26.1	28.5	37.8	48.0	59.0	67.4	72.8	71.0	63.6	52.9	42.6	30.9	50.05
	27.0	29.8	38.7	48.8	59.7	68.0	73.3	71.4	63.7	52.4	42.5	31.9	50.60
YORKTOWN HEIGHTS													
	24.7	27.0	36.7	47.6	58.1	66.5	71.6	70.0	62.9	52.1	42.2	30.3	49.15
	26.6	29.4	37.8	48.2	58.9	67.0	72.2	70.4	62.9	52.0	42.6	31.8	49.98
SUFFERN													
	26.0	28.1	37.6	48.5	58.8	67.4	72.4	70.6	63.2	52.0	42.5	31.4	49.88
	27.6	29.4	38.2	49.3	59.5	67.9	72.9	71.3	63.4	51.6	43.9	32.5	50.62
WEST POINT													
	25.8	27.9	37.6	47.6	58.4	66.4	71.4	70.5	63.2	52.6	41.8	30.2	49.45
	26.5	28.8	37.7	47.7	58.4	66.0	71.2	70.3	62.5	51.7	41.5	31.2	49.46

TABLE 2
CORRECTED SEASONAL AVERAGE TEMPERATURES
CARMEL / YORKTOWN HEIGHTS

Year	SPRING (Mar, Apr, May)	SUMMER (Jun, Jul, Aug)	FALL (Sep, Oct, Nov)	WINTER (Dec, Jan, Feb)	Year	Spring	Summer	Fall	Winter
					1944	46.5	70.0	50.8	24.0
					1945	51.0	68.3	52.4	26.1
1888	43.4	67.8	49.2	29.0 (1888-89)	1946	50.3	67.1	55.6*	29.4
1889	50.6	69.2	51.3	35.8?	1947	46.0	69.2	54.1	22.9
1890	47.9	70.0	50.1	29.3	1948	47.4	69.0	54.0	33.1
1891	28.6	68.8	51.6	31.5	1949	49.4	72.2	52.8	31.4
1892	45.6	71.0	49.2	23.5	1950	44.9	67.6	53.1	30.1
1893	44.1	68.4	49.1	27.0					
1894	48.1	69.0	50.4	24.4	1951	49.3	68.4	51.3	31.2(1951-52)
1895	46.1	69.2	51.3	28.4	1952	47.9	70.8	51.5	33.6
1896	48.8	70.2	51.4	27.5	1953	49.5	68.7	53.8	31.5
1897	49.3	68.6	51.2	28.7	1954	48.3	68.9	53.4	29.0
1898	47.5	70.2	52.1	25.0	1955	49.8	71.6	52.3	28.3
1899	45.8	69.3	50.9	28.4	1956	43.7	68.3	52.1	30.0
1900	45.7	71.2	54.5	25.4	1957	48.6	69.2	53.1	28.5
					1958	46.9	67.7	51.8	25.1
1901	45.7	71.1	49.2	26.5 (1901-02)	1959	49.1	70.2	53.6	31.1
1902	50.3	68.0	53.7	28.5	1960	45.8	67.6	52.2	23.1
1903	52.9*	65.6	48.5	20.0					
1904	45.9	67.6	48.0	21.0	1961	44.9	68.1	55.0	26.8(1961-62)
1905	46.5	68.2	50.1	29.9	1962	47.1	66.4	49.7	24.4
1906	45.7	69.9	51.7	23.3	1963	48.8	68.6	53.4	26.1
1907	44.0	68.7	49.5	27.9	1964	48.4	68.1	52.6	26.3
1908	48.6	71.2	52.1	29.5	1965	47.0	68.3	51.7	29.3
1909	46.6	68.4	49.9	25.0	1966	46.1	71.1	52.1	29.1
1910	50.0	68.2	51.4	25.2	1967	43.7	69.8	50.8	26.3
					1968	48.9	68.9	54.2	27.4
1911	46.9	69.0	49.3	24.1(1911 - 12)	1969	47.6	69.4	52.4	24.6
1912	46.2	67.1	52.2	30.6	1970	47.4	70.0	54.5	26.8
1913	48.8	68.8	52.2	25.2					
1914	45.2	67.4	52.0	29.4	1971	45.8	69.7	55.0	30.0(1971-72)
1915	46.6	66.9	52.8	26.3	1972	46.3	68.7	50.6	30.4
1916	43.0*	67.8	51.4	26.3	1973	49.1	71.3	54.6	30.2
1917	43.5	69.7	47.5*	19.7*	1974	48.2	68.8	51.0	32.2
1918	49.2	67.9	51.1	31.4	1975	47.0	69.6	54.0	29.3
1919	47.7	68.5	52.4	22.1	1976	49.9	69.0	48.8	24.4
1920	44.6	68.4	53.8	30.3	1977	51.6	69.5	53.0	25.8
					1978	46.0	69.5	51.6	26.1
1921	52.4	69.3	53.0	26.8(1921-22)	1979	49.4	69.4	53.7	29.2
1922	48.8	69.0	52.6	23.9	1980	48.6	70.8	51.5	26.6
1923	45.4	68.1	51.7	29.3					
1924	44.6	66.6	49.1	28.0	1981	49.2	70.3	50.8	25.9(1981-82)
1925	47.5	69.2	49.0	27.5	1982	47.5	67.6	53.3	32.1
1926	43.7	67.4	50.1	26.5	1983	47.9	71.3	54.0	29.3
1927	46.5	65.2*	52.7	29.7	1984	45.4	70.9	53.2	30.3
1928	45.0	68.8	51.4	28.8	1985	50.6	68.4	53.9	27.2
1929	49.1	68.3	51.4	30.5	1986	50.3	68.1	51.1	28.7
1930	47.4	69.4	52.3	28.7	1987	49.6	69.8	51.3	28.6
					1988	47.9	71.8	51.3	29.9
1931	47.9	69.4	55.4	35.4*(1931-32)	1989	47.6	69.4	53.2	29.0
1932	46.0	68.5	52.1	33.6	1990	47.2	70.1	54.8	33.1
1933	48.6	70.0	50.7	23.2					
1934	47.4	69.3	53.2	27.5	1991	52.3	71.4	52.6	31.8(1991-92)
1935	47.5	69.7	52.2	23.9	1992	46.2	67.4	50.7	28.7
1936	49.2	69.6	50.7	34.6	1993	47.5	71.1	51.5	28.5
1937	47.0	71.0	50.7	30.0	1994	48.2	70.8	53.5	32.1
1938	49.8	70.4	52.1	30.7	1995	48.2	71.2	52.4	30.4
1939	47.4	71.6	50.9	27.3	1996	46.0	69.2	51.3	32.9
1940	44.8	67.9	50.1	29.2	1997	46.7	69.8	51.5	34.7
					1998	51.1	71.7	54.3	32.9
1941	48.0	68.7	54.2	29.0(1941-42)	1999	48.9	73.0*	54.3	30.6
1942	50.2	68.4	51.5	25.3	2000	49.9	67.8	52.2	
1943	45.7	70.8	50.0	26.2					

TABLE 2a

SEASONAL 20TH CENTURY TEMPERATURE TRENDS
(°Fahrenheit)

	Average through 1930	Average through 1940	1931-1960	1941-1970	1951-1980	1961-1990	1971-2000
WINTER (Dec, Jan, Feb)							
Scarsdale	28.2	29.0	30.0	30.0	29.8	30.1	
BedfordHills	27.3	28.1	29.7	29.3	28.4		
Carmel/Yorktown	26.1	26.6	27.9	26.9	27.1	28.5	29.7
Wes Point	29.4	29.6	29.6	28.0	29.3	28.0	28.8
SUMMER (Jun, Jul, Aug)							
Scarsdale	68.4	69.2	71.0	70.7	70.5	70.5	
Bedford Hills	68.5	69.5	71.0	70.6	70.2		
Carmel/Yorktown	69.2	69.1	69.2	68.9	68.6	69.4	69.9
West Point	71.1	71.3	72.5	72.5	72.7	69.4	69.2
SPRING (Mar, Apr, May)							
Scarsdale	47.0	46.9	47.2	47.5	48.0	48.2	
Bedford Hills	46.6	47.0	48.6	48.0	48.2		
Carmel/Yorktown	46.4	46.3	46.7	46.5	46.6	47.8	48.3
West Point	48.0	48.1	49.2	49.4	49.9	47.9	47.9
FALL (Sep, Oct, Nov)							
Scarsdale	52.2	52.5	53.7	53.5	53.8	53.4	
BedfordHills	51.2	52.0	53.2	52.9	52.8		
Carmel/Yorktown	51.0	51.1	52.0	52.1	51.6	51.2	52.5
West Point	53.0	53.2	54.5	54.8	54.6	52.5	51.9

The above seasonal average temperatures are taken from the four weather stations with the longest continuous temperature records . Averages shown have been corrected for the time-of-observation bias but not for urbanization effects in Scarsdale and Bedford Hills. Averages for those locations should be decreased from 0.1 to 0.5 degrees Fahrenheit to show the true non-urbanized average. Averages for West Point have been corrected only for the time-of-observaation bias for the 1961-2000 periods.

Only the concurrent time period averages after 1931 can be compared, since readings began in different years as shown below.

Station Temperature Periods of Observation
Scarsdale 1904 - 1990
Bedford Hills 1896 - 1977
Carmel/Yorktown Heights 1888-2000

TABLE 3
HOTTEST MONTHS

	Jan	Feb	Mar	Apr	May	June	July	Aug	Sep	Oct	Nov	Dec	Year
SCARSDALE (1904-1990)													
	40.0	38.4	48.0	55.1	65.0	73.4	77.0	76.0	70.8	60.0	50.0	40.0	54.0
	1932	1976	1945	1945	1944	1943	1955	1944	1961	1947	1975	1984	1990
BEDFORD HILLS (1894-1977)													
	39.5	37.0	49.0	55.6	65.6	75.5	77.2	75.6	70.2	59.8	49.4	37.6	53.5
	1932	1949	1945	1941	1944	1943	1955	1944	1961	1971	1931	1923	1949
CARMEL/YORKTOWN (1888-2000)													
	38.5	36.4	45.4	53.3	64.3	70.9	77.5	74.3	68.0	58.6	47.6	38.3	53.2
	1932	1998	1946	1941	1896	1943	1999	1955	1961	1971	1975	1998	1998
SUFFERN (1941-1998)													
	35.7	37.9	48.4	52.8	63.8	72.2	73.8	75.3	66.9	57.8	47.0	38.0	53.2
	1990	1998	1945	1945	1944	1952	1977	1980	1980	1946	1979	1990	1998
WEST POINT (1821-2000)													
	38.0	37.5	46.2	54.2	64.6	75.0	78.6	75.0	70.0	59.0	47.7	38.0	51.9
	1932	1976	1946	1878	1872	1831	1876	1955	1961	1971	1931	1923	1991

TABLE 4
HOTTEST DAILY MAXIMUM TEMPERATURES

	Jan	Feb	Mar	Apr	May	June	July	Aug	Sep	Oct	Nov	Dec
SCARSDALE												
	73	75	88	94	99	100	105	104	102	92	84	70
	26th	24th	29th	18th	31st	27th	9th	7th	2nd	5th	1st	4th
	1950	1985	1945	1976	1938	1952	1936	1918	1953	1941	1950	1982
BEDFORD HILLS												
	71	74	91	96	100	100	104	104	103	97	83	69
	26th	16th	29th	27th	24th	25th	19th	26th	2nd	5th	1st	1st
	1950	1954	1945	1915	1964	1943	1942	1948	1953	1941	1950	1908
CARMEL/YORKTOWN												
	70	73	85	93	97	99	103	102	103	90	81	73
	26th	16th	28th	18th	31st	25th	9th	26th	2nd	4th	1st	7th
	1950	1954	1945	1976	1939	1952	1936	1948	1953	1941	1950	1998
SUFFERN												
	67	74	87	91	95	101	102	100	104	92	82	70
	28th	16th	31st	28th	30th	25th	4th	31st	2nd	4th	1st	10th
	1974	1954	1998	1990	1969	1952	1966	1953	1953	1951	1950	1946
WEST POINT												
	71	72	86	96	97	102	104	104	105	92	82	70
	26th	25th	28th	18th	19th	6th	9th	7th	2nd	5th	1st	7th
	1950	1930	1945	1976	1962	1925	1936	1918	1953	1941	1950	1998

TABLE 5
COLDEST MONTHS

	Jan	Feb	Mar	Apr	May	June	July	Aug	Sep	Oct	Nov	Dec	Year
SCARSDALE (1904-1990)													
	18.0	16.0	28.0	42.0	51.6	64.4	63.4	65.3	60.3	46.2	35.7	20.4	46.0
	1918	1934	1916	1907	1917	1958	1933	1927	1924	1988	1904	1917	1904
BEDFORD HILLS (1894-1977)													
	16.2	16.3	27.4	42.2	50.4	61.3	66.0	65.0	57.4	45.4	35.0	20.0	46.2
	1918	1934	1916	1965	1917	1903	1920	1903	1924	1925	1901	1917	1904
CARMEL/YORKTOWN (1888-2000)													
	15.6	13.4	25.5	41.2	50.1	60.8	66.4	63.6	58.0	45.4	35.1	18.6	44.8
	1904	1934	1916	1943	1917	1916	1962	1927	1963	1925	1904	1989	1904
SUFFERN (1941-1998)													
	18.0	18.0	28.5	43.4	50.7	62.0	67.8	66.3	57.5	47.6	36.8	20.2	46.7
	1994	1994	1960	943	1967	1958	1962	1963	1963	1958	1967	1989	1958
WEST POINT (1821-2000)													
	17.4	15.6	26.3	41.3	51.8	62.4	67.9	64.7	59.5	44.0	34.2	18.5	46.2
	1918	1934	1843	1927	1907	1928	1996	1982	1950	1888	1873	1989	1904

TABLE 6
COLDEST DAILY MINIMUM TEMPERATURES

	Jan	Feb	Mar	Apr	May	June	July	Aug	Sep	Oct	Nov	Dec
SCARSDALE												
	-12	-18	-3	10	28	38	45	40	29	21	8	-16
	6th	9th	19th	1st	10th	11th	12th	25th	22nd	28th	26th	30th
	1904	1934	1967	1923	1947	1980	1945	1940	1904	1976	1938	1917
BEDFORD HILLS												
	-17	-19	-4	7	27	38	42	36	28	16	7	-12
	5th	9th	5th	1st	10th	10th	11th	29th	28th	28th	27th	28th
	1904	1934	1948	1923	1947	1957	1898	1965	1947	1936	1947	1896
CARMEL/YORKTOWN												
	-24	-26	-10	6	24	33	41	35	28	16	5	-19
	22nd	16th	19th	1st	10th	1st	1st	25th	28th	28th	26th	30th
	1961	1943	1967	1923	1947	1945	1943	1940	1947	1936	1938	1917
SUFFERN												
	-16	-15	0	12	26	38	43	34	27	15	9	-10
	22nd	2nd	9th	4th	4th	12th	9th	25th	24th	29th	30th	21st
	1961	1994	1943	1954	1978	1974	1963	1940	1963	1940	1958	1942
WEST POINT												
	-15	-17	-10	12	28	39	45	41	28	20	8	-16
	13th	9th	7th	2nd	6th	18th	19th	29th	29th	31st	26th	30th
	1912	1934	1911	1923	1907	1908	1965	1899	1909	1897	1938	1917

TABLE 7
WEEKLY TEMPERATURES
SCARSDALE

Week Beginning	Average Temperature	Average Maximum	MAXIMUM ° F Normal Limits	Hottest	Average Minimum	MINIMUM ° F Normal Limits	Coldest
Jan 3	29.0	37.0	28.2 - 45.8	65	21.1	11.1 - 31.1	-12
10	27.2	36.3	27.5 - 45.1	69	18.0	7.0 - 29.0	-10
17	28.0	37.8	28.9 - 46.7	64	18.2	6.2 - 30.2	-12
24	29.6	38.9	30.0 - 47 8	73	20.3	8.3 - 32.3	-9
31	29.1	38.1	29.2 - 47.0	64	20.1	8.1 - 32.1	-9
Feb 7	28.8	38.6	29.6 - 47.6	62	19.1	7.1 - 31.1	-18
14	31.8	41.6	31.6 - 51.6	74	22.8	10.8 - 34.8	-8
21	34.4	43.9	33.9 - 53.9	75	25.0	14.0 - 36.0	-3
Mar 1	36.7	46.4	37.4 - 55.4	71	27.0	17.0 - 37.0	0
8	45.6	45.6	35.6 - 55.6	82	27.9	18.9 - 36.9	1
15	40.2	50.7	41.7 - 59.7	85	29.6	20.6 - 38.6	-3
22	42.4	54.0	44.0 - 64.0	83	30.9	22.3 - 39.5	8
29	45.1	57.1	47.1 - 67.1	88	33.1	24.5 - 41.7	8
Apr 5	46.4	57.3	46.6 - 68.3	89	35.4	26.7 - 44.1	14
12	49.8	61.6	50.6 - 72.6	94	38.1	29.7 - 46.5	22
19	53.2	65.1	50.6 - 72.6	90	41.3	33.3 - 49.3	22
26	55.1	67.1	57.1 - 77.1	91	43.1	35.1 - 51.1	25
May 3	57.1	69.6	59.6 - 79.6	93	44.6	36.6 - 52.6	30
10	59.0	71.4	61.4 - 81.4	91	46.6	38.6 - 54.6	26
17	62.8	75.1	66.1 - 84.1	97	50.4	42.4 - 58.4	31
24	63.6	76.3	67.3 - 85.3	96	51.0	43.0 - 59.0	30
31	66.2	78.6	69.6 - 87.6	100	53.7	45.7 - 61.7	35
Jun 7	68.2	80.7	72.0 - 89.4	99	55.7	47.7 - 63.7	38
14	69.4	81.3	73.3 - 89.3	99	57.6	51.1 - 65.1	39
21	70.7	82.6	74.6 - 90.6	100	58.8	51.8 - 65.8	42
28	72.4	84.4	76.9 - 91.9	102	60.3	53.3 - 67.3	46
Jul 5	73.6	85.6	78.6 - 92.6	105	61.6	54.6 - 68.6	46
12	74.8	86.4	80.0 - 93.0	102	63.1	56.1 - 70.1	45
19	74.9	86.1	79.6 - 92.6	102	63.7	56.7 - 70.7	48
26	73.8	84.7	78.2 - 91.2	103	62.8	55.8 - 69.8	47
Aug 2	74.0	84.8	77.8 - 91.8	104	63.1	56.1 - 70.1	45
9	72.8	83.8	77.3 - 90.3	102	61.7	54.7 - 68.7	43
16	71.6	83.1	76.6 - 89.6	97	60.1	52.6 - 67.6	42
23	71.2	82.4	75.4 - 89.4	101	60.0	52.5 - 67.5	40
30	69.8	80.8	72.8 - 88.8	102	58.8	51.3 - 66.3	39
Sep 6	67.5	79.6	71.1 - 88.1	100	55.4	47.9 - 62.9	34
13	64.4	75.7	67.2 - 84.2	95	53.1	45.6 - 60.6	36
20	62.8	73.4	64.9 - 81.9	94	52.1	44.1 - 60.1	29
27	59.3	70.3	61.8 - 78.8	90	48.3	40.3 - 56.3	28
Oct 4	57.0	68.0	59.0 - 77.0	92	45.9	37.4 - 54.4	27
11	55.6	67.0	58.0 - 76.0	88	44.3	35.3 - 53.3	26
18	53.4	65.1	56.1 - 74.1	86	41.6	32.6 - 50.6	23
25	50.2	61.4	52.4 - 70.4	83	39.0	30.0 - 48.0	21
Nov 1	49.8	59.6	50.6 - 68.6	84	40.0	30.5 - 49.5	18
8	46.0	55.3	46.3 - 64.3	76	36.7	27.2 - 46.2	14
15	43.0	52.1	43.1 - 61.1	75	34.0	24.0 - 44.0	14
22	42.0	51.4	42.4 - 60.4	74	32.6	22.6 - 42.6	8
29	37.3	45.9	36.4 - 55.4	70	28.7	19.2 - 38.2	4
Dec 6	35.9	44.4	34.4 - 54.4	70	27.4	17.4 - 37.4	1
13	32.6	40.1	30.1 - 20.1	63	25.0	16.1 - 34.0	-7
20	31.7	39.9	29.9 - 49.9	66	23.4	14.4 - 32.4	-3
27	30.8	38.8	28.8 - 48.8	69	22.7	12.7 - 32.7	- 16

TABLE 8
WEEKLY TEMPERATURES
WESTCHESTER AIRPORT

| Week Beginning | Average Temperature | MAXIMUM °F | | | MINIMUM °F | | |
		Average Maximum	Normal Limits	Hottest	Average Minimum	Normal Limits	Coldest
Jan 3	27.8	34.1	25.3 - 42.9	66	21.0	11.0 - 31.0	- 20
10	25.2	32.3	23.5 - 41.1	64	18.0	7.1 - 29.1	- 15
17	26.5	34.0	25.1 - 42.9	62	19.0	7.0 - 31.0	-8
24	28.8	36.3	37.4 - 45.2	65	21.3	9.3 - 33.5	-9
31	26.6	33.7	24.8 - 42.6	68	19.6	7.6 - 31.6	-7
Feb 7	26.5	34.0	25.0 - 43.0	59	19.0	7.0 - 31.0	- 10
14	30.2	37.7	27.7 - 47.7	67	22.7	10.7 - 34.7	-7
21	32.4	40.1	30.1 - 50.1	75	24.8	13.8 - 35.8	1
Mar 1	35.2	42.7	33.7 - 51.7	70	27.6	17.6 - 37.6	2
8	36.4	44.1	34.1 - 54.1	82	28.6	19.6 - 38.6	5
15	38.3	46.6	37.6 - 55.6	76	30.0	21.0 - 39.0	-6
22	40.8	50.0	40.0 - 60.0	80	31.6	23.0 - 40.2	11
29	44.2	53.0	43.0 - 63.0	77	35.4	26.8 - 44.0	8
Apr 5	44.6	53.6	42.6 - 64.6	86	35.7	27.7 - 44.4	16
12	48.2	57.4	46.4 - 68.4	90	39.0	30.6 - 47.4	26
19	51.1	60.8	50.8 - 70.8	86	41.4	33.4 - 49.4	27
26	53.4	62.8	52.8 - 72.8	90	44.0	36.0 - 52.0	29
May 3	54.9	64.4	54.4 - 74.4	87	45.4	37.4 - 53.4	32
10	58.0	67.4	57.4 - 77.4	88	48.6	40.6 - 56.6	33
17	61.0	70.4	61.4 - 79.4	95	51.7	43.7 - 59.7	36
24	62.0	71.4	62.4 - 80.4	96	52.6	44.6 - 60.6	36
31	64.6	74.0	65.0 - 83.0	93	55.3	47.3 - 63.3	41
Jun 7	67.0	76.6	67.9 - 85.3	94	57.4	49.4 - 65.4	39
14	68.4	77.6	69.6 - 85.6	96	59.1	51.6 - 66.6	45
21	69.3	78.6	70.6 - 86.6	98	60.0	53.0 - 67.0	47
28	71.4	80.6	72.1 - 88.1	102	62.3	55.3 - 69.3	47
Jul 5	72.4	81.8	74.3 - 89.3	97	63.0	56.0 - 70.0	46
12	74.2	82.6	76.1 - 89.1	100	65.8	58.8 - 72.8	52
19	74.0	82.7	76.2 - 89.2	99	65.4	58.4 - 72.4	50
26	73.4	81.8	75.3 - 88.3	96	65.0	58.0 - 72.0	51
Aug 2	73.8	82.0	75.0 - 89.0	98	65.7	58.7 - 72.7	51
9	72.2	80.7	74.2 - 87.3	95	63.8	56.8 - 70.8	50
16	70.7	79.6	73.1 - 86.2	95	61.8	54.3 - 69.3	45
23	70.8	79.6	7 2.6 - 86.6	97	62.1	54.6 - 69.6	41
30	69.2	77.8	69.8 - 85.8	100	60.6	53.1 - 68.6	42
Sep 6	67.0	76.3	67.8 - 84.8	98	57.8	52.8 - 65.3	40
13	63.6	72.1	63.6 - 80.6	93	55.1	47.6 - 62.6	40
20	61.4	69.7	61.2 - 78.2	94	53.1	45.1 - 61.1	33
27	58.6	66.0	57.5 - 74.5	85	51.1	43.1 - 59.1	34
Oct 4	56.0	64.7	55.7 - 73.7	87	47.3	38.8 - 55.8	30
11	54.6	63.3	54.3 - 72.3	85	46.0	37.0 - 55.0	30
18	51.9	60.7	51.7 - 69.7	82	43.1	34.1 - 52.1	24
25	49.4	58.3	49.3 - 67.3	80	40.6	31.6 - 49.6	25
Nov 1	48.7	56.4	47.4 - 65.4	78	41.0	31.5 - 50.5	22
8	44.9	52.0	43.0 - 61.0	73	37.8	28.3 - 47.3	20
15	42.0	49.3	40.3 - 58.3	77	34.6	24.6 - 44.6	17
22	40.0	47.4	38.4 - 56.4	67	32.7	22.7 - 42.7	13
29	36.9	44.1	34.6 - 53.6	70	29.7	20.2 - 39.2	7
Dec 6	34.8	41.6	31.6 - 51.6	64	28.0	18.0 - 38.0	2
13	31.5	37.7	27.7 - 47.7	62	25.3	16.3 - 34.3	3
20	30.4	37.1	27.1 - 47.1	62	23.8	14.8 - 32.8	-5
27	29.8	36.4	26.4 - 46.3	68	23.3	13.3 - 33.3	-5

TABLE 9
WEEKLY TEMPERATURES
CARMEL/ YORKTOWN HEIGHTS

Week Beginning	Average Temperature	MAXIMUM ° F			MINIMUM ° F		
		Average Maximum	Normal Limits	Hottest	Average Minimum	Normal Limits	Coldest
Jan 3	25.8	33.7	25.0 - 42.4	63	17.8	7.8 - 27.8	- 20
10	23.2	31.7	23.0 - 40.4	68	14.6	4.1 - 25.1	- 16
17	24.4	33.8	25.1 - 42.5	62	15.0	4.0 - 26.0	- 24
24	26.6	35.2	26.2 - 44.2	70	18.0	6.5 - 29.5	- 18
31	24.9	34.0	25.0 - 43.0	66	15.8	4.3 - 27.3	- 20
Feb 7	24.7	34.3	25.3 - 43.3	60	15.1	3.6 - 26.7	- 23
14	28.2	37.3	27.3 - 47.3	73	19.1	7.6 - 30.6	- 26
21	30.6	39.8	30.8 - 48.8	73	21.5	11.5 - 31.5	- 24
Mar 1	33.0	42.0	33.0 - 51.0	68	24.0	14.0 - 34.0	-8
8	34.8	44.0	34.0 - 54.0	80	25.5	16.5 - 34.5	-5
15	37.1	46.5	35.5 - 57.5	84	27.7	18.7 - 36.7	- 14
22	43.5	50.1	40.1 - 60.1	85	29.7	21.2 - 38.2	-2
29	43.5	53.6	43.6 - 63.6	85	33.4	25.4 - 41.4	3
Apr 5	43.4	53.4	43.4 - 63.4	86	33.4	25.4 - 41.4	10
12	47.6	58.1	49.1 - 67.1	93	37.1	29.1 - 45.1	14
19	50.9	61.8	50.8 - 72.8	91	40.0	32.0 - 48.0	20
26	53.3	64.0	54.0 - 74.0	91	42.6	34.6 - 50.6	24
May 3	53.8	64.6	54.6 - 74.6	91	43.1	35.1 - 51.1	25
10	58.4	68.7	58.7 - 78.7	91	48.0	40.0 - 56.0	23
17	60.8	71.7	62.7 - 80.7	96	49.8	41.8 - 57.8	30
24	61.5	72.6	63.6 - 81.6	97	50.3	42.3 - 58.3	27
31	64.2	75.0	66.0 - 84.0	98	53.4	45.9 - 60.9	30
Jun 7	66.0	76.6	68.1 - 85.1	97	55.3	47.8 - 62.8	34
14	67.2	77.6	69.3 - 86.3	96	56.9	50.0 - 64.0	36
21	68.4	78.9	71.4 - 86.4	99	58.1	51.1 - 65.1	34
28	70.0	80.7	73.7 - 87.7	100	59.3	52.3 - 66.3	40
Jul 5	71.5	82.0	75.0 - 89.0	103	60.3	53.3 - 67.3	38
12	72.5	82.6	76.1 - 89.1	100	62.4	55.4 - 69.4	41
19	72.9	83.0	76.5 - 89.5	100	62.8	55.8 - 70.0	41
26	71.8	81.9	75.4 - 88.4	100	61.8	54.8 - 68.8	44
Aug 2	72.2	82.0	75.0 - 89.0	101	62.3	55.3 - 69.3	43
9	70.2	80.0	73.0 - 87.0	100	60.5	53.5 - 67.5	37
16	69.4	80.0	73.0 - 87.0	97	58.8	51.8 - 66.3	37
23	68.9	79.3	72.3 - 86.3	102	58.5	51.0 - 66.0	35
30	68.0	78.4	70.4 - 86.4	103	57.5	49.5 - 65.5	31
Sep 6	65.8	76.7	68.7 - 84.7	98	55.0	47.0 - 63.0	33
13	62.6	73.0	65.4 - 81.0	95	52.1	44.1 - 60.1	32
20	60.2	70.1	62.1 - 78.1	95	50.4	42.4 - 58.4	28
27	57.8	68.0	60.0 - 76.0	89	47.5	39.0 - 56.0	24
Oct 4	54.8	65.4	56.4 - 74.4	90	44.1	35.1 - 53.1	22
11	53.4	63.7	54.7 - 72.7	87	43.0	34.0 - 53.0	20
18	50.8	61.6	52.5 - 70.6	84	40.0	31.0 - 49.0	16
25	48.4	58.6	49.6 - 67.6	83	38.3	29.3 - 47.3	16
Nov 1	47.8	57.0	48.0 - 66.0	81	38.7	29.2 - 48.2	17
8	42.8	51.0	42.0 - 60.0	76	34.7	24.7 - 44.7	14
15	40.2	49.0	40.0 - 58.0	76	31.5	21.5 - 41.5	8
22	38.8	47.1	38.1 - 56.1	71	30.4	20.4 - 40.4	5
29	35.0	43.5	34.5 - 52.5	68	26.6	16.5 - 36.5	- 2
Dec 6	32.7	40.6	31.6 - 49.6	68	24.8	14.8 - 34.8	- 9
13	28.7	36.1	27.1 - 45.1	63	21.3	11.3 - 32.3	- 16
20	28.2	35.8	26.8 - 44.8	63	20.7	10.7 - 30.7	- 21
27	27.6	35.7	26.9 - 44.4	70	19.6	9.6 - 29.6	- 19

TABLE 9a
AVERAGE WEEKLY TEMPERATURES
°Fahrenheit

Week Beginning	Bedford Hills Average Maximum	Average	Average Minimum	Dobbs Ferry Average Maximum	Average	Average Minimum	West Point Average Maximum	Average	Average Minimum
Jan 3	35.1	28.2	21.3	35.6	29.4	23.3	34.2	26.9	19.6
10	34.2	26.5	18.7	35.0	28.2	21.4	33.4	25.4	17.3
17	36.5	27.6	18.8	37.1	29.7	22.4	35.8	27.0	18.1
24	36.7	28.6	20.5	37.7	30.8	23.9	36.3	28.2	20.1
31	35.8	27.6	19.3	35.9	28.5	21.1	34.6	25.8	17.0
Feb 7	37.5	29.1	20.7	37.6	30.0	22.5	36.4	27.3	18.3
14	39.6	31.3	23.0	39.9	32.2	24.6	38.9	29.8	20.7
21	42.3	33.5	24.7	42.6	35.0	27.5	42.5	33.4	24.3
Mar1	44.7	36.4	28.1	45.1	37.4	29.7	44.1	35.5	27.0
8	45.2	36.5	27.8	46.2	38.2	30.2	45.5	36.4	27.2
15	46.8	38.1	29.5	48.3	39.9	31.5	47.5	38.2	28.9
22	50.1	40.3	30.6	51.7	42.4	33.1	51.6	41.2	30.9
29	54.4	44.3	34.3	55.6	46.2	36.9	55.1	44.6	34.1
Apr5	56.0	45.7	35.3	57.2	47.3	37.4	56.4	45.8	35.2
12	61.6	50.0	38.5	62.7	51.5	41.0	62.2	50.6	39.0
19	65.0	53.4	41.8	66.3	55.3	44.4	66.3	54.4	42.4
26	65.8	54.7	43.5	65.8	55.7	45.6	65.8	55.0	44.2
May 3	68.7	56.4	44.2	68.9	58.0	47.1	69.2	57.2	45.3
10	71.9	59.9	47.9	71.5	61.0	50.5	72.1	60.3	48.5
17	74.0	62.1	50.3	74.1	63.7	53.3	75.2	63.5	51.8
24	73.5	61.8	50.1	73.9	63.7	53.5	75.1	63.6	52.1
31	78.2	66.3	54.4	77.7	67.4	57.2	79.5	67.5	55.4
Jun 7	80.9	68.7	56.5	79.4	69.1	58.9	80.4	68.7	57.0
14	79.8	68.5	57.1	79.8	69.8	59.8	81.1	69.5	58.0
21	82.2	71.5	60.7	81.9	72.2	62.5	83.3	72.1	60.9
28	85.1	73.5	62.0	84.4	74.4	64.6	85.6	74.0	62.4
Jul 5	83.9	72.2	60.6	83.8	73.7	63.7	85.5	73.5	61.5
12	85.1	73.9	62.7	85.6	75.8	66.0	86.9	75.4	64.0
19	85.0	74.1	63.3	85.7	76.2	66.6	87.0	75.8	64.5
26	84.7	73. 9	63.1	84.7	75.4	66.1	86.1	75.2	64.2
Aug 2	82.5	71.9	61.2	83.5	74.4	65.3	84.8	73.8	62.9
9	82.4	71.8	61.2	83.2	74.0	64.8	84.3	73.6	62.9
16	82.9	71.7	60.5	82.5	73.0	63.5	83.8	72.6	61.3
23	82.2	70.9	59.4	82.4	72.9	63.4	83.9	72.4	60.8
30	80.7	70.1	59.5	81.5	72.5	63.4	82.9	72.0	61.1
Sep 6	77.8	66.6	55.5	78.0	68.7	59.5	79.0	68.2	57.3
13	74.4	64.1	53.9	74.8	66.0	57.2	75.2	65.0	54.7
20	72.3	61.9	51.5	71.8	63.4	55.1	73.0	62.8	52.7
27	69.7	59.8	50.0	69.5	61.2	52.9	69.9	60.2	50.5
Oct 4	68.0	57.2	46.4	67.1	58.5	50.0	67.9	57.6	47.2
11	67.1	56.5	45.6	66.0	57.3	48.7	66.3	56.1	45.9
18	62.2	52.3	42.0	62.9	54.4	45.8	63.2	53.3	43.4
25	59.5	49.7	40.0	59.0	51.0	42.9	58.7	49.6	40.4
Nov 1	56.4	47.8	39.3	57.4	50.0	42.6	56.7	48.3	39.9
8	52.2	43.9	35.7	53.2	46.2	39.2	52.3	44.5	36.6
15	50.3	42.3	34.3	52.0	44.7	37.5	50.5	42.5	34.4
22	48.2	40.2	32.1	49.5	42.4	35.4	47.6	39.9	32.3
29	43.5	35.8	28.1	44.9	37.9	30.9	42.7	35.3	27.9
Dec 6	42.9	35.7	28.4	43.6	37.1	30.7	41.5	34.4	27.3
13	38.2	31.2	24.3	39.4	33.1	26.8	37.6	30.3	23.1
20	37.1	30.0	22.9	38.6	32.1	25.6	36.4	29.1	21.8
27	36.2	28.7	21.3	38.0	31.5	25.0	35.8	28.4	20.9

Averages are based on the period 1951 - 1980
* Bedford Hills Station - closed in 1977
   West Point averages are 1 -2 degrees high due to poor thermometer location

TABLE 10
AVERAGE TEMPERATURE*
(19th and 20th century through 1930)

	Jan	Feb	Mar	Apr	May	Jun	Jul	Aug	Sep	Oct	Nov	Dec	Annual
Ardenia	25.9	28.2	34.9	47.8	59.0	68.3	72.9	70.8	62.9	51.3	41.2	30.0	49.4
Bedford Hills	27.9	27.1	37.5	47.5	58.6	66.9	72.2	70.1	63.7	53.1	41.7	31.2	49.8
Carmel	24.5	24.7	34.6	46.4	57.7	66.9	71.4	69.2	63.0	51.1	39.6	28.7	48.2
Mount Hope	28.8	28.3	38.2	48.4	58.9	67.3	72.4	70.2	64.1	53.9	42.4	31.9	50.4
Mount Pleasant	28.0	29.4	38.0	48.3	57.9	67.8	71.2	71.1	62.5	50.6	40.3	30.2	49.6
Mount Vernon	30.5	31.5	39.7	49.3	59.3	68.4	73.4	71.7	66.2	55.8	44.5	33.7	52.0
North Salem	26.4	25.7	35.4	46.4	56.7	66.2	71.8	69.0	60.4	49.5	39.2	28.9	48.0
Scarsdale	28.7	28.5	37.9	48.0	59.1	67.3	72.4	69.8	64.1	54.0	42.6	31.8	50.4
West Point	29.6	27.9	36.5	48.2	59.4	68.7	73.3	71.3	64.3	53.0	41.7	31.1	50.4
White Plains	29.1	30.5	35.8	47.7	58.3	68.3	72.0	69.9	63.7	53.1	42.1	32.6	50.3

* uncorrected for time of observation

TABLE 10a
HEATING DEGREE DAYS
Average from 1969-70 through 1998-99

	July	Aug	Sep	Oct	Nov	Dec	Jan	Feb	Mar	Apr	May	June	Annual
Dobbs Ferry / Ardsley	1	3	66	307	583	912	1076	898	742	413	152	24	5175
Westchester Airport	3	8	101	370	638	939	1138	964	813	481	206	39	5730
Yorktown Heights	6	13	112	390	675	1030	1199	1018	853	496	207	45	6044
West Point	2	4	90	350	610	910	1120	954	800	470	200	40	5550

TABLE 11
AVERAGE MAXIMUM TEMPERATURE*
(Late 19th and 20th century through 1930)

	Jan	Feb	Mar	Apr	May	Jun	Jul	Aug	Sep	Oct	Nov	Dec	Annual
Bedford Hills	37.0	36.5	47.8	58.6	70.1	78.2	82.9	80.7	74.5	64.1	51.3	40.0	60.1
Carmel	32.0	32.9	43.4	55.8	68.1	76.7	81.7	79.2	72.8	60.8	47.6	35.5	57.2
Mount Hope	37.2	36.9	47.8	59.3	70.5	78.9	83.1	80.8	74.9	64.9	52.2	40.1	60.6
Mount Vernon	38.3	39.5	48.9	59.1	69.5	77.9	82.3	80.3	75.0	65.4	52.6	41.0	60.8
Scarsdale	37.0	37.2	47.6	58.3	69.8	78.1	83.0	80.0	74.3	64.3	51.3	39.5	60.0
West Point	34.9	35.1	46.2	59.6	71.5	80.5	84.8	82.3	75.5	62.6	50.1	38.9	60.2

* uncorrected for time of observation

TABLE 12
AVERAGE MINIMUM TEMPERATURE*
(Late 19th and 20th century through 1930)

	Jan	Feb	Mar	Apr	May	Jun	Jul	Aug	Sep	Oct	Nov	Dec	Annual
Bedford Hills	18.6	17.6	27.7	36.2	47.1	55.6	61.6	59.4	53.2	42.5	32.2	22.4	39.5
Carmel	16.4	16.4	26.1	36.7	47.3	56.1	61.3	59.2	53.1	42.0	32.0	21.3	39.0
Mount Hope	20.3	19.7	28.4	37.6	47.4	55.7	61.4	59.3	53.3	42.9	33.0	23.7	40.2
Mount Vernon	22.7	23.5	30.4	39.6	49.1	58.9	64.5	63.1	57.3	46.1	36.4	26.5	43.2
Scarsdale	20.4	19.8	28.2	37.8	48.4	56.6	61.8	59.6	53.7	43.7	33.9	24.1	40.7
West Point	19.1	18.7	27.6	38.2	48.4	57.8	62.4	60.9	54.3	44.1	34.3	23.7	40.8

* uncorrected for time of observation

TABLE 13
AVERAGE FIRST AND LAST FREEZE DATES

SPRING

Dates on which chance of last occurrence of indicated temperature or lower decreases to

SCARSDALE

Temperatures °F	90% or 9 in 10	75% or 3 in 4	67% or 2 in 3	50% or 1 in 2	33% or 1 in 3	25% or 1 in 4	10% or 1 in 10
32	4/12	4/18	4/20	4/24	4/28	4/30	5/6
28	3/30	4/4	4/6	4/10	4/14	4/16	4/22
24	3/17	3/23	3/26	3/30	4/3	4/6	4/12
20	3/6	3/12	3/15	3/19	3/23	3/26	4/1
16	2/15	2/22	2/26	3/3	3/8	3/12	3/19

CARMEL

Temperatures °F	90% or 9 in 10	75% or 3 in 4	67% or 2 in 3	50% or 1 in 2	33% or 1 in 3	25% or 1 in 4	10% or 1 in 10
32	4/20	4/28	5/1	5/6	5/11	5/14	5/22
28	4/5	4/12	4/15	4/20	4/25	4/28	5/5
24	3/28	4/3	4/6	4/10	4/15	4/17	4/23
20	3/17	3/22	3/25	3/29	4/2	4/5	4/10
16	3/6	3/13	3/16	3/20	3/24	3/27	4/3

AUTUMN

Dates on which the chance of first occurrence of indicated temperature or lower increases to

SCARSDALE

Temperatures °F	90% or 9 in 10	75% or 3 in 4	67% or 2 in 3	50% or 1 in 2	33% or 1 in 3	25% or 1 in 4	10% or 1 in 10
32	10/1	10/8	10/11	10/16	10/21	10/24	10/31
28	10/12	10/19	10/23	10/28	11/2	11/6	11/13
24	10/21	10/30	11/3	11/9	11/15	11/19	11/28
20	11/13	11/20	11/23	11/28	12/3	12/6	12/12
16	11/25	12/2	12/4	12/9	12/14	12/16	12/23

CARMEL

Temperatures °F	90% or 9 in 10	75% or 3 in 4	67% or 2 in 3	50% or 1 in 2	33% or 1 in 3	25% or 1 in 4	10% or 1 in 10
32	9/20	9/28	10/1	10/7	10/13	10/16	10/24
28	10/7	10/14	10/16	10/21	10/26	10/28	11/4
24	10/20	10/28	10/31	11/5	11/10	11/13	11/21
20	11/3	11/11	11/14	11/19	11/24	11/27	12/6
16	11/19	11/25	11/28	12/2	12/6	12/9	12/15

Based on the period 1947 - 1976

TABLE 14

ICE ON - ICE OUT DATES FOR SELECTED LAKES

Lake Mohansic		Amawalk Reservoir		Lake Mahopac	
Ice On	Ice Out	Ice On	Ice Out	Ice On	Ice Out
Dec 7, 1964	Mar. 23, 1965				
Dec. 20, 1965	Mar. 20, 1966				
Dec. 28, 1966	Apr. 4, 1967				
Dec. 25, 1967	Mar. 27, 1968				
Dec. 10, 1968	Apr. 5, 1969				
Dec. 24, 1969	Mar. 24, 1970				
Dec. 27, 1970	Mar. 29, 1971				
Dec. 3, 1971	Mar. 25, 1972				
Dec. 17, 1972	Mar. 14, 1973	Jan. 8, 1973	Mar. 13, 1973	Jan. 8, 1973	Mar. 13, 1973
Jan. 5, 1974	Mar. 6, 1974	Jan. 8, 1974	Mar. 7, 1974	Jan. 9, 1974	Mar. 7, 1974
Dec. 26, 1974	Mar. 1, 1975	Feb. 2, 1975	Mar. 18, 1975	Feb. 2, 1975	Mar. 18, 1975
Dec. 24, 1975	Mar. 1, 1976	Dec. 24, 1975	Mar. 1, 1976	Dec. 24, 1975	Mar. 1, 1976
Dec. 4, 1976	Mar. 14, 1977	Dec. 26, 1976	Mar. 15, 1977	Dec. 26, 1976	Mar. 17, 1977
Dec. 11, 1977	Apr. 2, 1978	Dec. 28, 1977	Apr. 6, 1978	Dec. 28, 1977	Apr. 7, 1978
Dec. 23, 1978	Mar. 19, 1979	Jan. 11, 1979	Mar. 21, 1979	Jan. 9, 1979	Mar. 23, 1979
Jan.4, 1980	Mar. 17, 1980	Jan. 10, 1980	Mar. 19, 1980	Jan. 10. 1980	Mar. 19, 1980
Dec. 7, 1980	Feb. 22, 1981	Dec. 21, 1980	Feb. 23, 1981	Dec. 26, 1980	Feb. 23, 1981
Dec. 19, 1981	Mar. 24, 1982	Dec. 22, 1981	Mar. 25, 1982	Dec. 22, 1981	Mar. 26, 1982
Jan. 14, 1983	Mar. 6, 1983	Jan. 20, 1983	Mar. 8, 1983	Jan. 22, 1983	Mar. 12, 1983
Dec. 21, 1983	Mar. 16, 1984	Dec. 30, 1983	Mar. 21, 1984	Jan. 1, 1984	Mar. 22, 1984
Jan. 9, 1985	Mar. 5, 1985	Jan. 12, 1985	Mar. 9, 1985	Jan. 12, 1985	Mar. 11, 1985
Jan. 8, 1986	Mar. 16, 1986	Jan. 15, 1986	Mar. 20, 1986	Jan. 14, 1986	Mar. 22, 1986
Dec. 22, 1986	Mar. 26, 1987	Dec. 28, 1986	Mar. 28, 1987	Jan. 1, 1987	Mar. 28, 1987
Dec. 30, 1987	Mar. 24, 1988	Jan. 10, 1988	Mar. 25, 1988	Jan. 3, 1988	Mar. 25, 1988
Dec. 13, 1988	Mar. 16, 1989	Dec. 15, 1988	Mar. 18, 1989	Dec. 14, 1988	Mar. 26, 1989
Dec. 4, 1989	Mar. 10, 1990	Dec. 14, 1989	Mar. 10, 1990	Dec. 12, 1989	Mar. 10, 1990
Jan. 1, 1991	Mar. 2, 1991	Jan. 11, 1991	Mar. 3, 1991	Jan. 13, 1991	Mar. 3, 1991
Dec. 20, 1991	Mar. 5, 1992	Feb. 2, 1992	Mar. 10, 1992	Jan. 18, 1992	Mar. 10, 1992
Dec. 25, 1992	Apr. 1, 1993	Jan. 2, 1993	Apr. 7, 1993	Jan. 2, 1993	Apr. 7, 1993
Dec. 24, 1993	Apr. 4, 1994	Dec. 30, 1993	Apr. 7, 1994	Dec. 30, 1993	Apr. 7, 1994
Jan. 5, 1995	Mar. 9, 1995	Feb. 3, 1995	Mar. 16, 1995	Feb. 3, 1995	Mar. 17, 1995
Dec. 11, 1995	Mar. 19, 1996	Dec. 29, 1995	Mar. 25, 1996	Dec. 29, 1995	Mar. 25, 1996
Jan. 9, 1997	Mar. 1, 1997	Jan. 18, 1997	Mar. 3, 1997	Jan. 17, 1997	Mar. 3, 1997
Winter 1997 - 1998		None of the above three lakes completely frozen over			
Dec. 24, 1998	Mar. 3,1999	Jan. 3, 1999	Mar. 11, 1999	Jan. 3, 1999	Mar. 11, 1999
Jan.15, 2000	Mar. 10, 2000	Jan. 15, 2000	Mar. 12, 2000	Jan. 15, 2000	Mar. 14, 2000
December 23, 2000					

During the winter seasons of 71-72, 72-73, 73-74, 74-75, 79-80, 82-83, 84-85, and 95-95 in the frozen over periods noted above, parts of the above lakes came unfrozen due to thaws.

TABLE 15
RETURN FREQUENCY OF EXTREME TEMPERATURES
SCARSDALE

Hottest / Coldest (°F)

	2 YEAR RETURN	10 YEAR RETURN	25 YEAR RETURN	50 YEAR RETURN	100 YEAR RETURN
January	54 / 4	64 / -8	70 /-14	73 /-19	79 /-25
February	54 / 5	65 /-7	72 /-13	75 /-17	82 /-23
March	67 /15	78 / 6	85 / 0	90 /-2	94 / -8
April	79 /26	88 /19	93 /15	96 /13	101 / 9
May	86 /36	94 /31	99 /28	102 /26	106 /23
June	92 /45	98 /40	102 /37	104 /34	107 /32
July	94 /52	101 /48	104 /46	107 /44	110 /42
August	92 /50	99 /43	103 /40	106 /37	109 /34
September	88 /40	96 /33	100 /30	102 /27	107 /24
October	80 /30	88 /24	92 /21	96 /19	99 /16
November	68 /21	77 /13	81 / 9	85 / 6	89 / 3
December	57 / 9	65 / -2	70 / -9	73 /-14	77 /-19
Annual	96 / 0	102 /-10	105 /-16	107 -21	110 /-25

Based on the period 1904 - 1990

TABLE 16
RETURN FREQUENCY OF EXTREME TEMPERATURES
CARMEL

Hottest / Coldest (°F)

	2 YEAR RETURN	10 YEAR RETURN	25 YEAR RETURN	50 YEAR RETURN	100 YEAR RETURN
January	50 / -2	60 /-16	65 /-22	67 /-25	74 /-33
February	51 / -2	62 /-15	68 /-22	71 /-25	78 /-33
March	63 / 9	77 / -3	84 /-10	87 /-12	96 /-20
April	77 / 23	86 / 16	92 / 12	95 / 10	100 / 6
May	84 / 33	92 / 28	96 / 25	99 / 23	102 / 20
June	90 / 43	96 / 37	99 / 34	102 / 31	104 / 29
July	92 / 49	98 / 44	101 / 40	104 / 37	106 / 35
August	91 / 47	97 / 41	101 / 37	104 / 34	107 / 32
September	87 / 37	94 / 31	99 / 27	102 / 24	105 / 22
October	78 / 27	87 / 22	91 / 18	95 / 16	99 / 14
November	66 / 17	74 / 10	79 / 6	82 / 3	86 / 0
December	54 / 4	63 / -8	67 / -15	71 /-21	75 / -26
Annual	94 / -7	99 / -19	102 / -26	104 /-32	106 / -37

Based on the period 1896 - 1980

All About Precipitation

Precipitation Factors

Water vapor is ever present in the atmosphere. The factors that turn this vapor into precipitation depend in large part on changes in temperature. Greater moisture in the form of invisible water vapor can be held by the atmosphere at higher temperatures than at lower temperatures. The upper limits of the amount of moisture that the air can hold is also dependent on the temperature. When air is cooled to specific level, the moisture contained within it will change to the visible vapor form, namely clouds or fog, and with further cooling result in precipitation. Generally, greater amounts of precipitation are produced when a lowered air pressure brings about the lifting of large amounts of air. When this air rises it is cooled and further precipitation results. The rate and duration of this precipitation are dependent on the speed and further inflow of moisture laden air to replace that which has lost its moisture. The largest and most efficient air lifting mechanisms that affect our region are the low pressure storm systems that generally move north, northeastward along the Atlantic coast. Low pressure systems can also occur in the form of hurricanes, but are more likely to be "northeasters" originating near the Gulf coast or forming off the Carolina coast. The amount of precipitation produced by these storms is dependent on their size and rate of movement through any particular area. Precipitation in the form of rain or snow can occur from "northeasters" named after the predominant direction the wind is coming from as it heads towards the storm center.

A thin layer of below freezing air over frozen land can result in freezing rain, producing a glaze condition of ice (rain freezing on contact with a solid surface) or sleet. Lesser amounts of precipitation occur with the passage of cold fronts which force warmer air to condensation heights. Nearby low pressure systems to the west or north can also lesser amounts of precipitation through a combination of lifting and horizontal convergence.

Summer rainfall can also result from frontal systems passing through our area or by air mass instability, producing thunderstorms. These develop on warm, humid days when the sun heats the lower layers of the atmosphere. These heated layers rise and develop clouds at high altitudes, usually in the late afternoon or early evening. Some of the more severe of these will result in the formation of hailstones, a strictly summer phenomenon. Tropical storms or hurricanes that have passed through our two counties on many occasions have caused heavy rainfalls in a relatively short period of time in the warm months from June through October.

Annual precipitation within the lower Hudson Valley is fairly uniform, that is, there is little difference among the presently monitoring weather stations. Average annual precipitation totals range from 44 to 49 inches (See Figure 27). There are normally between 120 and 140 days a year that have .01 inches or more of precipitation A mean difference of about three inches is necessary for statistical significance (.01 level) to occur between any two stations. Precipitation, which includes rain, snow, sleet and hail is plentiful. The yearly amounts that fall here, as well as nearly all of the eastern United States are generally more than adequate for all vegetation. Even in drought years such as the mid 1960s, over 30 inches that fell each year was still greater than most states west of the Mississippi. Precipitation in dry years however, is not adequate for the water demands of the population of the greater New York City metropolitan area (See Appendices G to X).

At the present time there are about eighteen rain gauges within the three county region. Nine of these are maintained by the New York City Water Department in the Croton watershed. Two gauges of Westchester county monitor precipitation in the Bronx and Saw Mill Rivers. Three U.S. Weather Service stations monitor daily precipitation and three of their other gauges monitor hourly precipitation.

FOG

The average number of days per year with fog is thirty. This number is even greater for areas near large bodies of water. There are many days particularly in the fall when the water content of the air above and near such bodies condenses to fog a few days following the passage of cold air from the north. This phenomenon is noticeable over and within one mile of the Hudson River.

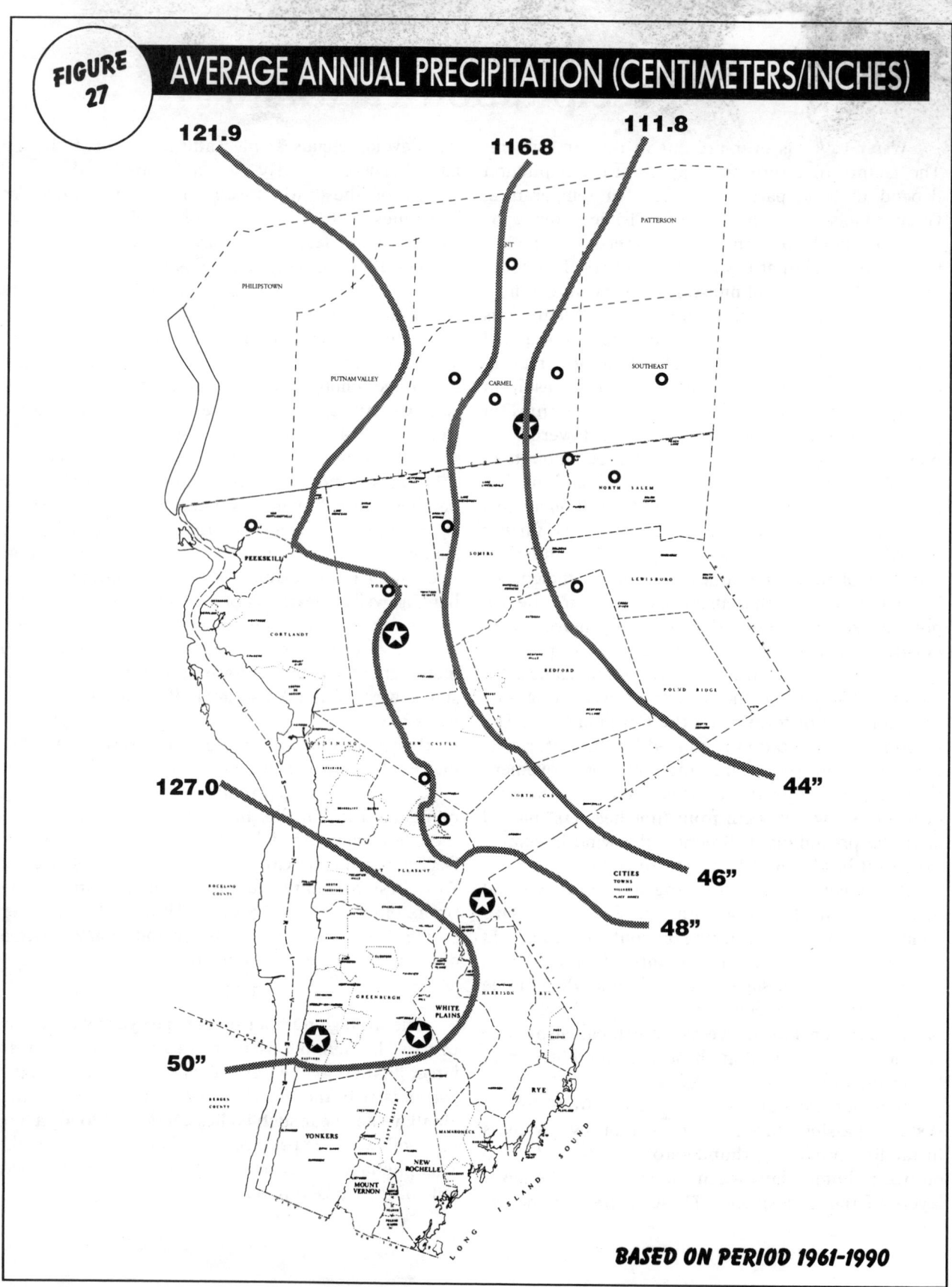

FIGURE 27

AVERAGE ANNUAL PRECIPITATION (CENTIMETERS/INCHES)

BASED ON PERIOD 1961-1990

EXTREME RAINFALL PROBABILITIES

"However big floods get, there will always be a bigger one coming; so says one theory of extremes, and experience suggests it is true."
President's Water Commission

With the increasing urbanization of Westchester, Rockland and Putnam counties, a growing concern for keeping local rivers, brooks, kills and streams within their beds has focused on the need for properly designed culverts, drains and catch basins to contain large amounts of runoff water within relatively short periods of time. The increased speed of runoff water has been caused by building of homes and businesses on slopes, the increase of pavement and the decrease of water absorbing top soil, wet lands, and vegetation in areas where they slow runoff or retain water.

How large should these drain pipes and catch basins be? The drains and basins should be just large enough to hold all of the expected runoff from their drainage area. If too small, the drain pipe will serve no useful purpose, while a drain or basin larger than necessary will be too expensive for its function. The size of the drain pipe or catch basin depends on the amount of rainfall that is expected as runoff from the drainage area. The runoff amount that is most important is not the monthly or yearly maximum but the maximum that can be expected in six, twelve hours, and one to four days (See Tables 18, 19 and 20). Other variables that can influence the amount of runoff are the degree of soil saturation prior to heavy rainfall and rain falling on snow covered terrain.

Long term records of over 100 continuous years at the Croton Lake and Carmel rain gauges shows than on average a three inch 24 hour rainfall can be expected every other year.

An analysis of past and present short and long-term precipitation records provides information on how often extreme amounts of rainfall have occurred and can be expected. Maximum hourly precipitation amounts are shown in Tables 22 - 27. Return frequency amounts for one to ten days are shown in Table 19 and show what can be expected once in a specified period of years.

The most recent extreme rainfalls of September 1999 required a revision of the return frequency for the rain gauge of the New York City Water Department at and Carmel (West Branch). The return period of the 10.0 inches that fell at that site is about once in 1000 years.

However there is a one in ten probability that such an amount can occur in its 107 year period of record. The probability is greater than expected since the fact that ten inches has fallen once in 107 years increases the likelihood of such an event recurring more often than every1000 years.

Tropical Storm "Floyd" at one point in the late afternoon of September 17th deposited as much as 1.30 inches of rain in a 45 minute period at Yorktown Heights.

Data sources are as follows: Scarsdale - Village Engineer; Dobbs Ferry/ Ardsley - U.S. Weather Service Cooperative Station; Bedford Hills - Chief Engineer, Hillcrest Home; Croton Lake - New York City Department of Water Supply; Peekskill Water Department; Carmel - New York City Department of Water Supply and West Point and Suffern - Climatological data - New York periodical.

With the exception of the One Day amounts in Table 19, where 71 - 104 years of data are used for Scarsdale, Bedford Hills, Carmel and Croton Lake, the estimates of the frequency of heavy rainfall have been determined by using by 31 years of daily extremes through 1976.

The values shown in Table 19 were derived for each rain gauge through a statistical analysis of the greatest amounts to have fallen in the time periods listed. The values shown represent the greatest rainfall expected to occur in the period specified. For example: at Scarsdale a one day rainfall amount of 2.69 inches is expected at least once every two years; 4.58 inches at least once every ten years; 5.66 inches at least once every 25 years; and 7.29 inches at least once every 100 years.

These estimated return frequency amounts for 1, 2, 4, 7, and 10 days should be employed with caution when considering drainage areas larger than a few square miles because the figures given are point values and were derived using rainfall from specific locations and do not take into consideration that rains often occur at nearby locations with other intensities.

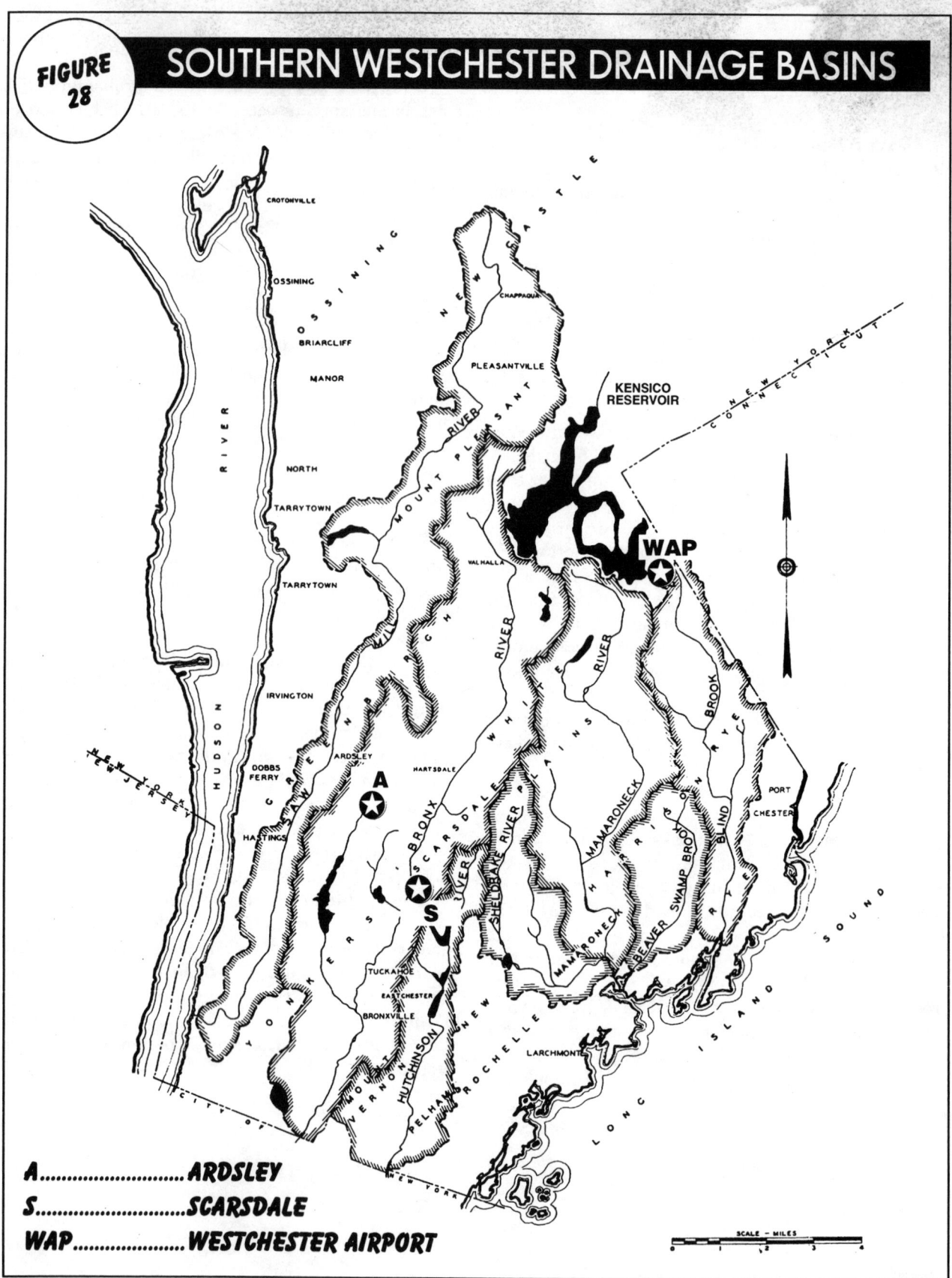

SOUTHERN WESTCHESTER DRAINAGE BASINS

FIGURE 28

A...................ARDSLEY
S...................SCARSDALE
WAP..............WESTCHESTER AIRPORT

TABLE 17

AVERAGE NUMBER OF DAYS WITH
.01 INCH OR MORE OF PRECIPITATION
(through 1930)

	Jan	Feb	Mar	Apr	May	June	July	Aug	Sep	Oct	Nov	Dec	Annual
Bedford Hills	10	9	10	10	12	11	11	10	9	8	8	9	117
Carmel	10	9	10	10	10	9	10	9	8	7	8	9	122
Mount Hope	8	7	8	9	10	9	10	8	7	6	6	8	96
Mount Vernon	10	10	10	10	11	10	11	10	8	8	8	11	117
West Point	8	8	9	9	9	8	9	8	7	7	8	7	97

TABLE 18

24 HOUR PRECIPITATION EXTREMES
(Inches)

Station	Jan	Feb	Mar	Apr	May	June	July	Aug	Sep	Oct	Nov	Dec
Bedford Hills	2.60	3.98	2.80	4.41	3.10	3.50	8.00	4.00	7.00	4.79	3.29	3.22
1895-1977	1940	1896	1953	1901	1946	1972	1960	1904	1938	1955	1896	1941
Scarsdale	3.20	2.50	4.10	4.00	5.65	4.25	5.30	9.00	8.00	6.00	4.83	4.00
1904-1990	1979	1941	1953	1980	1946	1972	1942	1955	1938	1955	1977	1909
Carmel	2.65	2.56	3.68	3.55	5.57	4.39	5.03	6.60	10.00	7.70	3.07	3.54
1896-2000	1979	1896	1980	1901	1900	1969	1897	1955	1999	1955	1903	1901
DobbsFerry/	3.79	3.20	3.25	5.34	5.44	5.69	3.22	4.77	4.84	5.75	5.27	4.21
Ardsley	1979	1973	1951	1984	1968	1972	1984	1955	1954	1955	1977	1973
1946-2000												
Peekskill	3.70	3.40	3.25	4.02	3.40	3.50	4.00	5.00	9.00	6.00	4.08	2.98
1946-2000	1980	1973	1951	1984	1968	1969	1946	1955	1999	1955	1977	1948
Yorktown	3.33	3.30	4.60	3.60	3.75	3.40	3.75	6.86	11.00	8.00	3.47	3.29
1940-2000	1979	1973	1980	1987	1989	1972	1984	1971	1999	1955	1947	1941
White Plains												
1873-1892												
Westchester Airport												
1949 -2000	5.50	4.72	3.79	4.46	4.80	6.40	5.90	6.00	6.00	6.90	5.04	4.45
	1874	1882	1951	1884	1968	1884	1875	1955	1971	1955	1889	1879
Suffern												
1941 - 1999	2.64	3.00	5.00	2.88	4.00	4.52	6.27	7.20	5.00	3.60	6.00	2.43
	1979	1973	1951	1971	1968	1973	1945	1955	1971	1987	1977	1990
West Point												
1895 -2000	3.96	3.18	4.40	4.20	6.00	3.63	6.00	4.80	8.00	6.00	4.14	4.90
	1996	1977	1951	1910	1984	1952	1897	1955	1999	1955	1927	1957

Heavy rainfall dates common to above rain gauges:
January 21,1979; February 2,1973; March30, 1951; March 13,1953; April 5, 1984; May 27, 1946, May 29, 1968; June 16, 1969, June 19, 1972 (Hurricane Agnes); July 7, 1984; August 13, 1955 (Hurricane Connie); September21, 1938 (Great Hurricane), September 11, 1954 (Hurricane Edna); October 16, 1955; November 8, 1977; December 14, 1941; September 17, 1999

TABLE 19

EXTREME RAINFALL AND EXPECTED RETURN FREQUENCY

	2 Year Return	10 Year Return	25 Year Return	50 Year Return	100 Year Return
ONE DAY RAINFALL					
Scarsdale	2.69	4.58	5.66	6.50	7.29
Dobbs Ferry	2.66	4.80	6.02	7.00	7.86
Bedford Hills	2.45	4.42	5.54	6.40	7.23
Croton Lake	3.00	4.80	6.40	7.00	9.00
Peekskill	2.61	4.48	5.54	6.50	8.80
Carmel	3.10	4.40	5.40	6.60	8.50
TWO DAY RAINFALL					
Scarsdale	3.23	6.18	7.85	9.00	10.39
Dobbs Ferry	3.39	6.15	7.72	8.90	10.10
Bedford Hills	2.93	5.87	7.55	8.80	10.08
Croton Lake	3.39	5.88	7.30	8.60	9.50
Peekskill	3.21	5.76	7.21	8.50	10.00
Carmel	3.42	5.97	7.65	8.85	11.00
FOUR DAY RAINFALL					
Scarsdale	3.75	7.19	9.14	11.20	12.10
Dobbs Ferry	3.90	7.24	9.14	11.15	12.00
Bedford Hills	3.40	7.34	9.58	11.70	12.96
Croton Lake	3.86	6.98	8.76	10.10	11.45
Peekskill	3.73	6.68	8.36	9.70	11.00
Carmel	3.60	6.93	8.87	10.20	12.00
SEVEN DAY RAINFALL					
Scarsdale	4.32	8.00	10.08	11.40	13.25
Dobbs Ferry	4.51	8.68	11.05	12.90	14.64
Bedford Hills	3.94	7.98	10.28	11.60	13.77
Croton Lake	4.43	7.48	9.21	10.60	11.84
Peekskill	4.26	7.65	9.80	10.90	12.50
Carmel	3.95	8.15	10.57	12.00	14.50
TEN DAY RAINFALL					
Scarsdale	4.91	9.31	11.82	13.80	15.61
Dobbs Ferry	5.10	9.74	12.37	14.20	16.37
Bedford Hills	4.53	8.92	11.43	13.40	15.22
Croton Lake	4.95	8.25	10.14	11.60	12.98
Peekskill	5.07	8.53	10.49	12.00	13.50
Carmel	4.60	8.83	11.30	13.20	15.04

TABLE 20
ONE TO FOUR DAY PRECIPITATION AMOUNTS (Inches)
ASSOCIATED WITH TROPICAL STORMS

Storm Name and/or Date	Location	1st Day	2nd Day	3rd Day	4th Day
Oct 9, 1877	White Plains	9.70			
July 29-31, 1889	Yonkers	2.52	7.08	9.55	
July 27, 1942	Mamaroneck	5.86			
Sept. 19-21, 1938	Scarsdale	1.85	2.15	6.55	
	Bedford Hills	2.00	1.35	6.00	
	Croton Falls	1.00	3.26	5.37	
	Carmel	2.90	2.27	3.77	
CAROL Aug. 31, 1954	Scarsdale	2.80			
	Bedford Hills	3.06			
	Croton Falls	1.75	4.18		
	Carmel	1.70	1.15		
	Suffern	2.45	2.78		
EDNA Sept. 11,12, 1954	Scarsdale	4.70			
	Bedford Hills	5.22			
	Croton Falls	3.10	1.58		
	Carmel	3.45	1.20		
	West Point	4.58			
CONNIE Aug. 12-14, 1955	Scarsdale	4.04	5.17		
	Bedford Hills	2.00	3.05		
	Croton Falls	1.03	3.75	1.70	
	Carmel	1.12	2.30	3.44	
	Suffern	2.10	5.63		
Oct. 14 - 17, 1955	Scarsdale	1.35	1.92	4.38	.41
	Bedford Hills	1.80	3.90	4.79	.51
	Croton Falls	2.55	6.79	.60	
	Carmel	2.55	6.77	.65	
DONNA Sept. 12,13, 1960	Scarsdale	3.60			
	Bedford Hills	5.20			
	Croton Falls	1.83	3.15		
	Carmel	1.52	2.51		
	West Point	.35	4.76		
AGNES June 16-19, 1972	Scarsdale	1.25	.12	.58	4.25
	Bedford Hills	.47	1.32	.12	3.50
	Croton Falls		3.49	.51	
	Carmel	.60	1.45	.50	
ELOISE Sept. 23-25, 1975	Scarsdale	2.65	1.45	1.00	4.00
	Bedford Hills	1.56	1.88	1.46	5.22
	Croton Falls	1.05	2.50	.61	4.20
	Carmel	.80	1.03	3.03	4.07
	Suffern	.89	2.01	2.16	
FLOYD Sept. 16, 17 1999	Carmel	1.05	9.90		
	Yorktown Hts	1.30	10.95		
	Peekskill	.61	8.81	.19	
	Ardsley	7.62	.75		
	West Point	.97	7.28		

TABLE 21

CROTON WATERSHED PRECIPITATION - SEPTEMBER 1999
(Inches)

Date	Amawalk	Cross River	Westchester Croton Falls	Croton Lake	Titicus	Yorktown Heights	Putnam Boyd's Comers	East Branch	Middle Branch	West Branch
1										
2										
3										
4										
5										
6	.52	.47	.46	43	.41	.81	40	40	.44	.43
7	.05	.21	28	.27	.32	.02	.39	.75	.39	.39
8	.32	.70	.48	.21	.26	28	.93	.21	.46	.90
9	.31	.56	T	.42	.05	.83	.02	-	T	.03
10	1.15	1.50	1.12	1.24	1.06	.78	1.94	.47	1.04	.93
11	.30	.26	.24	.37	.15	.62	.36	.26	.25	.11
12										
13										
14										
15										
16	1.40	1.58	1.29	1.10	1.52	1.30	1.11	1.35	1.27	1.05
17	11.00	9.00	8.77	7.50	8.70	10.95	6.90	8.60	8.77	9.90
18										
19										
20										
21	.20	.18	.22	.19	.19	.20	.12	.08	.21	
22	.82	.80	1.14	.58	1.09	.85	.62	1.67	1.70	1.10
23	.03									
24										
25	.03	.02	.07	.04	.06	.02	.05	.05	.06	.10
26										
27										
28										
29										
30	1.39	1.26	1.47	1.25	1.43	1.51	1.25	1.26	1.52	1.29
TOTALS	17.47	16.59	15.54	13.60	15.24	18.00	14.17	15.14	15.92	16.44
	Wettest Month	Wettest Sept. 16.62 Oct.1955	Wettest Sept. 16.93 Aug.1955		Wettest Month	Wettest Month	Wettest Sept. 16.68 Oct. 1955	Wettest Sept. 16.94 Oct.1955	Wettest Sept. 17.15 Aug.1955	Wettest Month

FIGURE 29

FLOOD DAMAGE IN NORTHERN WESTCHESTER SEPTEMBER 17TH, 1999

GREATEST 24 HOUR RAINFALL (7-11 INCHES) OF THE 20TH CENTURY.

TABLE 22
MAXIMUM HOURLY PRECIPITATION (Inches)
WOODLANDS-DOBBS FERRY/ARDSLEY (1944 - 1999)

	1 HOUR	2 HOURS	3 HOURS	6 HOURS	12 HOURS	24 HOURS
JAN	1.09 24 1979	1.63 24 1979	1.91 24 1979	2.70 24 1979	3.27 24 1979	3.27 24 1979
FEB	.68 2 1973	1.30 2 1973	1.39 2 1973	1.70 2 1973	2.30 2 1973	2.85 2 1973
MAR	.81 13 1953	1.10 13 1953	1.62 13 1953	2.95 22 1977	3.58 12,13 1953	4.28 12,13 1953
APR	.89 9 1980	1.36 9 1980	1.88 9 1980	2.77 9 1980	3.54 9 1980	5.34 5 1984
MAY	1.14 17 1946	1.65 17 1946	2.40 17 1946	2.90 29 1968	4.82 29 1968	5.44 28,29 1968
JUNE	2.20 15 1969	2.90 15 1969	3.22 15 1969	3.62 15 1969	5.21 19 1972	5.80 18,19 1972
JULY	2.43 10 1955	2.57 10 1955	3.63 10 1955	3.93 19 1960	4.51 19 1960	4.51 ??? 19 1960
AUG	1.82 19 1960	2.32 19 1960	2.56 19 1960	3.40 19 1960	3.74 19 1960	4.77 13 1955
SEP	2.59 3 1974	2.73 24 1946	2.97 26 1975	4.42 26 1975	4.82 26 1975	5.49 26 1975
OCT	1.52 22 1984	2.08 22 1984	2.52 22 1984	3.61 15 1955	4.40 15 1955	5.17 15 1955
NOV	.84 8 1947	1.37 8 1947	1.71 8 1972	2.73 8 1972	3.52 8 1972	5.60 8 1977
DEC	.61 26 1947	1.14 26 1947	1.36 26 1947	1.98 26 1947	2.37 26 1947	3.21 21 1973

TABLE 23
MAXIMUM HOURLY PRECIPITATION (INCHES)
LARCHMONT (1940 - 1976)

	1 HOUR	2 HOURS	3 HOURS	6 HOURS	12 HOURS	24 HOURS
JAN	57 21 1974	.78 21 1974	96 2 1959	1.28 20,21 1958	2.07 28 1943	2.41 28 1943
FEB	60 7 1941	.94 7 1941	1.20 13 1966	1.71 7 1941	2.48 7 1941	2.51 7 1941
MAR	.74 13 1953	1.10 30 1951	1.36 12 1953	1.84 12,13 1953	3.20 6,7 1944	3.31 30 1951
APR	.47 6 1949	.85 6 1958	1.20 6 1958	1.69 6 1958	2.28 6 1958	2.57 6 1953
MAY	.87 19 1966	1.40 19 1966	1.75 19 1966	2.33 27 1946	3.32 29 1968	3.48 29 1968
JUNE	1.76 21 1945	2.10 21 1945	2.16 21 1945	2.46 5 1962	3.06 19 1972	3.49 18,19 1972
JULY	3.284.98 27 1942	5.86 27 1942	6.20 27 1942	6.37 27 1942	6.77 27 1942	27 1942
AUG	1.902.52 10 1942	2.58 10 1942	3.24 9 1942	4.55 9 1942	4.59 9,10 1942	9,10 1942
SEP	1.50 2 1974	2.00 3 1957	2.67 26 1975	3.76 26 1975	4.45 3,4 1974	4.88 21 1966
OCT	1.09 7 1951	1.83 16 1955	1.92 16 1955	2.42 16 1955	2.75 16 1955	3.26 16 1955
NOV	1.64 4 1950	1.98 4 1950	2.15 4,5 1950	2.53 7 1951	2.64 6,7 1951	3.12 4,5 1950
DEC	.52 13 1941	.95 13 1941	1.43 13 1941	2.59 13 1941	3.27 13 1941	3.54 13,14 1941

TABLE 24
MAXIMUM HOURLY PRECIPITATION (INCHES)
PLEASANTVILLE (1976 - 1998)

	1 HOUR	2 HOURS	3 HOURS	6 HOURS	12 HOURS	24 HOURS
JAN	6 20 1995	1.1 20 1995	1.5 20 1995	1.8 23 1979	2.4 4 1982	2.9 23 1979
FEB	.6 24 1977	1.1 24 1977	1.6 24 1977	2.1 24 1977	2.4 24 1977	2.5 24 1981
MAR	.5 20 1990	.9 20 1990	1.1 13 1993	1.5 13 1993	2.1 13 1993	2.5 31 1987
APR	.8 9 1980	1.3 9 1980	2.1 9 1980	2.8 9 1980	3.8 9 1980	5.6 5 1984
MAY	.5 29 1984	.8 14 1978	.9 10 1990	1.7 14 1978	2.8 16 1989	4.4 17 1989
JUNE	1.3 13 1996	1.6 13 1996	1.6 13 1996	1.8 30 1984	2.4 30 1984	2.4 30 1984
JULY	1.2 17 1979	2.5 17 1979	2.5 17 1979	2.5 17 1979	3.1 9 1996	3.3 9 1996
AUG	1.4 7 1986	1.9 9 1976	2.5 9 1976	3.0 9 1976	3.8 9 1976	8.9 1 1984
SEP	.7 25 1991	1.1 25 1991	1.6 25 1991	2.1 25 1991	3.1 25 1991	3.4 25 1991
OCT	.6 19 1996	1.1 28 1987	1.5 28 1987	2.3 20 1989	3.1 19 1996	3.7 19 1996
NOV	1.3 28 1993	1.5 28 1993	1.6 28 1993	2.8 8 1977	3.9 8 1977	5.1 8 1977
DEC	.5 21 1993	.9 21 1993	1.1 21 1993	1.6 21 1993	2.0 3 1986	2.6 11 1992

TABLE 25
MAXIMUM HOURLY PRECIPITATION (Inches)
SCARSDALE (1944 - 1989)

	I HOUR	2 HOURS	3 HOURS	6 HOURS	12 HOURS	24 HOURS
JAN	.60 4 1982	.90 21 1979	1.30 21 1979	2.30 21 1979	3.00 21 1979	3.30 21 1979
FEB	.58 2 1973	1.00 13 1950	1.50 13 1950	2.60 13 1950	4.20 13 1950	5.74 13,14 1950
MAR	.85 30 1951	1.24 30 1951	1.42 30 1951	2.11 13 1953	3.13 12,13 1953	4.10 12,13 1953
APR	1.00 9 198	1.55 9 1980	2.10 9 1980	2.65 9 1980	3.00 9 1980	3.93 9 1980
MAY	.66 14 1947	.98 17 1946	1.00 17 1946	1.45 26,27 1946	2.90 26,27 1946	5.80 26,27 1946
JUNE	1.1 21 1945	1.32 21 1945	1.60 24 1984	2.68 19 1972	3.69 18,19 1972	4.83 18,19 1972
JULY	1.87 10 1955	2.11 10 1955	2.30 30 1960	2.98 30 1960	3.70 12,13 1955	5.03 12,13 1955
AUG	1.76 19 1960	2.21 19 1960	2.53 19 1960	3.36 19 1960	4.08 12,13 1955	6.28 12,13 1955
SEP	1.40 14 1944	2.58 14 1944	3.65 14 1944	4.88 14 1944	4.89 14 1944	6.55 14 1944
OCT	1.02 15 1955	1.94 15 1955	2.41 15 1955	3.14 15 1955	3.70 15 1955	4.67 15 1955
NOV	.70 7 1951	1.30 7 1951	1.90 7 1951	2.65 8 1972	3.80 8 1977	4.75 8 1977
DEC	.90 16 1950	1.50 16 1950	1.70 16 1950	2.04 16 1950	2.72 26 1947	3.16 26 1947

TABLE 26
MAXIMUM HOURLY PRECIPITATION (Inches)
SHRUB OAK (1953 - 1969) • YORKTOWN HEIGHTS (1970 -1999)

	1 HOUR	2 HOURS	3 HOURS	6 HOURS	12 HOURS	24 HOURS
JAN	.80 20 1995	1.10 20 1995	1.30 20 1995	1.50 4 1982	2.00 26 1986	3.33 211979
FEB	.42 8 1965	.78 7,8 1965	1.00 7,8 1965	1.31 7,8 1965	1.80 13 1966	3.30 3 1973
MAR	1.20 17 1973	1.30 17 1973	1.30 17 1973	1.70 22 1977	2.10 22 1977	4.60 22 1980
APR	.70 5 1984	1.00 4 1987	1.40 4 1987	2.30 4 1987	3.20 4 1987	4.30 5 1984
MAY	1.30 28 1985	1.80 28 1985	1.90 28 1985	2.40 14 1978	3.40 29 1968	3.75 28,29 1989
JUNE	1.60 21 1994	1.98 17 1960	2.00 30 1984	2.60 15 1969	3.30 15 1969	3.82 1 1952
JULY	1.90 15 1996	2.30 4 1973	2.50 4 1973	3.00 7 1984	3.80 7 1984	4.24 23 1946
AUG	1.50 16 1968	2.30 16 1968	2.40 16 1968	2.90 9,10 1976	3.70 28 1971	6.86 28 1971
SEP	1.20 11 1954	2.35 11 1954	2.80 17 1999	5.00 17 1999	6.90 17 1999	11.00 17 1999
OCT	.90 22 198	1.70 22 1984	1.90 22 1984	2.40 15 1955	4.05 15 1955	5.95 15,16 1955
NOV	.80 21 1994	1.10 21 1994	1.50 21 1944	2.60 21 1994	2.90 8 1972	3.47 12 1947
DEC	.60 6 1972	.75 6,7 1953	.90 21 1993	1.39 6,7 1953	2.60 21 1973	3.29 14 1941

TABLE 27
MAXIMUM HOURLY PRECIPITATION (Inches)
CARMEL (1954 -1999)

	I HOUR	2 HOURS	3 HOURS	6 HOURS	12 HOURS	24 HOURS
JAN	.40 26 1986	.80 21 1979	1.10 21 1979	1.60 21 1979	2.40 21 1979	2.80 21 1979
FEB	.70 2 1973	1.40 2 1973	1.70 2 1973	2.20 2 1973	2.90 2 1973	3.40 2 1973
MAR	.40 17 1973	.80 21 1974	1.00 21 1974	1.40 20 1990	1.90 20 1990	3.06 23 1977
APR	.58 24 1968	1.13 24 1968	1.49 24 1968	1.93 24 1968	2.65 24 1968	2.82 24 1968
MAY	.70 12 1974	1.10 12 1974	1.20 12 1974	1.47 29 1968	2.67 29 1968	3.00 29 1984
JUNE	.88 15 1969	1.39 15 1963	1.80 15 1969	2.57 15 1969	3.13 15 1969	4.30 15,16 1969
JULY	1.30 4 1973	1.70 4 1973	2.50 4 1973	3.70 4 1973	3.90 4 1973	5.03 2 1987
AUG	2.14 15 1960	2.54 15 1960	2.62 15 1969	3.10 13 1955	3.92 13 1955	6.00 13 1955
SEP	1.70 3 1959	2.00e 17 1999	4.00e 17 1999	6.00e 17 1999	7.00e 17 1999	10.00 17 1999
OCT	.90 15 1955	1.30 15 1955	2.05 15 1955	3.20 15 1955	4.43 15 1955	7.10 15 1955
NOV	.60 28 1958	.94 28 1958	1.33 28 1958	1.93 28 1958	2.15 28 1958	3.07 28 1958
DEC	.80 6 1983	1.00 6 1983	1.27 29 1966	1.42 29 1966	2.34 20 1957	3.05 31 1948

e = estimated from Yorktown Heights

THE WETTEST DAYS

Before September 1999, official records of the U.S. Weather Service Cooperative Stations dating back to the 1890s had never recorded a 24 hour rainfall four digits or greater than ten inches at its ten rain gauges that had been in operation at one time or another since then. The unofficial New York City Croton watershed network of nine gauges had three and seven day totals greater than ten inches. A nine inch 24 hour amount at the Croton Lake rain gauge site with daily records dating back to 1868 was considered to be the one in one hundred year storm event. All other rain gauge stations with records less than 100 years measured greatest 24 hour amounts between six and seven inches.

The September 16,17 1999 rainfall event has shattered the above record pluvial benchmark. Tropical Storm "Floyd" will be remembered locally as the wettest 20th century days. Within the Croton watershed ten or more inches was registered on the 17th at Carmel and Amawalk and Yorktown Heights, with the latter two sites recording eleven inches. Preliminary estimates based on the Carmel and Croton Lake long term record rank the return period for these amounts as at least a once in five hundred year event.

All Croton watershed stations except the Croton Lake rain gauge had their greatest September total with amounts ranging from 14 inches (WestBranch) to 18 inches(Yorktown Heights). Four sites recorded their wettest month of their 20th century record. At Peekskill 15 inches ranked as its second wettest month in its seventy four year record.

Unofficially, there have been past reports of daily amounts in excess of ten inches in otherparts of Westchester. An account of one of these is given as follows:

On August 6, 1990 about 5:30 PM this cooperative weather observer noted an immense darkthunderstorm cloud distantly to the northwest. Contrary to normal this storm did not move in the usual NW to SE manner but remained stationary till at least dark, 8 - 10 miles to the north at the Westchester - Putnam line in the vicinity of Shrub Oak. Telephone and radio reports that evening spoke of road washouts, flooded basements and home foundations on slopes washed away. Without an actual rain gauge in that area, I despaired of ever learning the exact amount that fell there. During the following week however, a friend informed me that he had heard that over 11 inches had fallen that day. Not one to ignore any source claiming such an extreme weather event nearly triple the normal August total, which if confirmed would break every previous two county record, I began a documentation search. After two days of meteorological sleuthing through phone calls, a TV network and four different people, I was able to track down the original source, Mr. Bud Lockhart, who, using a six inch deep coffee can, told me of his successive measuring activity that day. In the days following I was directed by my son Daniel to another source, a Mr. James Janak, also residing in Shrub Oak who reported 11.75 inches in a 24 hour period that day, starting 5 AM. and an August total rainfall of 18.5 inches. He used a more acceptable rain gauge. Further investigation produced other local data from the New York City Department of Water Resources within the Croton River watershed. Two of their standard rain gauges at West Branch (Carmel) and Boyd's Corners respectively measured rainfall that day of 4.33 and 6.00 inches and monthly totals of 14.88 and 14.85 inches.

This climatological detective story has an important consequence for Westchester and Putnam hydrology. The official Westchester County once in one hundred year 24 hour storm of seven inches on which highway and drain culvert size is based, should be revised to eleven inches. The Westchester Weather Book figure of nine inches in one hundred years also needs correcting. In addition a questionable rainfall extreme discovered years ago in the old New York City Water Department records now assumes a greater respectability. This was the 11.26 inches that was measured on September 23, 1882 at the Croton Lake rain gauge.

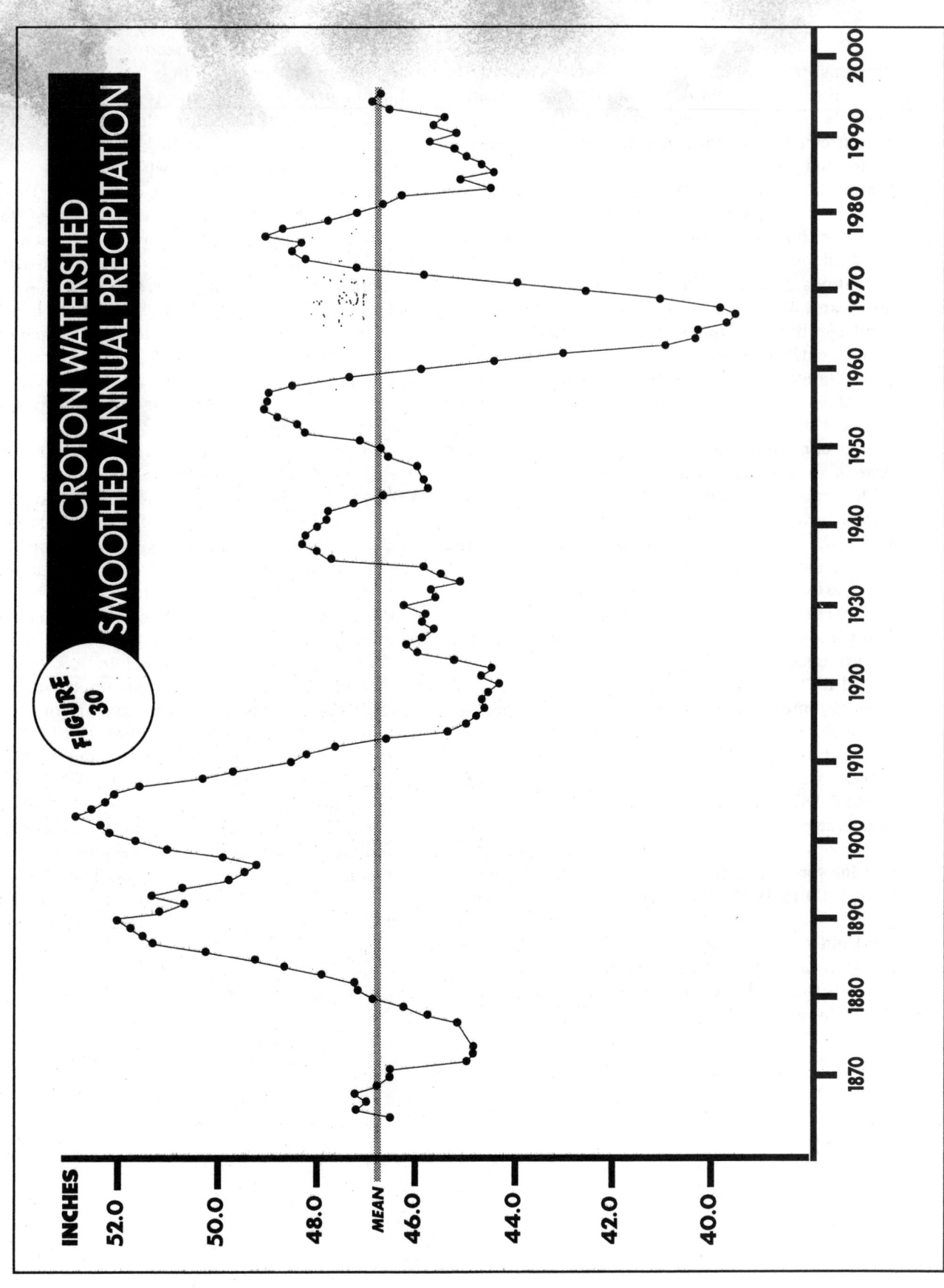

CROTON WATERSHED
SMOOTHED ANNUAL PRECIPITATION

FIGURE 30

CLIMATE TRENDS AND QUASI - PERIODICITIES

The determination of climate fluctuations, rhythms, trends, periodicities or cycles can only be made if a long enough record of continuous weather data is available. Since regular daily weather measurements by proper instrumentation have been performed for barely 200 years in the eastern United States, the data bank available from even the few stations currently in operation that long, is still too short for the best statistical time series analysis.

Besides the lack of long enough records, limitations regarding the length of time at any one site can also affect the usefulness of the data available. In the counties of the lower Hudson valley, while earliest recording of temperature and precipitation date back to the 1820s in all cases the record is not complete and the data comes from different sites. Since each weather station has its own unique climate profile its data can not be projected to past or future stations at different locations except under special conditions. In addition, individual stations are often not representative of the area in which they are located. This holds especially to the temperature record.

The longest temperature sets in the lower Hudson Valley are those of Bedford Hills, Scarsdale, West Point and Carmel. Unfortunately the Bedford Hills record ended in 1977, the Scarsdale station was closed in 1990 after 86 years of operation, and the Carmel temperature record obtained from the least urbanized site ended in 1980 after 92 years of daily observations. The West Point temperature while the longest of all, is flawed by numerous missing months in the 1870s and 1880s. Estimations of mean temperature have had to be made for these breaks in the record as well as for the complete years that are missing for the Civil war period and for the period from 1900 to 1905. The Carmel record was deemed the best as it was designated as one of the stations of the United States Historical Climatology Network by the Oak Ridge National Laboratory, Carbon Dioxide Analysis Center. Its record was integrated with that of the Yorktown Heights weather station located eleven miles to the southwest. Sixteen years of concurrent daily temperature readings allowed such an adjustment to be made. The result is a long - term record dating from 1888 through 1999. In Figures 20, 21, and 22 filtered or smoothed seasonal and annual temperature rhythms are shown.

The Annual and Winter figures reveal that the coldest period of the 20th century occurred during the first two decades, with succeeding fluctuating periods of warmth and relative coldness. Two decades of relative coldness in the 1960s and 1970s have been followed by gradually warmer times. There has been an overall 20th century upward trend of temperatures of two to four degrees Fahrenheit for annual and winter periods. Summer temperature, also reveal a similar pattern with the warmest, longest period in the last decade of the century.

The warming trend shown at the least urbanized site confirms what has been found worldwide. The warmest months, seasons and years have been phenomena mostly in the decade of the 1990s. Nearly all climatologists attribute the warming to the known increase of human produced greenhouse gases and they expect a further warming through the early part of the 21st century even if steps are immediately taken to limit the increase of such gases.

The longest continuous precipitation record in the region is that of the Croton watershed dating back to 1860. Figure 30 is based on an average of the total number of rain gauges in operation. Until 1900, no more than four gauges were in operation. By 1906 all nine gauges were in operation. The height of the peaks of precipitation shown about 1889 and 1902 are therefore suspect. The graph shows quasi-periodicities of fourteen to twenty two years averaging between 17 and 18 years. This periodicity has been found to be significant at the 95% confidence level. The major drought period as shown was that of the mid 1960s. Less severe droughts could also adversely affect the water supply of the New York City metropolitan region.

All About Snow

COUNTY SNOWFALL DIFFERENCES

Temperature is the critical factor when one compares monthly and seasonal totals within our three county region. Longer periods of time with below freezing temperatures provide a more likely chance of greater snowfall and also lengthen the time that the snow remains on the ground unmelted. Since temperature is affected by urbanization and elevation amounts will vary widely from one snow measuring site to another. As seen from Figure 31 and Table 29, seasonal snowfall in Westchester and Putnam increases from south to north as urbanization decreases and elevation increases. Comparisons between stations can only be valid for the years in common as changing urbanization effects can be unequal in effect. With only three snow measuring stations presently operating such comparisons can only be qualitative in nature.

In Rockland the seasonal total snow comparisons become even more tentative as the snow measuring sites have generally operated in different time periods. For Suffern and West Point the only five years in common between 1954 and 1974 show a nine inch seasonal difference (29 inches at West Point and 20 inches at Suffern). Three years of comparison between West Nyack and Suffern in the 1990s shows essentially no difference in seasonal snowfall (36 inches). Average seasonal snowfall at Garnerville for six years in the 1980s is also about 36 inches. The fragmented Suffern seasonal snowfall record for the second half of the 20th century shows an average of 33 inches. Currently there is no official snow measuring weather station in Rockland.

EXTREME SNOWFALL PROBABILITIES

"The improbable is bound to happen one day"
......Unknown Source

The economic effects of severe, heavy snowstorms are felt by urban and suburban areas alike. In Westchester, Rockland and Putnam where the predominant mode of transportation is by private automobile, heavy snowfall generally immobilizes this means of movement. Commercial vehicles are also adversely affected. Even the forecast threat of a snowstorm will reduce the traffic on most roads. The common use of powered snow removal equipment in the latter part of the 20th century has given homeowners and businesses greater flexibility in locating building sites away from major roads. This was not the case in the 19th century and earlier when homes were sited close to roads. Heavy snow does

pose greater demands on even our present snow removal equipment. As a consequence a single snowfall of a foot or greater will generally prevent nearly all suburban commuters from reaching their place of work that day. Schools will close with even a lesser depth of snow.

Snowfall records from the long-term weather stations provide information on how often large amounts of snow can be expected . The source of this data comes from the records of four weather stations with over 30 years of consecutive winter seasons. These are the National Weather Service Cooperative Stations at Dobbs Ferry/Ardsley (55 years), Scarsdale (76 years), Bedford Hills (83 years), Westchester Airport (50 years), Carmel/Yorktown Heights (100 years) and West Point (82 years). These records indicate that one or more inches of snow normally fall between ten and twenty days during the snowfall season.

An analysis of these continuous records allows us to show the frequency of heavy snowfalls based on past records of the heaviest one day amount for each winter season (See Table 30). The basic assumption made with the "order statistics" method used is that during the period involved there were no trends in climate that would have an effect on snowfall. Looking back to the mid and early 20th century we can see that winter temperatures have not been normally distributed and that urbanization has caused warming during the period that this data was recorded.

Future climate historians will have to weigh the quantitative effect of these factors and others such as topography, elevation, site location exposure and other micro-climate influences. In spite of these limitations the figures presented can serve as a guide to those interested in aspects of the snow regime.

The snowfall records used show the greatest single fall in each winter season. In Table 28 for example, a snowfall of 8.8 inches at Scarsdale can be expected at least once every two years; a snowfall of 26.0 inches can be expected at least once every 25 years and a snowfall of 30.9 inches can be expected at least once every 100 years.

Through 1998 the greatest single 24 hour snowfall have been: Dobbs Ferry/Ardsley - 28 inches, Scarsdale - 28.2 inches, Bedford Hills - 27 inches, and Carmel/Yorktown Heights - 25 inches.

OTHER HARD WATER FACTS

In a normal cold weather season there are between eight and twelve days when sleet has been observed and between four and eight days with glaze (freezing rain).

TABLE 28
TOTAL SEASONAL SNOWFALL
(Inches)

Winter Season	White Plains
1872-1873	61.5
1873 -1874	50.5
1874-1875	85.8*
1875 -1876	36.4
1876 -1877	60.5
1877-1878	11.0*
1878-1879	53.2
1879-1880	50.0
1880-1881	55.0
1881 -1882	63.3
1882 -1883	67.0
1883-1884	50.0
1884-1885	33.5
1885-1886	18.0
1886-1887	65.2
1887-1888	78.0
1888-1889	18.0
1889-1890	—
1890-1991	54.2
Average	48.0

Winter Season	Bedford Hills	Carmel	Scarsdale
1894-95	59.2		
1895-96	54.4		
1896-97	57.9		
1897-98	42.4	42.2	
1898-99	85.5	79.2	
1899-00	27.9	32.5	
1900-01	20.6	25.3	
1901-02	35.0	47.3	
1902-03	23.5	47.2	
1903-04	16.2	59.7	
1904-05	41.8	83.3	81.0
1905-06	24.6	33.0	25.7

Winter Season	Bedford Hills	Carmel	Scarsdale	West Point
1906-07	61.9	79.3	75.0	
1907-08	35.0	47.0	38.5	
1908-09	22.2	27.3	24.2	
1909-10	38.5	48.0	54.5	34.5
1910-11	25.0	37.5	41.7	30.7
1911-12	27.0	28.2	39.5	16.2
1912-13	16.0	16.5	24.0	12.9

1913-14	35.2	44.2	60.5				65.7
1914-15	19.0	24.5	35.0				60.5
1915-16	72.5	90.3	109.8*				67.0
1916-17	51.3	43.7	61.0				63.1
1917-18	23.4	50.1	42.9				23.8
1918-19	8.2	19.5	7.6				16.6
1919-20	49.7	64.4	54.7				35.7
1920-21	10.8	28.5	27.7				24.0
1921-22	43.3	32.5	34.4				29.4
1922-23	92.0*	84.3	83.5				68.4
1923-24	28.3	42.4	34.2				24.1
1924-25	35.2	29.7	37.0				27.0
1925-26	25.2	34.8	39.9				43.8
1926-27	33.7	49.0	28.4				41.6
1927-28	13.0	23.5	21.2				24.1
1928-29	11.0	21.7	17.0				
1929-30	16.5	20.2	17.2				
1930-31	26.0	39.6	15.8				
1931-32	6.5*	24.0	5.3*				
1932 - 33	32.0	48.5	25.4				42.8
1933 - 34	54.1	68.0	72.2				
1934 - 35	33.9	34.0	32.2				
1935 - 36	37.9	46.7	47.7				51.3
1936 - 37	12.8	21.5	10.3				28.4
1937-38	22.6	24.6	17.7				17.3
1938 - 39	36.5	34.6	42.0				30.2
1939-40	36.2	37.2	33.0				29.7

	Bedford Hills	Carmel	Scarsdale	Yorktown	Dobbs Ferry Ardsley	Westchester Airport	West Point
Winter Season							
1940-41	31.5	43.6	37.8	41.0	42.5		
1941-42	18.3	18.7	18.2	18.5			19.0
1942-43	37.5	51.2	33.0	44.6			45.0
1943-44	21.5	25.0	25.3	29.5			30.0
1944-45	35.8	22.5	36.5	57.0			34.2
1945-46	44.2	33.5	42.4	49.5	52.8		
1946-47	33.5	25.0	34.7	30.0	46.9		
1947-48	67.1	94.4*	64.9	74.5	73.5		
1948-49	46.0	56.0	36.8	41.3	53.0		
1949-50	21.5	30.5	18.0	19.0	23.4	21.5	26.8
1950-51	18.0	32.9	14.2	25.5	23.8	13.9	31.7
1951-52	34.4	38.5	25.9	28.5	29.5	25.1	33.0
1952-53	17.0	16.0*	16.1	17.0	21.6	14.8	20.0
1953-54	19.9	26.3	22.0	26.0	27.3	22.5	28.9
1954-55	11.5	16.6	12.0	17.5	15.7	13.0	14.0
1955-56	37.8	53.7	43.0	51.6	56.8	50.0	54.3
1956-57	25.0	23.1	27.8	28.0	33.0	24.8	27.7
1957-58	55.0	54.7	79.6	68.0	79.8	74.9	73.6
1958-59	20.4	21.8	33.1	16.5	26.5	21.4	28.2
1959-60	42.9	35.7	50.0	49.5	53.8	37.0	55.2

	Bedford	Carmel	Scarsdale	Yorktown Heights	Ardsley	Westchester Airport	West Point
1960-61	70.7	89.0	76.2	82.5	90.0*	84.2*	
1961-62	42.7	46.5	46.2	44.0	37.4	38.4	48.8
1962-63	39.4	58.0	48.9	38.1	42.5	37.8	45.0
1963-64	31.5	42.0	55.9	40.0	52.3	48.8	52.9
1964-65	32.8	43.0	63.6	42.4	37.2	35.1	49.9
1965-66	26.3	32.6	34.0	33.3	30.9	24.5	31.9
1966-67	75.1	79.0	50.5	76.5	70.3	75.5	93.1*
1967-68	26.5	30.5	23.5	28.5	27.2	24.0	23.2
1968-69	44.7	60.0	42.4	50.3	44.0	37.4	50.2
1969-70	48.6	45.5	37.7	49.0	44.4	39.6	49.7
1970-71	38.3	53.0	31.1	47.1	38.9	40.0	44.1
1971-72	38.1	46.5	28.0	41.9	35.2	29.0	33.0
1972-73	15.3	18.0	5.8	24.4	9.4*	15.3	12.7
1973-74	30.9	29.0	31.0	33.5	35.2	33.5	27.0
1974-75	20.3	22.5	16.5	26.5	23.2	15.5	19.1
1975-76	39.0	36.0	36.1	34.7	38.5	35.9	32.3
1976-77	37.0	50.0	29.0	41.0	33.8	37.9	28.8
1977-78			59.6	57.1	61.6	59.7	60.0
1978-79			25.0	29.4	33.8	23.0	24.0
1979-80				29.9	18.2	15.0	24.0
1980-81				19.5	23.8	20.0	
1981-82				43.5	33.0	38.5	40.0
1982-83			25.1	47.7	30.9	24.0	
1983-84			37.0	56.2	45.6	47.0	44.5
1984-85				28.5	27.8	23.5	
1985-86			20.9	33.0	26.3	22.1	32.0
1986-87			38.4	46.7	38.0	33.5	47.5
1987-88				45.2	30.3	37.0	42.0
1988-89				12.0*	10.7	9.3	7.0*
1989-90				44.5	26.9	29.1	37.0
1990-91				27.7	24.0	23.0	29.2
1991-92				20.1	14.1	12.9	12.0
1992-93				60.8	44.1	50.5	68.6
1993-94				59.5	53.9	46.3	52.0
1994-95				17.7	13.9	13.1	14.0
1995-96				103.7*	83.1	80.7	90.7
1996-97				39.2	25.1	17.0	30.0
1997-98				22.4	9.6	9.0*	15.0
1998-99				22.6	14.7	16.0	18.0
1999-2000				19.5	20.6	17.5	22.5

Average

(1949-50   - 1976-77)

	34.3	40.4	35.6	38.6	38.6	35.0	37.1

Average

(1960-61   - 1989-90)

	35.2(est.)	40.9	35.2 (est.)	40.9	36.6	34.8	36.7

Most & Least Snow = *

146

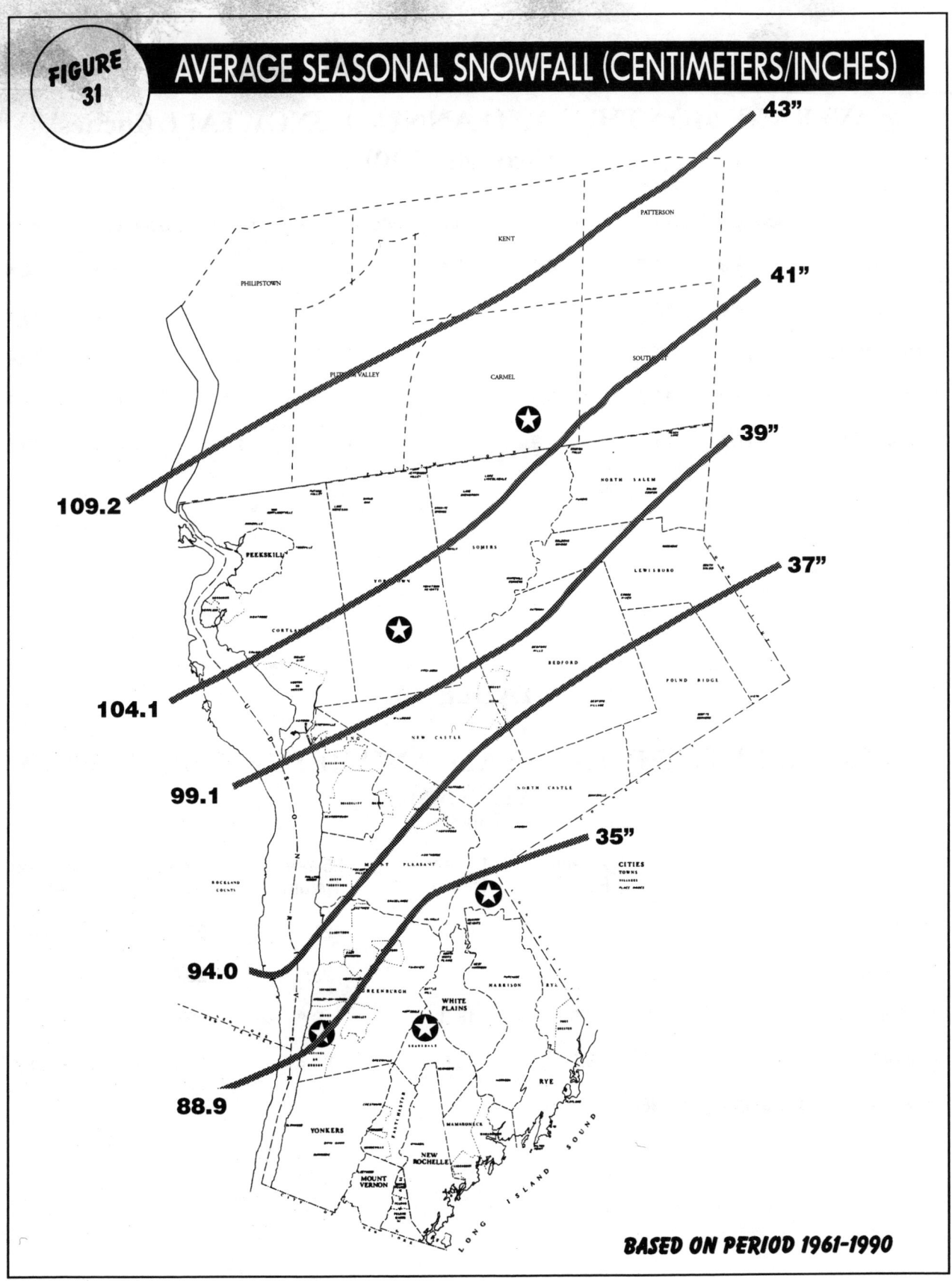

FIGURE 31 — **AVERAGE SEASONAL SNOWFALL (CENTIMETERS/INCHES)**

BASED ON PERIOD 1961-1990

TABLE 29

AVERAGE MONTHLY AND ANNUAL SNOWFALL (inches)
(through 1930)

	January	February	March	April	October	November	December	Annual
Bedford Hills	9.3	11.7	6.7	2.4	T	2.0	6.3	38.4
Carmel	9.9	13.4	7.6	2.0	.1	2.1	9.0	44.1
Mount Hope	10.5	12.9	8.6	1.2	.1	1.0	9.1	43.4
Mount Vernon	9.0	11.5	5.5	2.3	T.	.1	6.5	34.9
West Point	11.7	14.4	7.9	1.6	T	1.1	6.8	43.5

TABLE 30

24 HOUR EXTREME SNOWFALL AND RETURN FREQUENCY
(YEARS)
(Inches)

	2 Year Return	10 Year Return	25 Year Return	50 Year Return	100 Year Return
Dobbs Ferry	8.9	17.5	21.9	25.1	28.3
Scarsdale	8.8	17.8	23.0	26.0	30.9
Bedford Hills	7.5	15.3	19.8	22.0	26.5
Carmel	8.2	16.0	20.4	23.0	27.9

Based on the record ending in 1980

TABLE 31

GREATEST SNOWFALLS
BY WEEK

	SCARSDALE (1904 - 1990)		BEDFORD HILLS (1894 - 1977)		CARMEL/ YORKTOWN HEIGHTS (1892 - 2000)	
	Inches	Date	Inches	Date	Inches	Date
OCT 1 - 8					12	4 1987
9 -16					6.0	10 1979
17 -24	Trace	17 1929	Trace	19 1972	2.5	19 1972
25 - 31	3.0	26 1962	Trace	26 1962	5.0	26 1962
NOV 1 - 8	5.0	7 1953	4.0	8 1894	5.0	7 1953
9 - 15	3.0	15 1906	4.0	12 1968	7.0	12 1968
16 - 23	4.0	20 1961	6.0	20 1961	5.0	20 1961
24 - 30	11.0	25 1938	11.0	30 1898	8.0	30 1898
DEC1 - 8	11.0	4 1911	6.0	5 1926	8.0	3 1903
9 - 15	17.0	12 1960	16.0	12 1960	16.0	12 1960
16 - 23	12.0	20 1948	11.0	19 1945	11.0	20 1948
24 - 31	28.0	27 1947	20.0	27 1947	25.0	27 1947
JAN1 - 8	8.0	3 1904	9.0	1 1971	14.0	8 1996
9 - 16	18.0	15 1910	12.0	15 1910	9.0	14 1923
17 - 23	15.5	20 1961	16.0	20 1961	17.0	20 1961
24 - 31	22.0	25 1905	13.0	28 1897	13.5	25 1905
FEB 1 - 7	17.0	5 1907	15.0	5 1907	19.0	4 1961
8 - 14	24.0	10 1969	22.0	10 1969	25.0	12 1983
15 - 21	21.0	20 1920	18.0	16 1902	16.0	20 1934
22 - 29	13.5	25 1966	13.0	26 1934	19.0	22 1893
MAR 1 - 8	14.0	1 1914	16.0	4 1960	12.0	4 1960
9 - 16	2.0	12 1959	12.0	16 1896	13.5	13 1993
17 - 23	15.0	19 1956	15.0	20 1958	13.0	19 1956
24 - 31	9.0	29 1970	10.0	29 1970	12.0	29 1970
APR 1 - 8	14.0	3 1915	12.0	3 1915	17.0	1 1997
9 - 16	7.0	9 1907	14.0	12 1894	14.0	10 1907
17 - 23	Trace	19 1965	0		5.0	19 1983
24 - 30	4.5	24 1967	Trace	2 1967	2.5	30 1909
MAY 1 - 8	0	Trace		3 1911	Trace	6 1967
9 - 16	Trace	9 1977	Trace	9 1977	2.0	9 1977

TABLE 32

NUMBER AND PERIODS OF OCCURRENCE OF STORMS WITH 6 INCHES OR MORE OF SNOW IN PUTNAM AND NORTHERN WESTCHESTER

INCHES	NOV 1-15	NOV 16-30	DEC 1-15	DEC 16-31	JAN 1-15	JAN 16-31	FEB 1-15	FEB 16-29	MAR 1-15	MAR 16-31	APR 1-15
6.0-6.9	0	1	4	7	4	7	8	4	5	1	4
7.0-7.9	1	1	1	4	4	4	4	1	1	5	0
8.0-8.9	0	1	2	2	2	4	6	3	2	1	1
9.0-9.0	0	0	1	2	1	1	3	2	4	0	1
10-10.9	0	0	0	3	0	1	3	2	3	0	1
11-11.9	0	0	0	0	0	1	4	1	0	2	0
12-12.9	0	0	1	1	0	1	0	1	2	2	0
13-13.9	0	0	0	0	0	2	1	0	1	1	0
14-14.9	0	0	1	1	1	1	0	1	0	0	1
15-15.9	0	0	0	0	0	0	0	0	0	0	0
16-16.9	0	0	1	0	0	0	0	1	0	0	0
17-17.9	0	0	0	0	0	1	0	0	0	0	1
18-18.9	0	0	1	0	0	0	0	0	0	0	0
19-19.9	0	0	0	0	0	0	1	1	0	0	0
20-20.9	0	0	0	0	0	0	2	0	0	0	0
25.0	0	0	0	1	0	0	1	0	0	0	0

Based on records from Carmel (1892 - 1975) and Yorktown Heights (1976 - 2000)

WEATHER STATION HISTORY AND DATA LEGITIMACY

Knowledge of the climate of the lower Hudson valley is based on a network of weather stations distributed unevenly throughout three counties. Precipitation is monitored by personnel working for Water Departments of some county municipalities and by the New York City Department of Environmental Protection in the Croton Watershed, and daily temperature readings in nearly all cases are taken by these same employees. There are few stations that record both temperature and rainfall even less that also monitor snowfall. The National Cooperative Observer Network that was set up by the U.S. Weather Bureau about 100 years ago, continues to the present day, with three Westchester stations, one in Rockland and one in Orange county close to the northern tip of Rockland. These currently report both daily temperature and all precipitation data which is published in the monthly Climatological Data - New York periodical. Additionally, the Northeast Regional Climate Center based at Cornell University also lists two other sites that only monitor precipitation. Their monthly summary is published in New York Climate. Nationwide, many of these dedicated volunteer observers have performed this service for decades. There are also individual weather buffs that record significant weather events and keep records on a daily basis. However few of these records exceed ten years of length and are not published. Additionally the equipment used is not of the standard that the U.S. Weather Service specifies.

The key factors in obtaining a satisfactory climatological record are the longevity and consistency of the observational data. Generally, a 20 year unbroken record at one site is the minimum needed to obtain a clear climate profile of a local region. The Weather Service in its Climatological Data publications uses a 30 year average for determining what is normal.

Beginning in 2001 normal will be the period from 1971 through 2000.

The question of data legitimacy is always present regarding any specific weather station. Does the data produced truly represent the local region in which it is located? Are there identifiable factors that can adversely influence temperature or snowfall measurements?

Some of these factors that can greatly affect the quality and accuracy of a climate record are thermometer location, changes in site location (Schmidlin), and changes in the time of the daily observation. The time of normal observation is a key factor in the determination of the monthly mean temperature. In addition, mean temperature and snowfall amounts are affected by a north or south facing exposure, closeness of homes, closeness and amount of nearby blacktop or pavement and local bodies of water.

The following is a short history of each of the significant Westchester and Putnam active and discontinued data collecting weather stations of the late 19th and 20th centuries.

WESTCHESTER AIRPORT - This station has the longest Westchester record at one site of those in currently in operation of temperature and precipitation (precipitation since 1949 and temperature since 1951). Daily readings have been monitored by a succession of airport employees. It is located at an elevation of 400 feet above sea level on a flat and open terrain not typical of the general area. The temperature effect of this openness would be one of a slight cooling caused by greater air movement. This cooling however could be offset by the buildings and moderate amount of pavement and blacktop at the airport. Until about 1980 the thermometers were housed in the standard Weather Service shelter located between a roadway and the edge of the airfield, not a recommended location. At present thermometer sensors are located between two runways on the airfield and temperature is monitored continuously. In all likelihood winter temperatures are cooler than what is typical for the area and summer temperatures are warmer than what would be representative. Whether these average out to give a true annual average temperature for the year is an open question. We are thus left with some uncertainty as to whether this station represents its area in specific months or seasons (Fig 33).

DOBBS FERRY/ARDSLEY - Until 1989 when the station was relocated to its present location in Ardsley, following the death of its founder, G. Henry Weber, it was sited in a residential neighborhood of single family homes on 1/4 acre lots. The homes appeared to be of about the same age (October 1945) as the weather station itself. Other than the temperature effect caused by surrounding homes, there had been no additional home building in the area. However, until 1972, the minimum and maximum thermometers were positioned on the northwest corner of the observer's home, under a large tree. A standard thermometer shelter was not used before then. This thermometer location would have had the effect of raising winter temperatures from home heating during the cold months of the year. Shading from the house and trees in the summer would have had a cooling effect. Reverend Robert Duane assumed the responsibility of daily readings at the new site from 1989 to 1997 followed by John Clear. The relocation to Ardsley about 2 miles to the east has also created temperature differences. While the elevation of the two sites is the same 240 feet above sea level, the topographical land configuration is quite different. The Dobbs Ferry site sloped down to the Hudson River to the west, while the Ardsley station is sited at the bottom of a bowl with higher terrain all around. On cold still nights this site traps the sinking cold air giving colder minimum temperatures. A temperature assessment of this station would conclude that at Dobbs Ferry, for the period through 1989, annual mean and winter monthly temperatures were higher than the general area, while after 1989 at Ardsley they were colder (See Figure 32).

CARMEL/YORKTOWN HEIGHTS - As a consequence of the closing of the Carmel station in 1982, the monthly mean temperature record for Carmel dating back to 1888 was adjusted by a mean difference method to that of Yorktown Heights using data from the 18 year period of concurrent operation. This has resulted in retaining a continuous temperature record of 112 years, the longest in Westchester and Putnam. This station also monitors rain and snow, and is part of the United States Historical Climatology Network of long-term stations, used to determine climate normals and temperature trends.

The Carmel location in Putnam County, four miles north of the Westchester line, about 1000 feet east of the West Branch Reservoir at an elevation of 490 feet above sea level, was perhaps the best site possible for any weather station in southeastern New York State. Other than one office/barn building over 100 feet away, the station maintained by employees of the New York City Water Department, could be considered a climate benchmark since the area within one half mile has remained the same for over 80 years. There was no blacktop within 100 feet of the thermometer shelter. Daily low temperatures in the fall perhaps were raised 2 - 4 degrees and highs lowered by that amount in the summer by the influence of the nearby reservoir.

The Yorktown Heights component of the combined temperature record has been operated since 1964 by Dr. Jerome S. Thaler. Its location cannot be considered typical of the village one mile to the east, or for much of the town of Yorktown. Located on the northwest slope of French Hill at an elevation of 665 feet, it occupies the highest elevation of any weather station past or present within all counties. The station site is located within a one acre zone residential neighborhood on a street that did not exist before 1954. The surrounding homes were there

before 1964. The high elevation of the station results in minimum daily temperatures 2 - 5 degrees warmer than the areas that are 100 - 200 feet lower in elevation, which includes most of the town of Yorktown.

Generally the warmer minima occur on many fall, winter and spring nights after cold air masses have passed through the area and inversion conditions prevail. The daily maximum temperatures are generally 1 - 3 degrees cooler than most of the lower parts of the town due to the greater air movements at higher elevation. These two effects do not balance each other out and the site is certainly cooler than most of the Yorktown region, as snow amounts and duration of snow on the ground are greater at this location. What one can say about this site is that it represents much of Putnam and those areas of northern Westchester that have elevations equal or greater than 600 feet (See Figure 33).

PEEKSKILL - This station, not affiliated with the National Weather Service network of cooperative stations (daily data unpublished) and maintained by the Peekskill Water Department, has kept daily temperature records from 1945 to the present. Its precipitation record dates back to 1926. Snowfall amounts were measured only to 1968. It is located about one mile northeast of the Peekskill population center at an elevation of 370 feet. During most of its period of operation the thermometer and shelter used were not the standard ones employed by the National Weather Service. Reliable temperature and precipitation readings show this station to be truly representative of the suburban region just outside of Peekskill. The site location is on an open grassy field away from any large man made structures. The instruments employed in the past do not appear to have had any climate effect radically different than other past or present weather stations in the area (See Figure 32).

CROTON WATERSHED PRECIPITATION NETWORK - see The Croton Watershed & Figure 33.

KENSICO RESERVOIR - The rain gauge, located at an elevation of 365 feet has monitored precipitation since 1884 by the New York City Water Department. (unpublished data)

PLEASANTVILLE - Two rain gauges (automatic hourly and standard daily) are maintained by the Village of Pleasantville at an elevation of 320 feet. The precipitation amounts have been published since 1948. The record is noteworthy for its reliability and continuity.

SUFFERN - This Weather Service Cooperative Station began daily weather readings in 1940. Since then it has been relocated at five different sites in the Suffern area at elevations ranging from 270 to 500 feet elevation. From July 1940 through January 1941, readings were taken from a home location of 360 feet elevation 3.5 miles south of the Suffern Post Office. Readings were resumed 2.5 miles northeast of the Post Office in July 1941 and continued through July 1947. In August 1949, monitoring restarted and continued through December 1952 at a Suffern High School location 1.4 miles east north east of the Post Office (elevation 420 feet). In May 1953, daily readings resumed one mile south of the previous location at an elevation of 500 feet 2 miles east of the Post Office . In 1956, the Suffern Water Works took over the daily monitoring of temperature, rain and snow and has continued this with one break to early 1999. The numerous breaks and station relocations make it nearly impossible to determine an exact temperature profile of the Suffern area much less that of most of Rockland County. However, the flawed record as it exists is the only long-term data source available. With extrapolation from neighboring stations in adjoining counties it is possible to estimate in a qualitative way most of the climate parameters.

WEST POINT - This long-term weather station has the distinction of being one of the oldest in the United States. The earliest temperature readings date back to 1819 from the Post Hospital of the fledgling military academy, when readings were taken daily from one thermometer at 7 AM, 2 PM and 9 PM. In 1840, precipitation readings were monitored concurrently with temperature.

Following the Civil War when no readings were taken for about four years, a minimum/ maximum thermometer was employed along with the previous temperature determination. During the Civil War years and from 1900 through 1904 no readings were taken. In the 1870s and 1880s there were many months with missing data. For climate change studies this missing data has had to be extrapolated from other nearest stations. The present minimum/maximum thermometer has been employed through the 20th century to the present and daily readings are monitored by engineering and maintenance employees of the military academy. In 1946, the station was relocated it present courtyard site westward from an elevation of 167 feet to that of 360 feet. This location with the thermometer shelter on a concrete slab and bounded on three sides by a stone building has resulted in temperature readings significantly higher than what is expected in the surrounding area. Extreme high temperatures are suspect and monthly mean temperatures have had to be adjusted to reflect this disparity. Temperature readings are also adjusted for the Time of Observation Bias that results when readings are taken at times other than at midnight.

Other local weather stations that monitor temperature and precipitation are presently maintained by members of the Hudson Valley Weather Observers. In WHITE PLAINS, John Drohan and in CARMEL, Harold Schaefer have faithfully taken daily readings for many years.

DISCONTINUED STATIONS

ARDENIA (Garrison) - This Putnam County site at an elevation of 157 feet above sea level had precipitation monitored by Thomas B. Arden from 1854 through 1887, then by Richard R. Arden, except for sixteen months during the Civil War beginning 1862. Daily temperature readings were taken from 1864 through July 1890 less the years 1884 to 1887. This station provides the earliest climate information for Putnam County.

BEAR MOUNTAIN - Readings of temperature and precipitation were taken here from 1948 to 1953 and are published in Climatological Data - New York

GARNERVILLE - This Rockland County, U.S. Weather Service Cooperative Station took daily readings for eight years in the 1980s. Published data are in Climatological Data - New York. The observer was Reverend Robert Duane.

NORTH SALEM - This oldest Westchester weather station (elevation 361 feet) was part of the network of weather monitoring stations set up in 1826 by the New York State Regents, at sundry Academies (the first in the United States). For 19 years during the period from 1829 to 1850 (less 1836, 1837 and 1839) temperature, precipitation , cloud cover and wind direction were monitored. Temperatures are also available for the period of 1851 to 1860. There were five teacher observers during this period with John F. Jenkins who was Principal of the Academy, the one who did most of the observations. These were the first systematic weather observations in Westchester County.

Note: All 19th century temperature readings till about 1880 were taken on one thermometer three or four times a day.

MOUNT PLEASANT - This site, at an elevation of 125 feet, also part of the New York State Regents Academies, with standardized equipment, took daily readings of temperature and precipitation in the same manner as North Salem from 1831 through 1844 (less 1833 and 1836). There were six teacher observers during the period of observation with Albert Wells, Principal, the main observer.

WEST NYACK - This Rockland County, U.S. Weather Service Cooperative Station was maintained for nine years in the 1990s by Dr. Mitchell Mayers. Data is published in the Climatological Data - New York periodical.

WHITE PLAINS - From 1853 to 1860 this site was part of the New York State Regents Academy network, monitoring temperature, precipitation, cloud cover and wind direction. In May 1862, Dr. Oliver R. Willis as part of the Smithsonian Institution network began his 31 years of daily temperature observations . It is not known if the site of his station (elevation 100 feet) was the same as that of the Regents. During his 31 years of observations there were only a dozen months with missing data. Precipitation readings began in 1873 and continued through 1891. Nothing is known as to the siting of his instrumentation.

MOUNT HOPE - Located in the town of Greenburgh at an elevation of 200 feet above sea level, precipitation was monitored from 1897 to 1929 and daily temperature readings begun in 1900. The station was part of the Weather Bureau cooperative observer network.

MOUNT VERNON - Daily precipitation and temperature readings were taken at this location (elevation 155 feet) near Eastchester, at 39 E. 4th St. in a residential section, from 1915 through 1941 as part of the Weather Bureau cooperative observer network.

OSSINING - From 1941 through 1973, daily temperature and precipitation readings were taken at the Sing Sing prison (25 feet elevation) as part of the United States Weather Bureau (USWB) cooperative observer network.

SHRUB OAK - Daily temperature, rain and snow readings were taken by employees of the Yorktown Water Department from 1950 to 1969 at the pumping station (elevation 430 feet). As with all the USWB cooperative stations, this data is published in the periodical Climatological Data - New York

CHAPPAQUA - From 1956 to 1974 daily temperature readings were taken.

TARRYTOWN - Precipitation monitored through the Smithsonian Institution network from 1860 through April 1872 (elevation 152 feet) and from 1920 to 1976 by the Tarrytown Water Department (Unpublished).

YONKERS - Precipitation was monitored by the Water Department from 1878 to 1943.

BEDFORD HILLS - This long-term temperature and precipitation station operated from 1894 to early 1977 and was part of USWB cooperative observer network. The station location (elevation 425 feet)

higher than much of the surrounding area, for most of its history was sited at the Montefiore Hospital, later converting to the Hillcrest Center for Children and was operated by New York City. Multi-story buildings lay on one side of the weather station blocking air flow and shading the station for part of the day. The station was moved 250 feet northward to an improved site in 1972 but still did not conform to all Weather Service specifications. The overall effect on temperature and snowfall measurements by the previous and the subsequent station location was to increase the temperature and thus reduce snowfall depths. The temperature increase would be greater in the cold months of the year when the cooling effects of wind at this higher elevation would be offset by the heating of the complex of buildings. This would raise the temperature of the immediate area where the thermometer shelter is located. Despite these imperfections, this station represents local suburbs or villages in this part of northern Westchester. It provides a useful climate portrait with its many years of 30 year monthly and annual temperature and precipitation averages and departures from normal.

SCARSDALE - This USWB cooperative observer station was operated from 1904 to 1942 by C.H. Wilmarth and subsequently by the Village of Scarsdale to 1990. The station location 270 feet above sea level was changed in 1943 to that of the locale of the Scarsdale Municipal building at 200 feel elevation, a move about 0.6 miles to the south-south west. This move probably caused warmer winter temperatures. A 1976 station relocation a few hundred feet away, close to an expanded parking area would have also raised temperatures for most of the year. In the last two decades of this station's operation it's continuity of daily reporting has declined with many days of weekend readings not taken. In view of the effect of the location changes this station climate cannot truly be representative of the non-urbanized local region. It is more representative of the many urban areas that are located in southern Westchester. It's record and many 30 year averages shows the effects of the increased 20th century urbanization.

INSTRUMENTATION AND MEASUREMENT

While measurements of rainfall have been made since antiquity, it was not until the invention of the practical mercury thermometer in the early 1700s, that exact measurements of temperature became possible. The few thermometers that were available in colonial America were located at colleges such as Yale and Harvard. By the start of the 19th century, mercury thermometers were more available. In New York by the late 1820s uniform rain gauges and thermometers were assigned by the New York State Regents to various teaching academies throughout the state to monitor these elements daily. This was the first network in this country of weather measuring stations.

TEMPERATURE -

From the 1830s to about 1880 readings were taken from one thermometer three or four times each day. Readings at sunrise and sunset and at 2 or 3PM were among a number of specified times. It was assumed that sometime about sunrise and about 2 PM had the coldest and warmest temperatures of the day. Sometimes readings two hours after sunset were also taken. An average or specific formula was used to arrive at the average temperature of the day. Some time in the 1870s, minimum and maximum thermometers made their appearance and for a period of about ten years two methods of determining a day's average temperature were employed. By the 1890s multiple readings on one thermometer were terminated and the present convention adopted using the minimum and maximum thermometers. The high and low temperature of the day are added together and divided by two, giving the days average or mean temperature. In 1890 a cooperative observer network of data collecting stations was set up by the Weather Bureau of the U.S. Agriculture Department at that time, primarily for agricultural purposes. The thermometers were housed in a standard white slatted box (known as the Cotton Shelter), measuring about three by three by two feet and placed about three feet above ground. Temperature readings of minimum, maximum and at observation time are taken once a day and thermometers are reset at that time.

The placement of the thermometers four to five feet above ground level means that at many times there will be a difference between the surface level temperature and that of the thermometer located above. In fact government publications define a "freeze" as "an observation of 32°F on a thermometer in a standard shelter five feet above the ground." There are many days during the winter season when ground level temperatures are two or three degrees colder than five feet above ground level.

For climatological research on temperature, the 19th century temperatures have had to be adjusted for the present method of daily mean determination. In addition, mean monthly temperatures also need to be corrected for the "time of observation bias," since any readings taken other than at midnight do not result in a true monthly average. Since about 1990, the National Weather Service has replaced about 3000 of its older thermometers with a Minimum, Maximum Thermometer System that records the high and low temperatures electronically so that the observer is not required to go out to the shelter.

PRECIPITATION -

Because of the simplicity of equipment and the requirement of less than regular daily measurements, there have always been more gauges monitoring precipitation than thermometers recording temperature. In the 19th century differently shaped buckets or containers were employed.

The 20th century standard used at present by the National Weather Service employs an eight inch diameter, two foot high cylinder, with an over topping funnel that directs water into a narrower 2.5 inch diameter internal cylinder. This allows for measurements of as little as one-one hundred of an inch. In winter the inner cylinder and funnel is removed so that snow and frozen precipitation can be collected in the eight inch diameter opening. In the latter part of the 20th century recording rain gauges have been introduced allowing measurements of precipitation to be made every fifteen minutes. About six such gauges are presently in operation in Westchester, three of which have their measurements published in Hourly Precipitation Data - New York (Dobbs Ferry/Ardsley, Pleasantville and Yorktown Heights).

Automated snowfall measurements are now also possible. However snow depth on the ground in the days after the snow has fallen is still a daily measurement that can only be performed by a human being. New snow collected in the standard rain gauge is melted down after each snowfall so that its water equivalent can be obtained. While the water equivalent of snow is normally a ten to one ratio (ten inches of snow is the equivalent to one inch of water) this ratio can vary greatly depending on the character of the snow. The water equivalent of sleet will be very different than that of light fluffy flakes.

THE 20th CENTURY DAILY WEATHER WATCHERS

WESTCHESTER COUNTY

KENSICO RESERVOIR - 1884 to present - Rain gauge monitored by employees of the New York City Department of Environmental Protection

BEDFORD HILLS - About 1910 to 1914 - Dr. L. Rosenberg, 1915 to 1917 - Dr. Louis Shalet, 1918 to 1925 - Dr. B. Stivelman, 1926 - Dr. Casper Folkoff; 1927 to 1941- Dr. Arnold Shamaskin, 1942 to 1947- Albert Lasky, 1948 to 1970 - employees of the Montifiore Hospital, 1970 to 1977 - Kenneth Smith

SCARSDALE - 1904 to 1942 -C.H.Wilmarth, 1943 to 1945 -Arthur Boniface, 1946 to 1990 - Scarsdale Village Manager and employees

MOUNT HOPE - 1897 to 1929 - William A. Cornelius

MOUNT VERNON - 1915 to 1941 - J.W. Redway

OSSINING - 1941 to 1973 - Employees and/or inmates of Sing Sing Prison

PEEKSKILL - 1946-present. Current observers (see Figure 32)

YORKTOWN HEIGHTS - 1940 to 1950 - George D. Hancock

DOBBS FERRY/ARDSLEY - 1945 to 1989 - J. Henry Weber, 1989 to 1997 - Rev. Robert Duane, 1997 to present - John Clear (see Figure 32)

GRANITE SPRINGS

1998 - Stuart's Fruit Farm, Betsy and Robert Stuart (see Figure 32)

SHRUB OAK - 1950 to1969 - George D. Hancock

WESTCHESTER AIRPORT - 1949 to present - airport employees (see Figure 33)

YORKTOWN HEIGHTS 1W- 1964 to present - Jerome S. Thaler (see Figure 33)

CROTON WATERSHED RAIN GAUGES - 1903 to present - Five rain gauges in operation, (one dating back to the mid 19th century) maintained by employees of the New York City Department of Environmental Protection. (See Figure 33)

PUTNAM COUNTY

CARMEL - Observers unknown before 1910; 1910 to 1925 - Thomas Manning, 1926 to 1928 - Andrew Gridley, 1929 to 1941 - Ernest Burke, 1941 to 1949 - James Potter, 1950 to 1980 - James Stevens and Anthony Farina, all employees of the New York City Water Department

CROTON WATERSHED RAIN GAUGES - Four rain gauges currently in operation, three since the late 19th century, all serviced by employees of the New York City Department of Environmental Protection. (See Figure 33).

ROCKLAND COUNTY
SUFFERN

Observers were John D. Gallagher Jr from July 1940 through January 1941, George W. Sutherland from July 1941 through July 1947, Alfred Gruenwald in August 1949 and Neil L. Abell from October 1949 through December 1952. Employees of the Suffern Water Works monitored the station from 1956 through 1999.

ORANGE COUNTY

WEST POINT - Staff, cadets and employees of the U.S. Military Academy have taken daily readings during the 19th and 20th century

FIGURE 32

ARDSLEY...
Robert Duane
John Clear

GRANITE SPRINGS...
Betsy & Robert Stuart

PEEKSKILL...(L to R) • Steve Weigel • Arthur Morin • Glenn Allen
• Edward Khuns III • Not in picture: Vince Powell

FIGURE 33

CROTON WATERSHED: DEPT OF ENVIRONMENTAL PROTECTION...
(L to R) • Karen Oliviero • David Alderisio • Lori DiLorenzo • Christopher
Richie • Stephen McCaffrey • Michael Cassar • Paul Thiesing • Stacey Rabe

WESTCHESTER AIRPORT...
(L to R) • Gary Falk • Dogan Tekben • John Kastens • Scott Mealey
• John Starace • Not in Picture: Doug Byrne

YORKTOWN HEIGHTS...
Jerome S. Thaler

TABLE 33

Latitude 40° 59'N
Longitude 73° 48'W
Elevation 200 feet

CLIMATE SUMMARY
SCARSDALE
TEMPERATURE (°F)

Month	Means 1961 - 1990 Average Daily Maximum	Average Daily Minimum	Monthly Average	Extremes 1904 - 1990 Daily Hottest	Year	Daily Coldest	Year	1961 - 1990 Average Heating Degree Days
January	37.6	19.7	28.7	73	1950	-12	1948	1125
February	40.9	22.1	31.5	75	1985	-18	1934	938
March	50.3	29.4	39.9	88	1945	- 3	1967	778
April	61.8	38.5	50.2	94	1976	10	1923	444
May	72.9	47.8	60.4	99	1938	26	1907	174
June	81.1	56.8	69.0	100	1953	38	1979	13
July	85.7	62.5	74.1	105	1936	45	1945	0
August	83.7	61.5	72.6	104	1918	39	1965	0
September	76.2	53.8	65.0	102	1929	29	1904	82
October	65.5	42.8	54.2	92	1941	21	1976	346
November	54.3	35.4	44.9	84	1950	8	1938	603
December	42.1	25.5	33.8	70	1946	-16	1917	967
Annual	62.7	41.3	52.0					5470

AVERAGE NUMBER OF DAYS

	Maximum 90° and above	32° and below	Minimum 32° and below	0 and below	Cooling Degree Day Normals
January		9.4	27.5	1.3	
February		4.7	23.5	.5	
March		.5	20.4		
April					
May	1.0				32
June	3.4				133
July	8.2				282
August	4.3				239
September	1.5				82
October			4.1		11
November			11.2		
December		4.8	24.5		

PRECIPITATION
(Inches)

	1961-1990 Average	Greatest Daily	1904-1990 Year	Average # Days Pptn. .10 or more	Average	SNOW 1904-1990 Maximum Monthly	Year	Greatest Daily	Year
January	3.20	3.20	1979	7	8.2	36	1923	24	1905
February	3.07	2.50	1941	6	10.4	38	1934	24	1969
March	3.89	4.10	1953	8	4.8	39	1958	18	1960
April	4.09	4.00	1980	7	.6	14	1915	14	1915
May	4.25	5.76	1946	8					
June	3.60	4.25	1972	6					
July	4.11	5.30	1942	7					
August	4.10	5.50	1909	6					
September	3.92	6.55	1938	6					
October	3.58	4.38	1955	5		5	1962	5	1962
November	4.30	4.83	1977	7	.8	18	1938	11	1938
December	3.90	4.00	1909	7	5.7	30	1947	28	1947
Annual	46.01				30.5				

TABLE 34

CLIMATE SUMMARY
CARMEL / YORKTOWN HEIGHTS

Latitude 41º 16N
Longitude 73º48W
Elevation 670 feet

TEMPERATURE (0 F)

Month	Means 1961 - 1990			Extremes 1888-1999				1961 - 1990
	Average Daily Maximum	Average Daily Minimum	Monthly Average	Daily Hottest	Year	Daily Coldest	Year	Average Heating Degree Days
January	33.6	15.8	24.7	68	1932	-24	1961	1216
February	36.6	17.5	27.0	73	1985	-24	1934	1045
March	46.5	26.9	36.7	86	1998	-14	1916	860
April	58.2	36.9	47.6	93	1976	6	1923	502
May	69.3	46.8	58.1	97	1939	24	1947	217
June	77.5	55.5	66.5	99	1952	33	1945	49
July	82.4	60.7	71.6	103	1936	41	1963	7
August	80.7	59.3	70.0	102	1948	35	1940	16
September	73.6	52.1	62.9	103	1953	28	1947	114
October	62.9	41.3	52.1	90	1939	16	1936	387
November	50.9	33.5	42.2	81	1950	5	1938	669
December	38.2	22.3	30.3	73	1998	-19	1917	1063
Annual	59.2	39.0	49.1					6145

AVERAGE NUMBER OF DAYS

	Maximum		Minimum		Cooling Degree Day Normals
	90º and above	32º and below	32º and below	0 and below	
January		13.8	28	2.8	
February		10.0	25	2.0	
March		2.2	23		
April			9		
May	.5		1		25
June	1.7				100
July	4.5				225
August	2.0				175
September	1.0				50
October			5		
November			15		
December		9.0	27	.5	

PRECIPITATION
(Inches)

	1961-1990	1888-1999		Average # Days Pptn. .10 or more	SNOW 1896-1998			Greatest	
	Greatest Average	Daily	Year		Average	Maximum Monthly	Year	Daily	Year
January	3.50	3.33	1979	7	11.1	35	1923	17	1961
February	3.32	3.37	1900	6	11.6	47	1893	25	1983
March	3.82	3.44	1919	7	7.0	32	1967	14	1993
April	4.26	3.60	1987	8	1.4	18	1997	17	1997
May	4.73	5.57	1900	8		2	1977	2	1977
June	3.78	4.30	1969	7					
July	4.39	5.03	1897	7					
August	4.54	6.86	1971	6					
September	4.08	11.00	1999	6					
October	3.74	6.77	1955	5	.5	6	1962	4	1962
November	4.36	3.47	1947	7	2.0	18	1898	8	1898
December	3.83	3.29	1941	8	8.3	30	1947	26	1947
Annual	48.35				41.9				

Seasonal Maximum 104" 1995-96
Seasonal Minimum 12" 1988-89

TABLE 35

CLIMATE SUMMARY
SUFFERN

Latitude 41º7'N
Longitude 74 09' W
Elevation 270 feet

TEMPERATURE (º F)

	Means 1961 - 1990	Extremes 1940 - 1999		1961 - 1990								
Month	Average Daily Maximum	Average Daily Minimum	Monthly Average	Hottest Month	Coldest Month		Daily Hottest		Year	Daily Coldest	Year	Heating Degree Days
January	35.4	17.4	26.4	35.3	1990	18.0	1994	67	1967	-16	1961	
February	38.0	19.4	28.7	37.3	1998	18.0	1994	74	1954	-17	1943	
March	47.4	27.8	37.6	48.4	1945	28.5	1960	84	1945	0	1943	
April	58.2	38.2	48.2	53.2	1945	43.5	1943	90	1962	12	1954	
May	69.4	48.4	58.4	65.3	1991	50.7	1967	97	1962	27	1966	
June	77.0	57.0	67.0	71.3	1943	62.0	1958	101	1952	38	1957	
July	83.2	61.2	72.2	76.6	1955	67.8	1962	102	1966	43	1940	
August	81.0	59.8	70.4	74.3	1955	66.3	1963	100	1953	34	1940	
September	74.0	52.4	63.2	69.2	1961	57.5	1963	104	1953	27	1963	
October	62.0	42.0	52.0	58.0	1971	48.2	1988	92	1941	15	1940	
November	51.7	33.7	42.7	45.1	1990	36.8	1967	82	1950	9	1958	
December	41.7	21.7	31.7	37.6	1990	20.2	1989	70	1946	-10	1942	
Annual												6067

*Estimated - years 1983, 1984, 1985, 1986 are missing

PRECIPITATION
(Inches)

	Means* 1961 - 1990	Wettest Month		Driest Month		Greatest Daily		Average	SNOW Greatest Month		Greatest Daily	
January	3.26	9.48	1979	30	1970	2.64	21/1979	8	35.5	1996	2.70	1996
February	3.16	7.99	1981	.98	1968	2.56	8/1965	11	22.0	1994	14.0	1947
March	3.83	8.80	1980	.54	1981	4.00	22/1980	6	26.0	1960	6.0	1947
April	4.61	10.57	1980	1.10	1963	3.00	29/1980	1	10.0	1944	10.0	1944
May	4.96	12.40	1989	.38	1964	4.00	30/1968					
June	4.05	10.06	1972	1.02	1988	2.70	16/1969					
July	4.40	18.08	1945	.91	1998	3.21	18/1945					
August	4.55	15.68	1955	1.01	1981	8.40	28/1971					
September	4.45	10.09	1975	.38	1941	5.00	12/1971					
October	3.90	12.00	1955	.80	1963	2.75	9/1965					
November	4.53	9.78	1972	.37	1976	5.52	9/1972	1	4.0	1951	4.0	1951
December	3.62	9.66	1973	.43	1980	2.40	24/1941	6	31.0	1947	22.0	1947
Annual	49.32							33				

*Estimated - Some years and months missing

TABLE 36

CLIMATE SUMMARY
WEST POINT (1821 - 2000)

Latitude 41º 23'N
Longitude 730 58' W
Elevation 320 feet

TEMPERATURE (ºF)

	Means* Means Extremes 1961 - 1990	Average	Average		Extremes				
Heating									
Month	Daily Maximum	Daily Minimum	Monthly Average	Hottest Months	Coldest Months	Daily Hottest Date	Daily Coldest Date	Degree Days
January	33.8	17.8	25.8	38.1 1932	17.3 1888	71 26/1950	-11 19/1948	1169
February	36.9	18.9	27.9	37.5 1976	15.6 1934	70 16/1954	-15 1/1920	999
March	47.6	27.6	37.6	46.2 1946	26.3 1843	86 28/1945	-10 7/1911	793
April	58.6	36.6	47.6	54.2 1878	39.5 1874	93 19/1896	12 2/1923	442
May	69.4	47.4	58.4	64.6 1872	51.4 1917	97 19/1962	30 10/1966	157
June	78.0	65.0	74.5	75.0 1830	62.3 1927	102 6/1925	39 18/1908	21
July	82.4	60.4	71.4	78.6 1876	67.9 1996	104 4/1911	47 1/1899	1
August	81.5	59.5	70.5	75.7 1876	64.7 1982	105 7/1931	41 29/1899	5
September	73.2	53.2	63.2	70.0 1961	59.1 1899	105 2/1953	28 29/1909	74
October	62.6	42.6	52.6	59.0 1971	44.0 1888	92 5/1941	20 31/1897	332
November	50.0	33.6	41.8	47.7 1931	34.2 1901	82 1/1950	10 27/1932	630
December	37.2	23.2	30.2	38.0 1923	18.5 1989	67 10/1946	-16 30/1917	1030
Annual			49.4	51.9 1991	46.2 1904			5653

*Averages have been corrected for urbanization effects and for three different times of readings during this period

PRECIPITATION
(Inches)

	Means (1961 - 1990	Wettest Month	Driest Month	Greatest Daily		Average	SNOW Greatest Month	Least Month	Greatest
January	3.35	11.64 1996	.45 1970	3.78	19/1996	10.7	35.9 1961	1.0 1998	12 20/1961
February	3.37	8.58 1981	.63 1856	2.44	20/1981	11.3	27.3 1961	T 1981	15 14/1914
March	3.69	12.02 1896	.52 1915	3.80	1/1896	5.2	38.7 1967	T 1946	17 20/1958
April	4.05	10.53 1854	.50 1844	3.85	5/1952	.5	11.7 1956		17 20/1958
May	4.69	11.66 1868	.57 1911	3.70	14/1897				11 8/1956
June	4.02	9.56 1972	.76 1873	3.63	1/1952				
July	4.00	13.05 1897	1.04 1894	3.40	28/1922				
August	4.16	11.74 1955	.05 1876	3.22	13/1955				
Sept.	4.00	12.30 1999	17 1846	7.28	17/1999				
October	3.83	12.75 1955	T 1924	4.20	15/1955		T 1952		T 20/1952
Nov.	4.39	10.02 1846	25 1922	4.14	2/1927	1.2	9.8 1938		9 25/1938
Dec.	3.96	11.47 1983	.72 1988	3.89	20/1957	8.6	29.6 1969	T 1954	25 27/1947
Annual	47.51					37.5			

TABLE 37

PREVAILING WIND DIRECTION

	Jan	Feb	Mar	Apr	May	Jun	Jul	Aug	Sep	Oct	Nov	Dec	Annual
Carmel													
	nw	nw	nw	nw	nw	sw	sw	sw	nw	nw	nw	nw	nw
Mount Hope													
	nw	nw	nw	w	w	w	s	s	w	nw	nw	nw	nw
Mount Vernon													
	nw	nw	nw	nw	nw	nw	sw	s	s	nw	nw	nw	nw
West Point													
	nw	nw	nw	nw	nw	sw	sw	sw	nw	nw	nw	nw	nw

APPENDIX A

CORRECTED AVERAGE TEMPERATURES °Fahrenheit
CARMEL / YORKTOWN HEIGHTS

Year	Jan	Feb	Mar	Apr	May	June	July	Aug	Sep	Oct	Nov	Dec	Annual
1888	19.4	26.8	28.4	44.4	57.4	67.3	65.9*	69.4	60.4	45.8	41.2	31.6	46.52
1889	32.2	23.0	38.0	49.8	61.8	68.2	70.8	68.0	63.5	47.8	43.2	35.6	50.17
1890	35.6	36.3	32.8	49.6	59.2	68.3	70.8	70.4	61.4	50.8	38.9	25.4	50.01
1891	29.8	32.3	34.8	50.4	58.6	67.6	66.9	71.2	66.7	49.7	39.2	39.3*	50.55
1892	26.2	28.8	30.8	46.8	58.4	71.5	71.8	69.2	61.4	49.2	37.6	26.9	48.22
1893	18.7	24.8	31.3	46.4	57.3	68.9	71.2	69.6	59.5	51.8	37.9	30.5	47.34
1894	29.4	24.8	39.0	48.3	59.1	70.2	73.4	67.8	66.1	51.8	36.0	30.4	49.69
1895	24.6	20.8	32.3	47.8	59.7	71.2	69.2	70.6	65.7	45.7	43.1	33.6	48.70
1896	23.1	28.4	29.2	51.0	64.4*	66.8	73.0	70.4	62.1	48.9	44.0	26.7	49.00
1897	26.9	28.6	37.0	49.4	59.4	64.9	73.0	67.6	61.8	52.4	39.9	31.7	49.38
1898	27.6	29.9	43.3	46.5	58.3	69.1	73.8	72.6	67.4	54.8	40.4	29.2	51.13
1899	26.4	25.0	34.2	48.6	60.0	71.0	71.4	71.5	62.4	55.0	41.4	34.0	50.07
1900	30.2	28.7	32.1	50.2	60.7	70.0	75.2	74.4	67.5	57.8	44.6	30.8	51.86
1901	27.5	21.7	35.5	49.4	58.1	70.8	75.2	72.0	64.3	52.1	35.5	30.2	49.36
1902	24.8	25.9	41.2	49.0	58.8	65.8	69.6	68.0	62.9	52.1	46.8	27.4	49.36
1903	27.5	30.4	45.4	49.4	61:9	61.7	70.6	63.8	59.9	50.3	36.0	22.9	48.31
1904	15.6*	19.3	32.1	42.9	62.0	66.5	69.2	66.5	60.2	47.1	35.2*	21.7	44.85*
1905	22.3	18.5	34.4	45.1	58.1	64.9	72.6	66.7	61.5	51.0	38.6	32.1	47.15
1906	31.4	25.9	29.5	47.2	58.4	67.4	70.8	71.0	65.3	50.6	39.9	27.0	48.72
1907	25.9	16.7	35.4	42.0	52.2	64.3	72.6	68.6	63.9	45.6	39.7	32.7	46.63
1908	27.3	23.6	36.2	46.9	60.7	69.7	74.4	69.0	64.1	53.1	39.8	28.9	49.48
1909	27.6	31.9	33.9	46.2	57.6	68.6	70.0	66.0	60.4	47.5	42.6	25.6	48.16
1910	25.2	23.8	40.1	50.5	57.5	64.6	72.4	67.1	63.4	54.5	37.1	22.6	48.23
1911	28.2	24.6	32.0	43.7	63.1	64.7	72.4	69.4	62.2	49.9	36.5	34.2	48.41
1912	16.0	21.8	31.1	46.2	59.2	62.9	71.4	66.6	62.8	53.3	41.1	33.3	47.14
1913	35.0	23.1	39.5	47.9	57.1	66.0	71.6	68.2	60.7	55.2	41.3	33.1	49.89
1914	24.0	18.2	30.4	43.1	60.1	63.6	68.2	70.0	62.5	55.1	39.1	27.3	46.81
1915	29.1	31.6	33.1	49.6	55.1	64.3	69.4	66.3	66.4	52.1	40.7	27.0	48.74
1916	29.5	22.0	25.6*	44.4	57.2	60.8*	71.8	70.2	63.3	52.2	39.5	29.2	47.13
1917	26.6	22.9	34.1	44.4	50.1*	65.4	71.5	71.7	59.1	48.1	35.9	18.7*	45.71
1918	16.0	24.3	37.8	46.2	61.6	63.1	69.4	70.7	59.0	53.6	41.3	32.6	47.97
1919	30.5	30.9	38.2	45.3	57.6	68.0	71.0	66.0	62.6	54.6	40.5	24.7	49.17
1920	18.2	23.0	33.5	43.4	55.0	64.8	68.9	70.9	65.0	57.8	39.3	33.7	47.80
1921	27.2	29.7	43.9	52.6	58.7	67.0	73.8	66.5	67.7	52.4	39.5	28.3	50.61
1922	22.3	29.4	36.6	47.3	60.4	67.4	70.4	68.5	64.3	53.4	40.6	28.3	49.08
1923	23.5	19.5	31.5	47.1	55.7	67.6	68.6	67.5	64.2	51.1	40.6	36.5	47.79
1924	28.2	23.0	34.7	44.3	52.8	63.5	68.4	67.5	59.1	50.2	38.8	29.0	46.63
1925	21.8	33.0	38.8	47.3	54.5	71.8*	67.5	67.7	63.3	45.4*	39.1	30.7	48.41
1926	27.7	23.9	30.8	42.6	55.7	61.4	70.9	69.4	60.9	49.5	40.6	24.5	46.49
1927	23.5	31.3	38.6	44.1	54.8	62.0	69.3	63.7*	62.0	54.0	42.9	31.2	48.12
1928	29.0	28.5	33.8	43.7	55.5	62.9	72.3	70.7	59.9	52.7	42.3	33.7	48.75
1929	26.0	26.3	39.9	47.1	58.3	67.4	70.9	66.2	64.2	49.1	41.4	30.4	48.93
1930	28.0	32.9	36.4	44.7	59.0	68.5	70.8	68.2	65.4	50.2	41.9	31.0	49.75
1931	26.0	28.2	36.5	47.5	57.8	65.7	72.6	69.4	65.2	54.8	35.7	28.6	50.57
1932	38.6*	31.6	33.1	44.3	58.7	65.3	69.6	70.0	63.7	54.1	39.1	33.7	50.14
1933	35.3	31.4	34.8	48.1	61.1	68.3	71.6	69.6	64.2	51.6	37.0	27.5	50.04
1934	28.4	13.5*	32.9	46.8	60.4	68.6	72.3	66.5	65.7	49.7	44.7	29.8	48.27
1935	24.4	27.9	38.6	46.3	55.6	65.7	73.3	69.5	59.6	52.6	45.0	26.0	48.71
1936	24.6	20.8	42.5	44.4	58.6	65.5	71.6	71.1	63.6	52.1	37.0	35.5	48.94
1937	35.7	32.3	32.1	46.5	60.4	67.7	71.5	73.2	60.5	50.7	41.5	30.5	50.21
1938	27.0	32.1	40.1	50.4	57.0	66.5	72.0	72.1	59.7	54.6	42.8	32.0	50.52
1939	26.9	33.0	33.7	45.4	61.2	68.2	72.0	73.9	63.5	51.5	38.2	30.7	49.86
1940	21.5	29.5	31.1	43.7	57.8	64.4	71.3	67.5	61.0	48.6	41.4	34.0	47.65

Year	Jan	Feb	Mar	Apr	May	June	July	Aug	Sep	Oct	Nov	Dec	Annual
1941	25.7	27.6	29.5	53.3*	59.1	66.2	71.3	68.0	64.3	54.8	44.1	34.4	49.85
1942	25.7	26.7	38.7	49.5	60.5	66.5	70.5	68.6	61.6	52.7	40.9	24.9	48.81
1943	24.3	26.5	34.8	41.2*	58.7	70.9*	71.7	69.2	61.8	50.4	38.4	25.0	47.75
1944	27.1	26.1	31.1	43.6	62.8	66.3	72.0	71.3	63.6	49.4	40.0	26.6	48.32
1945	18.0	27.3	43.7	52.4	55.0	65.9	70.1	68.5	65.5	50.6	41.8	24.8	48.64
1946	26.7	26.6	45.5*	46.3	57.5	64.3	70.4	66.4	65.1	56.8	45.6	32.3	50.29
1947	30.7	25.2	33.4	46.3	56.4	64.0	71.3	72.1	65.8	58.2	39.0	27.4	49.15
1948	18.2	23.0	35.3	47.8	57.3	64.5	71.8	70.5	64.4	51.6	46.8	32.1	48.61
1949	33.5	33.6	38.4	49.5	58.5	69.0	75.4	71.8	60.6	57.4	41.2	31.5	51.71
1950	35.2	27.4	31.9	44.8	56.2	65.0	69.1	68.4	60.0	55.8	44.2	29.3	48.93
1951	29.5	31.5	37.3	49.3	59.5	65.8	70.3	68.8	62.2	54.0	38.3	32.1	49.88
1952	30.3	31.0	35.5	50.8	55.7	68.0	74.2	69.7	63.0	49.3	42.8	34.0	50.37
1953	31.9	34.8	39.0	48.0	59.6	65.9	71.2	68.7	64.6	54.3	43.3	35.6	51.41
1954	23.9	34.9	38.7	49.8	56.2	67.6	71.0	68.1	61.5	57.6	41.7	31.4	50.21
1955	26.2	29.1	37.2	50.2	61.6	64.5	76.0	74.4*	61.9	54.4	40.8	24.8	50.07
1956	28.1	31.8	32.8	43.7	54.2	67.2	68.8	68.6	60.3	53.0	43.3	34.9	48.89
1957	22.2	32.6	38.0	50.0	57.6	69.6	70.8	67.1	63.9	50.8	44.8	35.1	50.21
1958	26.5	23.6	37.2	48.7	54.4	62.1	71.2	69.5	62.0	50.4	43.3	23.1	47.66
1959	25.5	26.5	36.0	49.3	61.5	66.0	71.8	72.5	66.0	53.5	41.6	32.7	50.23
1960	27.6	32.7	28.8	50.4	57.8	65.6	67.8	69.0	62.1	51.1	43.8	23.0	48.31
1961	18.1	28.0	36.2	44.1	54.0	65.0	70.1	68.8	68.1*	54.2	43.1	29.8	48.28
1962	25.2	25.0	35.8	47.2	57.8	65.7	66.6	66.7	59.6	51.4	38.3	27.2	47.18
1963	23.8	22.0	38.0	49.8	58.1	66.5	72.0	66.9	58.1*	56.2	46.4	24.6	48.52
1964	27.7	25.8	37.8	45.8	61.0	65.2	72.3	66.5	63.9	49.6	44.5	29.8	49.16
1965	22.5	26.0	34.7	44.4	61.4	65.1	69.8	69.8	63.5	50.4	41.5	32.7	48.49
1966	26.1	28.8	37.8	44.9	55.0	68.0	73.5	71.4	61.2	50.9	44.6	30.4	49.39
1967	31.6	24.8	32.6	46.2	51.8	68.3	71.6	69.0	62.0	51.6	38.9	32.6	48.43
1968	21.2	24.5	38.7	51.4	56.0	64.4	72.2	69.6	66.0	55.1	41.7	27.7	49.05
1969	25.8	28.2	34.6	49.9	57.9	66.8	69.7	71.4	63.5	52.2	41.7	27.9	49.15
1970	18.0	27.3	34.5	47.8	59.3	65.8	72.0	71.7	64.6	54.6	44.6	29.8	49.19
1971	21.2	28.9	36.0	45.6	55.4	67.8	71.1	69.7	65.9	58.7*	40.3	35.0	49.64
1972	29.2	25.2	34.5	43.9	60.1	63.7	72.3	69.5	64.6	48.2	38.7	32.8	48.57
1973	30.7	27.1	42.4	49.2	55.3	69.3	71.7	72.3	64.1	55.0	44.0	34.1	51.29
1974	29.0	26.9	37.0	50.7	56.6	64.7	71.0	70.1	61.6	47.9	43.2	33.6	49.37
1975	31.5	31.0	35.6	42.9	62.1	66.7	72.2	69.3	59.4	54.6	47.8*	30.5	50.29
1976	22.2	34.8	39.7	51.8	57.6	69.0	68.8	68.7	61.2	47.6	37.2	24.8	48.62
1977	18.5	29.5	43.0	49.9	61.3	64.9	72.6	70.5	63.8	50.7	44.0	29.2	49.83
1978	24.6	23.0	33.8	46.8	57.0	66.9	70.0	71.2	60.5	50.6	43.2	32.1	48.32
1979	27.0	18.7	40.5	47.1	60.0	65.5	72.6	69.6	63.0	51.0	46.8	33.7	49.62
1980	27.9	25.5	34.8	49.6	61.0	65.4	73.4	73.0	65.6	49.8	38.8	25.1	49.16
1981	19.0	35.1	36.6	50.7	59.9	67.4	72.8	70.2	61.5	48.5	42.1	30.0	49.48
1982	17.8	29.3	35.6	46.0	60.4	63.6	71.8	66.9	62.8	52.0	44.7	36.0	48.91
1983	28.1	31.6	39.4	47.3	56.6	68.6	73.1	71.7	65.9	52.1	43.5	28.6	50.54
1984	23.6	35.1	30.9	46.9	57.8	69.2	71.0	72.2	60.9	55.7	42.6	37.4	50.27
1985	23.0	30.5	40.0	50.2	61.5	63.5	71.3	69.9	64.3	53.2	43.8	28.1	49.94
1986	27.5	26.0	38.9	50.4	61.6	65.4	70.9	67.6	60.9	52.5	39.5	32.9	49.50
1987	26.1	27.1	40.1	49.9	58.6	67.9	73.0	68.2	62.4	48.6	42.5	33.8	49.84
1988	22.7	29.3	38.5	46.7	58.5	67.6	74.4	73.4	61.9	47.6	44.5	29.6	49.56
1989	31.4	29.2	37.2	46.7	58.9	67.7	71.2	69.2	63.4	54.6	41.4	18.7	49.13
1990	35.2	33.6	39.6	47.2	54.7	67.9	72.1	70.3	62.3	56.8	45.4	37.0	51.84
1991	28.4	35.0	40.7	51.9	64.2	69.2	72.9	72.0	62.2	52.8	42.8	34.4	52.21
1992	29.4	31.2	34.4	45.8	58.4	65.3	69.5	67.4	62.4	50.0	40.6	31.6	48.83
1993	30.6	23.8	33.0	48.8	60.7	67.3	74.2	71.7	62.3	50.0	42.0	31.0	49.62
1994	18.7	25.0	35.8	51.0	57.8	69.6	74.3	68.5	61.8	52.1	46.5	36.3	49.78
1995	32.7	27.3	40.6	47.5	56.4	68.1	74.4	72.5	62.0	57.0	38.1	26.5	50.26
1996	24.9	28.3	34.3	47.6	56.2	67.6	69.6	70.3	63.5	51.7	38.5	36.4	49.08
1997	26.6	33.8	37.6	46.8	55.8	67.1	71.7	70.4	63.1	51.5	39.7	33.4	49.78
1998	34.4	36.4*	40.8	50.4	62.2	67.3	72.9	73.0	66.4	53.1	43.3	38.3*	53.19*
1999	28.0	32.3	36.9	49.9	60.0	70.0	77.5*	71.6	65.6	51.0	46.4	34.5	51.98
2000	25.2	32.0	43.0	47.0	59.7	66.4	68.7	68.4	62.4	52.5	41.6	26.1	49.42

APPENDIX B
CORRECTED AVERAGE TEMPERATURES °Fahrenheit
DOBBS FERRY / ARDSLEY

Year	Jan	Feb	Mar	Apr	May	June	July	Aug	Sep	Oct	Nov	Dec	Annual
1945										53.0	43.8	27.0	
1946	29.8	28.0	46.5*	47.5	59.0	67.1	72.7	68.3*	66.5	58.0	47.3	34.4	52.09
1947	33.1	25.8	34.7	47.4	57.8	65.6	73.1	72.9	65.1	59.5	40.2	29.6	50.40
1948	21.6	26.0	38.1	48.1	57.8	66.8	73.2	72.3	66.3	52.5	48.3	33.8	50.40
1949	35.5	37.0	41.0	51.4	60.8	72.0	77.4	74.2	63.4	59.3	43.2	35.6	54.23*
1950	37.8*	28.7	34.3	46.6	58.5	68.4	72.6	70.8	62.6	57.0	46.2	31.7	51.27
1951	33.0	33.7	39.6	51.0	61.4	67.7	73.4	71.5	64.6	55.6	40.2	35.1	52.23
1952	32.3	33.1	37.8	52.4	58.0	71.0	77.0	72.8	65.8	52.2	45.0	35.3	52.72
1953	33.8	36.5	40.6	50.2	61.3	71.2	75.1	72.7	67.5	56.5	46.0	38.3	54.14
1954	27.7	38.1	40.0	52.4	58.0	70.0	74.7	71.7	64.6	59.1	43.1	33.5	52.74
1955	28.0	31.8	39.7	53.2	64.6	67.4	79.0*	76.2	65.1	57.2	42.2	27.0	52.62
1956	29.6	34.1	35.3	46.3	57.5	70.6	72.0	72.3	62.4	55.1	49.1	37.7	51.83
1957	25.6	34.2	39.6	52.4	62.2	73.0*	75.2	70.6	66.7	53.2	46.2	37.1	53.00
1958	28.6	25.4	38.0	51.5	58.2	66.3	75.0	72.4	65.0	52.5	45.8	26.7	50.46
1959	28.8	29.2	38.0	51.7	63.8	69.1	74.5	75.3	68.8	56.8	43.8	35.0	52.90
1960	31.0	34.0	31.5*	53.1	60.4	69.4	72.5	71.8	64.8	54.5	46.8	27.8	51.47
1961	24.3	32.7	38.7	46.4	58.7	69.7	74.1	72.8	71.0*	57.3	45.3	32.4	51.95
1962	29.5	27.7	38.7	50.6	61.4	70.4	72.1	70.5	62.4	55.1	40.0	28.4	50.57
1963	27.2	25.3	39.6	50.3	60.0	69.7	74.1	70.7	61.8*	59.9	49.0	27.5	51.26
1964	32.0	29.0	40.6	48.3	64.4	69.1	74.3	70.8	66.7	53.0	47.6	33.2	52.42
1965	26.5	30.2	36.8	47.7	65.2	69.5	73.2	72.6	67.0	53.2	43.2	36.1	51.77
1966	28.5	31.5	40.2	46.5	57.0	70.5	76.7	74.0	63.5	53.7	46.4	33.2	51.81
1967	34.9	27.6	35.4	48.7	54.2*	70.8	73.5	72.0	64.6	55.0	40.2	35.2	51.01
1968	24.3	26.4	40.9	53.0	57.7	68.2	76.0	73.7	67.8	57.4	44.1	30.9	51.70
1969	24.4	29.6	36.8	52.8	61.7	70.4	72.7	75.0	66.7	55.0	44.0	30.7	51.65
1970	22.9	31.1	36.1	50.2	62.1	69.0	75.4	75.2	68.0	56.7	46.4	32.0	52.09
1971	25.3	32.7	37.8	49.0	58.7	71.4	74.7	73.4	68.5	60.0*	43.0	38.3	52.73
1972	32.6	29.0	37.3	47.7	61.7	66.4	75.3	73.1	67.3	51.2	41.4	35.5	51.54
1973	33.7	30.0	45.0	51.4	57.8	72.0	75.8	75.8	67.4	57.5	46.8	36.0	54.15
1974	32.7	30.1	41.0	54.2*	59.5	68.1	75.5	74.5	65.1	51.3	46.0	36.6	52.88
1975	35.0	34.6	38.3	46.2*	65.0	69.6	75.6	73.0	62.5	57.4	50.1*	34.0	53.44
1976	25.4	38.4*	42.7	54.0	60.0	72.2	73.1	73.5	64.5	51.0*	39.8	28.4	51.92
1977	21.3*	32.0	45.0	52.0	64.2	68.8	76.3	73.5	66.3	52.6	46.0	32.0	52.50
1978	26.0	24.3	36.6	49.5	59.3	69.5	73.2	74.4	63.7	54.0	44.8	35.5	50.89
1979	30.0	21.6*	43.4	49.4	62.4	67.7	75.0	73.3	65.6	53.4	48.8	37.0	52.30
1980	30.5	27.6	37.7	51.7	63.5	68.5	77.2	77.4*	69.5	54.8	42.5	30.0	52.58
1981	23.0	37.1	39.3	53.3	61.8	71.4	76.5	73.5	65.0	52.2	45.3	32.7	52.59
1982	22.4	32.4	28.3	48.2	63.1	67.0	74.7	71.7	66.4	55.7	48.0	39.4	51.44
1983	31.5	33.0	41.8	49.8	58.2	71.4	77.1	75.4	69.4	55.8	46.5	32.7	53.47
1984	26.2	37.8	34.2	49.4	59.6	72.5	73.6	75.8	64.5	59.4	45.0	40.3*	53.19
1985	26.0	33.3	43.1	53.0	63.3	66.7	74.2	73.1	67.6	56.3	46.6	30.7	52.82
1986	31.4	28.4	42.0	51.5	63.3	69.3	73.9	70.5	65.4	55.6	43.1	36.2	52.55
1987	30.0	30.7	43.0	51.5	61.1	71.1	75.4	71.4	65.3	51.7	46.4	37.0	52.88
1988	27.5	32.5	41.5	49.1	59.5	69.5	76.6	76.0	65.0	51.0*	46.8	34.0	52.42
1989	34.9	32.2	40.2	49.2	60.4	70.1	73.3	72.1	66.3	56.3	42.4	21.7*	51.59
1990	36.6	36.5	41.0	49.3	57.2	68.5	73.3	72.0	63.7	58.2	45.6	38.8	53.39
1991	30.4	35.9	41.6	52.0	65.3*	70.3	74.1	73.6	63.2	54.8	44.2	36.5	53.49
1992	32.0	33.4	36.6	46.6	57.8	66.3	70.5	68.7	64.0	51.0*	42.3	34.3	50.29*
1993	32.9	26.9	35.5	49.1	60.6	68.6	75.1	72.7	65.0	51.7	42.8	32.1	51.08
1994	23.0	26.5	36.7	51.0	58.2	71.2	76.1	69.9	63.4	52.0	48.0	37.5	51.12
1995	34.6	28.3	41.8	47.7	58.0	68.3	75.1	73.1	63.7	57.0	40.5	29.3	51.45
1996	27.4	31.2	35.4	48.6	57.7	68.5	71.2	71.6	65.0	53.0	39.7*	38.4	50.64
1997	29.4	37.6	39.1	47.8	58.1	67.3	73.5	70.7	63.4	52.5	41.0	34.5	51.24
1998	37.2	37.4	42.2	50.1	62.0	67.0	74.4	72.7	67.0	54.0	43.5	38.7	53.85
1999	30.9	33.1	40.0	49.8	59.0	70.0	76.5	72.0	66.2	52.7	47.7	36.9	52.90
2000	29.3	34.1	44.1	49.0	60.1	69.6	69.4*	70.6	64.9	54.1	43.2	29.4	51.48

APPENDIX C
AVERAGE TEMPERATURES °Fahrenheit
PEEKSKILL

Year	Jan	Feb	Mar	Apr	May	June	July	Aug	Sep	Oct	Nov	Dec	Annual
1945									52.6	54.0	26.5		
1946	28.7	27.8	46.9*	47.5	58.4	66.6	72.4	68.6	67.2	58.4	46.8	33.4	51.90
1947	31.3	25.9	34.8	46.6	57.4	65.4	73.0	72.8	65.3	59.5	41.0	29.6	50.19
1948	20.2	25.0	32.0	49.1	57.0	67.1	74.4	73.2	66.9	53.6	50.8*	35.1	50.38
1949	34.9	34.9	40.0	51.8	60.4	71.1	77.8	74.8	63.8	60.2*	43.0	34.1	53.86*
1950	35.2	27.0	32.3	46.4	58.2	67.5	71.8	70.8	61.9	57.4	47.0	32.0	50.64
1951	31.4	30.8	38.4	50.6	60.4	66.8	72.5	71.0	63.4	56.2	39.3	33.4	51.18
1952	31.5	32.6	34.9	52.2	56.8	69.2	73.8	71.2	63.6	50.6	43.5	35.8	51.31
1953	33.7	36.0	39.8	50.8	61.2	68.6	73.2	70.1	65.7	55.7	43.8	37.2	52.98
1954	26.2	36.8	38.3	50.6	56.4	67.5	72.6	70.4	63.7	58.9	42.6	31.8	51.32
1955	27.2	29.6	37.4	50.8	61.9	66.2	77.0	74.8	64.2	56.5	40.6	24.6	50.90
1956	27.8	31.5	32.2	43.6	54.4	68.2	69.2	69.2	59.1	52.5	41.4	34.3	48.62
1957	22.4	32.0	37.4	49.6	58.4	70.9	72.0	68.0	64.3	51.4	43.8	34.8	50.42
1958	26.4	23.2	36.3	49.0	54.9	62.6	72.6	70.7	62.4	50.4	42.6	23.8	47.91
1959	29.3	37.6*	34.5	49.5	61.0	67.2	72.3	72.3	66.4	54.9	40.6	32.4	51.50
1960	25.0	31.8	28.9*	50.6	56.4	67.2	71.1	70.1	61.5	51.9	43.0	24.4	48.48
1961	20.6	30.2	35.6	44.3	55.3	67.2	78.1	70.5	67.2	55.3	42.3	30.4	49.75
1962	26.0	25.3	36.6	48.1	46.4*	66.2	69.1*	66.5	60.3	52.8	38.9	24.5	46.72*
1963	24.0	21.7	37.2	47.8	55.7	67.5	71.8	67.6	58.7*	56.8	46.2	23.7	48.22
1964	29.1	26.3	37.2	45.6	60.9	66.3	72.3	68.5	62.1	54.5	40.7	33.9	49.78
1965	22.6	27.5	32.3	42.3	60.7	66.3	71.0	69.5	63.2	48.5	40.2	34.9	48.25
1966	25.4	28.9	37.7	40.9*	54.6	66.0	71.9	72.0	61.0	51.5	44.6	30.9	48.78
1967	33.1	24.5	32.5	45.8	51.4	68.7	69.7	66.4*	62.5	51.3	37.1*	32.7	47.98
1968	22.6	24.4	38.7	49.7	55.3	65.3	72.3	70.4	64.7	54.6	41.8	27.9	48.98
1969	25.9	27.7	35.6	50.5	58.6	60.4*	69.9	71.6	63.4	54.6	41.1	27.7	48.92
1970	19.3	27.5	33.7	47.4	59.5	66.8	70.9	73.0	64.8	55.1	44.5	30.8	49.47
1971	22.1	30.1	34.8	45.2	55.5	67.7	70.7	69.2	66.5	57.4	40.4	33.9	49.46
1972	29.7	25.2	34.4	44.3	63.8	63.9	72.3	69.7	64.2	47.8*	38.3	31.7	48.78
1973	30.4	27.0	42.5	48.6	55.6	69.5	72.7	73.2	64.0	54.6	42.5	33.4	51.17
1974	30.2	29.1	39.6	50.3	57.3	64.5	73.0	73.2	63.7	50.6	44.5	35.9	50.99
1975	34.4	32.5	37.5	46.1	64.0	69.4	74.6	71.4	59.0	54.2	47.4	28.1	51.55
1976	21.0	34.5	39.6	51.8	57.1	70.2	70.1	70.2	62.8	49.6	37.6	24.8	49.12
1977	18.4*	29.2	43.2	50.0	61.6	66.2	74.2	71.2	64.6	51.2	43.6	29.0	50.20
1978	24.0	22.2	33.1	46.5	56.6	67.0	70.8	72.7	61.6	51.4	43.4	32.0	48.44
1979	27.0	19.0*	40.9	47.4	60.2	66.2	72.9	71.4	64.0	51.8	46.8	35.2	50.23
1980	28.8	26.0	36.6	50.6	62.8	66.6	75.8	75.8*	67.0	52.6	40.0	27.2	50.82
1981	21.3	35.9	38.0	52.0	61.3	69.2	76.6	72.6	63.6	50.4	43.7	31.2	51.37
1982	19.5	30.5	40.0	46.9	61.4	64.8	73.4	69.4	65.1	53.3	44.8	36.5	50.47
1983	28.6	31.8	40.5	45.1	56.6	71.2	74.8	73.3	67.6*	52.8	44.0	29.7	51.33
1984	23.0	35.6	32.9	50.1	59.4	71.4*	72.3	73.7	61.8	57.5	43.8	38.0*	51.62
1985	24.5	32.3	42.0	52.5*	63.0	65.8	72.8	71.6	66.6	54.8	45.3	29.7	51.74
1986	29.7	27.7	40.5	51.4	63.6	67.5	73.3	69.6	63.6	52.8	40.0	34.2	51.15
1987	27.5	29.6	42.0	50.9	58.6	70.2	75.6	70.4	63.4	49.6	43.4	33.9	51.26
1988	24.7	30.9	39.1	47.2	59.8	68.6	76.6	74.3	63.8	48.6	44.6	30.7	50.74
1989	32.5	29.7	38.8	47.6	60.7	70.7	72.8	71.0	64.8	54.4	40.2	19.2*	50.21
1990	36.7*	33.5	41.4	50.8	57.3	69.2	71.8	71.5	61.8	56.6	44.9	36.8	52.69
1991	28.8	35.9	42.9	51.6	64.2*	69.6	73.6	72.3	62.2	55.4	42.7	34.0	52.77
1992	29.0	31.3	35.4	45.3	59.9	66.8	70.0	68.0	62.2	48.5	40.0	30.7	48.92
1993	30.4	24.1	33.0	48.9	60.7	66.7	75.0	71.7	61.6	49.7	41.0	29.7	49.33
1994	17.4	24.2	34.8	51.4	57.3	69.1	75.1	69.1	62.1	51.1	46.4	36.2	49.52
1995	33.2	23.8	41.2	48.1	57.2	68.7	76.0	71.0	63.2	55.6	37.3	26.2	50.12
1996	23.4	27.1	33.8	46.2	55.1	63.8	70.0	71.1	63.8	50.6	39.2	35.3	48.28
1997	25.6	34.3	37.4	47.9	57.1	68.6	72.0	68.9	61.3	50.6	38.1	31.8	49.47
1998	33.2	35.6	41.3	50.5	60.4	65.0	71.0	71.5	64.0	51.5	42.0	37.0	51.92
1999	27.1	30.8	38.8	51.9	61.6	71.2	78.8*	73.1	67.4	53.4	48.2	36.8	49.64
2000	27.2	34.1	44.8	48.7	61.2	69.4	70.8	70.0	62.6	54.1	41.2	27.2	50.94

APPENDIX D

AVERAGE TEMPERATURES °Fahrenheit
WESTCHESTER AIRPORT

Year	Jan	Feb	Mar	Apr	May	June	July	Aug	Sep	Oct	Nov	Dec	Annual
1952				51.8	57.2	70.7	76.2	72.3	65.3	51.4	44.7	34.7	
1953	34.8	35.1	40.0	48.7	59.6	70.0	73.6	71.6	65.4	55.9	45.0	37.0	53.06
1954	26.7	36.8	38.1	50.3	56.6	68.5	72.9	69.4	63.2	58.0	42.4	32.5	51.28
1955	27.4	31.0	40.4	50.3	62.0	66.4	77.1	75.2	64.0	56.3	41.2	26.3	51.47
1956	29.3	33.5	33.3	44.5	55.3	68.7	70.4	71.3	61.2	54.0	42.9	36.8	50.10
1957	24.3	32.7	38.5	50.3	59.7	71.3*	73.6	69.3	66.1	52.8	45.7	36.6	51.74
1958	28.5	24.7	37.4	50.0	56.0	64.5	74.2	72.6	64.3	52.5	44.5	25.6	49.57
1959	27.7	28.2	36.8	50.3	62.8	68.4	73.8	74.9	68.7	56.1	42.8	34.2	52.06
1960	29.9	33.6	30.0*	50.6	59.7	68.9	72.0	72.0	64.3	53.7	45.3	26.9	50.58
1961	22.5	30.1	37.2	46.1	56.5	69.0	74.0	72.3	71.1*	56.9	44.2	31.4	50.94
1962	29.8	26.7	38.4	48.9	60.8	69.0	71.0	70.0	62.1	53.8	39.9	29.5	49.99
1963	24.9	22.7	38.0	49.5	58.8	68.8	74.4	70.7	61.3	58.6	47.5	26.6	50.15
1964	30.2	28.5	38.6	46.1	62.6	67.5	73.5	69.8	65.3	53.3	46.3	32.6	51.19
1965	25.0	29.4	36.1	45.9	64.2	68.6	72.3	72.2	66.9	53.5	42.8	34.7	50.97
1966	29.0	30.2	39.4	46.1	55.8	69.6	76.8	73.3	64.0	54.1	46.2	33.2	51.48
1967	33.8	26.6	33.7	47.5	53.3*	70.2	73.5	71.8	65.9	54.7	39.5	34.5	50.42
1968	23.7	26.5	40.2	52.2	56.9	66.7	75.7	73.2	67.5	57.1	43.3	30.4	51.12
1969	28.3	28.9	35.9	51.4	60.1	69.2	72.1	74.1	66.1	54.9	43.5	30.6	51.26
1970	21.3	29.9	35.3	48.1	60.0	67.8	74.5	75.1	67.8	56.2	45.7	32.4	51.18
1971	24.6	31.0	36.9	46.5	56.6	69.9	73.3	72.7	68.0	60.3*	42.7	37.6	51.68
1972	31.3	26.8	35.7	45.0	59.9	64.7	73.3	70.1	66.8	48.4*	39.2	33.7	49.58
1973	30.7	28.1	42.6	49.4	54.8	69.4	73.3	73.4	64.3	55.1	44.1	34.8	51.67
1974	31.1	27.8	38.4	51.6	58.3	65.2	72.6	71.8	62.4	49.3	44.2	34.6	50.61
1975	32.6	30.9	35.4	43.7*	61.4	67.4	74.4	71.9	60.5*	54.8	48.0	31.1	51.11
1976	23.3	35.0	39.0	50.8	57.0	69.9	70.3	69.9	61.7	48.7	37.4*	25.7	49.06
1977	17.6*	28.2	41.4	48.4	60.1	65.1	72.6	70.8	63.1	50.2	43.9	29.5	49.24
1978	23.3	21.2	33.7	46.7	56.0	65.8	70.3	72.4	59.1	51.2	42.5	33.0	47.93*
1979	27.3	18.9*	40.9	46.0	58.6	63.7*	71.0	69.7	61.4	51.0	45.6	35.0	49.09
1980	27.9	25.5	37.1	50.4	60.2	64.6	74.1	74.0	66.0	52.0	40.5	28.2	50.04
1981	20.7	35.2	36.8	50.0	58.8	67.9	73.3	70.6	62.1	48.9	42.5	31.3	49.82
1982	20.1	32.5	38.2	47.1	61.9	67.2	72.7	67.9*	62.9	52.8	45.8	38.3	50.62
1983	30.0	32.7	42.5	50.9	56.9	70.0	76.4	75.6*	68.2	53.4	45.4	32.4	52.87
1984	26.2	37.9	34.0	48.5	57.8	69.7	72.0	73.9	62.0	57.8	44.1	40.1	52.00
1985	25.0	33.0	42.7	53.1*	62.5	66.9	74.9	73.5	67.7	55.5	45.9	30.3	52.58
1986	29.7	27.6	39.6	50.0	61.7	66.7	71.1	69.0	62.7	52.4	41.0	34.6	50.51
1987	28.8	28.1	39.8	49.3	59.2	69.0	74.4	69.4	63.4	49.3	44.0	35.4	50.84
1988	24.8	31.3	39.4	48.0	60.5	67.7	75.1	73.9	63.0	49.0	44.7	32.1	50.79
1989	33.0	30.0	37.7	47.5	58.4	68.4	72.1	71.4	64.2	54.5	42.9	21.9*	50.17
1990	37.1	35.1	40.6	49.3	56.4	68.1	72.7	72.1	63.0	57.7	45.8	38.5	53.03
1991	29.9	35.9	41.5	52.4	65.1*	70.4	73.4	71.9	62.2	54.2	43.8	35.4	53.01
1992	31.4	32.0	35.6	45.5	56.3	65.8	70.2	69.2	63.5	50.2	42.8	34.0	49.71
1993	32.1	26.0	34.8	48.7	60.5	68.3	75.5	72.9	63.5	51.2	43.1	32.7	50.78
1994	21.3	25.9	37.1	51.0	57.8	70.7	76.0	69.7	63.4	53.6	49.2*	38.5	51.18
1995	35.0	28.1	42.3	47.8	57.5	68.8	76.0	73.7	63.9	57.9	40.8	29.9	51.81
1996	27.5	30.8	36.1	49.2	59.0	69.7	72.4	72.4	64.6	53.2	39.8	38.5	51.10
1997	29.3	38.0	40.4	50.0	57.9	68.7	73.7	70.7	64.2	53.4	42.2	35.5	52.00
1998	37.5*	38.5*	42.4	50.1	62.4	67.8	74.0	74.1	67.9	54.5	45.7	41.4*	54.69*
1999	32.4	35.8	40.4	51.2	60.0	71.3	77.2*	73.6	67.2	53.3	48.0	37.5	53.99
2000	28.6	34.0	44.5*	48.7	60.3	67.5	69.5*	70.9	64.7	55.5	44.6	29.2	51.50

APPENDIX E
AVERAGE TEMPERATURES °Fahrenheit
SUFFERN

Year	Jan	Feb	Mar	Apr	May	June	July	Aug	Sep	Oct	Nov	Dec	Annual
1941							72.5	68.4	65.0	56.1	45.8	34.2	
1942	26.4	26.6	40.1	52.4	62.4	67.3	72.0	68.8	63.5	54.2	42.5	27.0	50.3
1943	26.8	30.2	37.1	43.4*	60.4	71.8	72.3	70.6	62.6	52.0	40.2	28.3	49.6
1944	30.1	29.4	34.8	46.3	64.2	69.2	73.6	73.6	64.2	52.2	41.3	28.4	50.6
1945	21.6	29.8	48.4*	53.2*	56.8	68.4	71.4	70.0	66.5	51.7	43.4	26.2	50.6
1946	29.1	28.8	46.8	47.0	58.5	66.7	72.0	67.2	66.2	57.8	46.6*	33.7	51.7
1947	33.2	26.6	34.6	48.2	58.2	65.2	72.8						
1948													
1949											42.3	33.8	
1950	35.2	27.3	32.4	45.9	56.3	65.6	70.0	68.7	59.0	55.3	43.5	31.2	49.2
1951	31.8	32.0	38.4	49.9	60.6	67.1	72.6	68.7	62.5	53.3	38.5	31.7	50.6
1952	30.3	27.1	31.5			72.6*						31.7	
1953					63.0	70.1	73.7	71.7	66.1	55.9	44.3	36.6*	
1954	26.6	37.0	39.6	51.8	57.4	69.2	71.7	68.8	62.7	57.3	41.9	32.4	51.4
1955	27.4	31.2	38.4	52.4	62.7	66.2	76.6*	74.3					
1956					56.3	68.5	69.7	69.4	59.7	51.8		35.0	
1957	32.9	32.1	37.5	50.0	58.9	71.1	71.0	67.5	62.9	49.6	42.8	33.5	50.0
1958	25.6	23.0	36.0	49.0	54.1	62.0	71.5	69.0	60.7	47.6*	41.3	20.9	46.7*
1959	23.5	27.2	35.1	50.3	62.0	68.2	73.5	73.3	66.4	54.8	41.0	33.1	50.7
1960	28.9	32.6	28.5*	50.9	58.4	67.0	69.7				24.2		
1961	20.5	29.2	35.9	44.5	55.0	67.0	71.4	69.7	69.2*	53.5	42.2	29.4	48.9
1962	25.5	24.2	35.7	47.8	58.6	67.2	67.8*	67.1	58.5	51.5	37.0	27.0	47.3
1963	22.5	20.3	35.6	46.9	55.6	65.8	70.7	66.3*	57.5*	54.7	44.4	23.5	47.0
1964	26.8	25.2	36.5	44.1	60.0	66.7	73.2	68.6	64.8	50.2	44.8	30.6	49.3
1965	24.7	28.0	35.8	45.4	63.1	66.3	69.7	69.2	63.3	48.4	39.9	32.3	48.8
1966	25.7	28.2	37.8	44.2	54.3	68.2	73.5	70.5	60.7	49.9	43.1	30.6	48.9
1967	31.3	23.9	31.9	45.8	50.7*	68.8	70.8	68.7	60.9	50.0	36.8*	32.3	47.7
1968	20.9	24.1	37.8	50.4	54.2	64.3*	72.4	69.7	63.7	53.9	39.9	29.3	48.4
1969	27.4	28.6	34.9	50.5	59.4	68.6	70.8	72.5	64.2	51.8	41.7	28.9	49.9
1970	20.2	28.3	34.7	48.2	60.1	66.5	73.6	72.9	65.3	54.7	44.1	30.9	50.0
1971	23.3	29.4	37.0	46.8	56.4	69.2	71.7	70.1	66.8	58.0*	40.6	36.2	50.5
1972	30.2	26.2	35.4	45.7	60.2	64.4	73.8	69.8	64.2	48.4	39.4	34.7	49.4
1973	31.2	27.7	42.9	50.6	55.9	70.2	73.2	73.2	63.9	54.4	44.1	34.7	51.8
1974	29.3	27.0	38.2	51.7	57.0	65.2	72.0	70.5	61.7	47.9	42.9	34.8	49.8
1975	32.4	32.5	36.1	45.5	62.8	67.0	72.5	68.5	58.9	54.8	46.4	31.3	50.7
1976	22.9	33.6	39.0	51.0	58.5	67.9	68.6	70.0	61.5	48.9	38.5	25.9	48.9
1977	19.4	30.2	43.1	49.5	61.7	66.8	74.0*	71.0	64.9	51.4	45.2	31.0	50.7
1978	25.4	22.3	35.1	48.7	57.8	67.8	70.0	72.0	61.1	50.9	43.5	33.4	49.0
1979	29.1	20.2	42.2	48.8	61.5	66.2	73.0	71.6	63.3	51.7	45.7	34.8	50.8
1980	29.4	27.0	36.3	52.2	63.2	67.0	74.0	75.5*	66.9*	51.1	40.1	27.1	50.8
1981	20.7	34.8	38.2	52.6	61.1	69.3	75.7	72.4	63.3	48.9	44.0	31.7	51.1
1982	19.4	31.2	38.3	49.5		66.1							
1983													
1984													
1985													
1986													
1987	35.0	28.5	40.8	51.0	59.7	69.6	74.7	69.9	63.7	48.5	43.2	35.4	51.6
1988	22.7	28.7	39.5	48.4	59.6	68.4	76.0	74.8	62.8	48.2	43.9	30.5	50.3
1989	32.2	29.0	37.5	47.2	59.4	69.1	71.9	70.4	64.5	54.0	41.5	20.2*	49.7
1990	35.3*	34.2	41.1	49.5	57.1	68.5	73.1	72.0	64.5	57.2	45.1	37.6	50.3
1991	28.5	34.4	41.6	52.1	65.3*	70.6	73.9	73.2	63.3	53.5	43.6	35.5	53.0
1992	30.7	32.2	35.6	46.7	58.6	66.5	70.7	68.2	63.6	49.3	41.5	32.4	49.7
1993	31.9	24.5	34.3	49.2	61.3	68.4	74.6	72.7	63.0	49.7	41.8	31.4	50.2
1994	18.0*	18.0*	34.3	49.9	58.2	70.2	75.2	69.2	62.7				
1995												28.1	
1996	25.5	28.9	33.9	48.2	57.2	68.5	70.0	71.2	64.0	52.4	38.3	36.5	49.6
1997	26.6	35.1	38.5	47.5	55.3	67.4	71.9	69.8	61.9	51.9	40.1	34.2	50.0
1998	35.2	37.3*	41.1	50.8	62.5	66.6	72.6	72.5	65.2	52.7	43.0	39.0	53.2*
1999	28.7	32.9											
Average 1961-90	26.0	28.1	37.6	48.5	58.8	67.4	72.4	70.6	63.2	52.0	42.5	31.4	49.9

APPENDIX F
CORRECTED AVERAGE TEMPERATURES °F
WEST POINT

Year	Jan	Feb	Mar	Apr	May	June	July	Aug	Sep	Oct	Nov	Dec	Annual
1821	22.0	34.8	36.0	40.5	55.6	71.4	73.1	75.6	66.1	53.8	41.0	28.5	49.87
1822	20.5	27.4	31.0	48.0	58.5	72.0	76.0	74.0	66.9	56.2	42.6	31.7	50.40
1823	24.5	19.2	32.0	47.7	58.6	69.0	76.9	74.3	60.2	53.3	38.6	32.4	48.89
1824	31.5	29.0	36.4	51.3	61.0	69.3	77.5	75.0	63.5	52.0	41.7	37.0	52.10
1825	31.5	31.4	44.2	47.2	59.2	73.5	77.0	73.6	61.4	54.0	42.0	30.0	52.04
1826	29.0	31.6	38.6	46.0	65.0	72.2	75.3	73.3	66.4	55.5	43.3	31.5	52.31
1827	22.8	31.3	38.0	51.7	61.8	69.6	73.2	72.5	65.0	53.8	37.3	31.0	50.67
1828	32.8	36.0	38.5	44.0	61.7	73.0	73.0	75.0	64.6	50.0	43.0	37.0	52.38
1829	25.0	22.2	34.3	49.3	64.2	70.0	72.7	71.0	60.0	52.6	41.0	38.0	50.17
1830	27.5	26.4	39.6	53.8	59.5	69.4	76.0	75.0	63.0	50.4	46.0	34.3	51.74
1831	24.0	23.4	40.0	51.4	62.5	75.0*	74.0	74.0	65.2	56.3	40.0	20.0	50.48
1832	27.0	30.0	37.0	47.8	58.7	66.5	72.0	70.4	62.2	52.0	41.0	34.0	49.88
1833	32.6	27.4	34.8	52.0	62.0	66.9	72.7	71.4	62.8	50.0	40.3	33.3	50.52
1834	25.8	35.3	39.0	50.8	58.0	67.4	76.8	73.5	64.8	50.0	40.2	29.8	50.95
1835	26.3	24.8	36.0	46.3	59.6	68.2	74.5	70.8	60.4	53.0	41.0	25.4	48.86
1836	26.7	20.0	31.7	45.3	60.8	66.0	73.6	67.2	62.0	44.0*	37.0	28.7	46.92
1837	21.3	27.0	32.1	45.0	56.5	67.2	71.6	69.4	61.2	50.7	41.5	30.7	47.85
1838	34.2	21.4	38.0	42.2	56.8	72.2	75.8	74.2	64.1	50.0	39.0	26.0	49.49
1839	28.0	27.6	37.0	50.0	58.0	64.0	73.7	67.7	63.7	55.0	38.0	32.0	49.56
1840	22.0	33.0	38.0	50.3	60.4	67.4	74.2	73.5	63.0	53.0	43.0	28.4	50.52
1841	29.0	25.2	35.7	45.3	58.0	71.9	73.9	72.1	66.8	45.4	38.4	34.5	49.68
1842	30.0	35.0	40.0	52.0	59.2	67.1	74.8	70.2	63.4	50.0	36.0	29.0	50.56
1843	32.7	20.6	26.3*	46.7	59.0	71.0	73.0	71.5	66.1	48.2	35.8	29.5	48.38
1844	18.7	25.2	35.5	52.5	61.7	67.5	71.5	68.8	62.2	49.2	38.7	29.4	48.39
1845	27.8	27.4	39.1	47.6	57.8	69.2	74.5	74.2	61.4	52.0	42.7	23.4	49.76
1846	26.8	22.8	36.8	49.5	60.2	67.4	72.2	72.3	68.7	50.7	44.7	30.0	50.12
1847	28.1	27.4	31.9	44.7	58.4	64.9	75.5	72.7	63.0	50.0	43.8	35.0	49.62
1848	31.7	28.0	34.0	48.0	60.8	68.6	71.3	71.1	61.1	50.6	36.8	35.5	49.79
1849	23.3	21.0	36.8	45.7	55.4	67.6	72.0	69.2	61.4	50.0	47.0	30.7	48.34
1850	30.0	32.0	35.0	44.1	53.5	68.6	73.0	68.4	61.3	51.3	42.3	28.7	49.02
1851	28.7	31.5	38.0	46.3	57.1	65.6	71.7	68.3	63.3	52.3	38.0	24.3	48.75
1852	21.0	28.0	33.0	42.0	58.4	68.4	73.0	67.5	61.4	53.0	39.4	35.8	48.41
1853	25.6	29.0	38.1	48.3	59.9	69.2	70.9	71.1	64.4	50.0	40.8	29.7	49.75
1854	27.3	26.6	36.0	45.4	60.6	68.2	75.7	72.5	63.8	53.0	41.8	24.8	49.64
1855	30.3	22.0	34.3	46.0	60.0	68.4	73.5	71.6	64.8	52.7	44.4	35.0	50.25
1856	21.6	25.2	32.6	50.0	58.0	69.6	76.7	70.5	64.8	51.0	41.0	29.5	49.21
1857	18.6	32.0	33.0	44.0	59.0	67.4	74.4	72.2	63.6	51.2	40.0	34.0	49.15
1858	33.6	20.0	34.0	46.0	54.0	72.0	72.0	70.0	63.0	52.0	38.0	30.0	48.72
1859	26.0	30.0	40.0	48.0	61.0	67.0	72.0	71.0	62.0	53.4	43.0	27.0	50.03
1860	27.0	26.0	39.0	46.0	60.0	70.0	74.0	73.0	63.0	54.6	44.7	29.6	50.58
1861	24.0	30.0	34.0	49.0	57.0	71.0	74.0	70.8	65.6	57.0	40.0	30.0	50.20
1862	26.0	24.0	32.0	47.0	61.0	67.7	74.0	73.0	66.3	54.0	39.0	33.0	49.75
1863	31.2	28.6	32.0	49.0	61.0	68.0	75.3	74.0	61.0	52.8	44.0	30.0	50.58
1864	29.7	31.4	36.2	42.4	64.4	70.0	73.0	75.0	62.0	50.0	44.0	32.0	50.84
1865	20.0	26.0	40.0	51.8	62.0	74.0	74.6	72.0	69.4	50.0	42.0	33.8	51.30
1866	21.0	28.0	33.4	52.0	59.7	70.6	72.0	67.0	64.8	54.0	42.2	30.6	49.61
1867	20.0	32.0	33.0	47.8	58.4	71.6	73.0	73.0	65.0	52.0	41.0	25.0	49.32
1868	22.0	19.0	34.0	45.0	56.8	69.0	77.0	74.5	64.3	48.0	40.0	25.0	47.88
1869	28.0	30.0	29.0	47.0	59.0	73.7	72.5	71.0	64.0	50.0	40.0	30.0	49.52
1870	32.0	26.0	30.0	49.0	60.0	73.0	75.0	74.0	65.0	54.0	42.0	31.0	50.92
1871	27.3	28.9	43.0	53.6	63.8	68.0	72.0	73.0	62.0	54.0	35.0	27.3	50.66
1872	28.0	29.6	29.9	52.0	64.6*	73.2	77.3	74.0	66.0	52.7	39.7	24.1	50.94
1873	22.4	25.5	32.4	45.5	57.7	70.1	74.7	70.8	64.2	52.6	34.2*	31.6	48.48
1874	29.4	25.8	35.4	39.5*	59.8	71.5	73.9	70.0	67.2	53.8	40.3	29.7	49.69
1875	20.2	18.8	29.0	41.5	60.0	69.7	72.6	71.6	63.4	50.7	36.0	29.6	46.92

Year	Jan	Feb	Mar	Apr	May	June	July	Aug	Sep	Oct	Nov	Dec	Annual
1876	32.2	28.1	33.0	46.7	60.0	74.7	78.6	75.7	63.2	49.0	43.2	21.3	50.48
1877	22.9	33.0	34.8	49.4	62.4	71.6	75.9	75.2	67.6	56.3	44.2	34.9	52.35
1878	28.3	29.1	42.6	54.2*	59.6	67.4	76.7	73.4	67.6	57.0	42.1	30.7	52.39
1879	20.6	22.3	33.4	44.5	61.4	69.6	73.5	70.6	62.8	58.0	40.0	31.7	49.03
1880	34.8	32.2	34.0	48.7	65.0	71.0	73.0	70.0	66.2	52.0	37.6	23.0	50.63
1881	20.5	23.5	35.0	47.0	61.6	66.2	71.9	72.2	70.0	53.1	39.4	36.0	49.70
1882	25.0	29.0	37.0	46.0	55.5	69.2	71.8	71.2	66.7	53.5	36.0	28.0	49.08
1883	22.0	27.0	29.0	47.0	59.5	72.2	72.0	68.2	61.3	49.5	40.0	30.0	48.12
1884	21.0	30.0	34.0	46.3	58.2	69.4	69.7	71.2	67.8	53.0	41.4	31.4	49.45
1885	27.4	17.7	26.7	46.4	56.4	67.9	74.2	69.0	63.9	53.5	42.1	32.4	48.13
1886	23.7	24.8	35.6	50.9	59.1	66.1	72.6	71.1	66.2	55.3	42.8	25.8	49.50
1887	24.0	28.3	30.9	44.5	64.0	66.9	74.8	68.4	60.3	51.3	41.0	30.2	48.72
1888	17.5	22.6	28.4	46.0	56.7	69.0	71.2	70.6	61.3	44.0*	41.6	30.3	46.58
1889	30.8	22.5	36.6	46.7	59.9	65.7	69.9	68.0	62.3	47.3	43.2	34.9	48.98
1890	32.5	32.2	30.5	44.5	55.2	66.3	68.9	68.5	60.9	46.0	35.8	20.0	46.78
1891	29.8	32.0	34.0	48.3	56.8	67.6	69.0	68.0	67.0	47.5	38.6	38.0	49.72
1892	26.0	28.0	30.0	47.5	55.2	68.5	71.7	69.4	61.9	51.1	39.0	28.4	48.06
1893	18.4	25.0	32.5	47.1	59.3	69.1	43.6	70.0	60.0	52.5	39.9	31.3	48.22
1894	28.8	23.0	39.0	48.0	60.4	69.7	74.8	68.0	66.0	52.0	35.0	31.2	49.66
1895	23.1	18.0	32.3	47.5	59.3	70.6	67.9	70.9	67.8	47.5	42.8	34.1	48.48
1896	22.4	25.9	30.2	50.5	63.3	64.5	72.4	72.0	63.2	49.4	46.4	27.7	48.99
1897	25.2	28.1	37.4	49.5	60.3	64.7	73.5	70.4	60.8	50.3	40.8	32.2	49.43
1898	27.3	28.4	44.4	46.0	56.5	68.4	73.4	71.4	68.8	55.5	41.0	29.2	50.86
1899	24.7	21.4	34.0	49.2	60.7	69.2	70.5	67.4	59.1*	54.7	40.7	32.6	48.68
1900	27.4	25.8	31.5	47.9	59.9	69.1	74.9	74.7	67.5	58.5	43.6	30.6	50.95
1901	26.6	21.1	35.6	46.0	57.5	69.4	76.0	71.8	64.4	51.3	35.2	29.8	48.66
1902	24.0	23.8	41.0	49.0	58.5	65.6	71.0	68.2	61.5	52.3	45.9	27.9	49.06
1903	25.8	28.6	45.0	47.7	61.0	62.7	72.2	65.4	62.4	52.4	36.6	25.6	48.78
1904	18.2	20.0	33.6	43.8	61.0	67.3	70.9	68.6	62.0	48.6	36.5	23.3	46.15*
1905	22.4	18.8	36.5	48.2	58.9	67.1	73.8	68.4	62.4	52.5	39.5	32.9	48.45
1906	31.7	25.6	32.0	48.3	58.8	68.6	71.9	71.6	64.3	50.6	39.5	25.7	49.05
1907	24.0	18.3	38.1	41.9	51.8	64.3	72.5	68.7	62.7	44.5	39.3	32.9	46.58
1908	26.8	22.2	36.9	47.4	60.6	71.1	76.2	69.7	65.3	54.3	41.4	29.7	50.13
1909	26.8	30.7	33.8	47.3	57.2	68.7	70.9	68.5	60.4	47.1	44.0	27.6	48.58
1910	25.0	23.2	41.0	51.3	58.5	65.2	73.7	68.7	64.5	53.9	38.2	23.7	48.91
1911	28.3	23.8	32.0	44.0	63.6	66.0	73.4	69.5	62.4	50.2	37.3	34.5	48.75
1912	18.6	23.8	33.7	47.6	61.4	64.0	72.0	66.4	65.0	55.1	44.1	35.6	48.94
1913	35.4	25.2	41.4	49.5	58.5	67.0	72.1	70.0	62.4	55.9	43.5	34.5	51.28
1914	26.0	19.2	33.0	42.2	60.8	66.6	69.2	70.4	63.9	56.6	41.0	29.5	48.20
1915	30.5	32.5	34.2	52.7	55.5	64.3	70.2	67.2	67.0	54.4	42.5	27.6	48.99
1916	31.4	21.9	28.5	47.6	60.4	63.8	72.2	71.2	64.9	53.9	42.3	31.2	49.11
1917	28.2	24.8	36.3	46.0	51.4*	65.6	71.3	72.2	60.0	49.3	36.0	20.4	46.79
1918	17.4*	24.5	39.3	48.1	63.8	64.9	71.1	72.2	59.5	53.6	43.0	33.2	49.22
1919	30.5	29.4	40.0	45.5	56.6	67.6	71.2	66.6	60.4	55.5	40.5	24.2	49.00
1920	19.4	22.8	36.0	46.0	58.1	64.8	69.0	70.8	65.5	57.1	38.7	31.6	48.32
1921	28.0	29.9	45.7	53.4	59.0	68.3	74.2	66.9	68.7	52.8	42.0	28.8	51.48
1922	22.8	29.5	40.3	48.7	60.2	67.3	70.5	68.3	64.6	54.3	41.6	29.7	49.82
1923	25.5	23.6	33.0	48.5	56.0	68.2	69.2	66.4	65.0	51.4	40.5	38.0*	48.82
1924	30.0	24.9	37.0	46.0	53.5	64.7	72.0	71.7	60.0	51.0	43.7	31.7	48.77
1925	23.0	31.8	40.0	50.0	56.0	72.0	73.6	71.9	64.0	47.0	41.0	31.4	50.14
1926	28.8	25.8	33.8	44.6	56.8	62.8	73.6	68.8	61.5	49.9	42.1	27.4	47.99
1927	25.0	32.2	36.5	41.3	53.7	62.3*	69.8	64.4*	63.3	54.7	43.8	30.7	48.15
1928	30.0	28.0	34.9	44.8	57.0	62.4	71.3	70.8	59.6	52.9	42.8	34.1	49.05
1929	27.2	28.3	41.7	46.8	57.4	68.7	73.0	68.6	66.3	50.7	41.5	28.7	49.91
1930	26.8	32.7	37.0	45.4	59.9	70.0	72.0	70.0	66.7	50.5	42.2	30.0	50.27
1931	27.9	29.3	36.5	48.9	58.5	66.0	74.0	71.0	67.0	56.0	47.7*	36.4	51.60
1932	38.0*	31.5	33.6	45.3	59.8	66.0	71.0	70.8	64.6	53.9	38.4	32.4	50.44
1933	35.2	30.5	34.9	47.5	61.0	68.5	72.0	69.2	64.3	50.1	36.3	25.7	49.60
1934	28.3	15.6*	34.2	46.8	61.0	69.3	73.2	67.0	65.3	50.8	45.5	30.0	48.92
1935	24.7	28.7	39.6	47.2	56.5	66.5	74.5	70.6	60.6	53.0	44.7	26.3	48.41
1936	25.2	21.7	43.3	45.9	61.4	66.6	73.3	71.8	64.6	52.9	38.6	33.5	49.90
1937	34.9	31.7	33.7	46.6	60.6	65.8	72.8	73.4	72.2	51.0	43.3	31.4	50.62

171

Year	Jan	Feb	Mar	Apr	May	June	July	Aug	Sep	Oct	Nov	Dec	Annual
1938	26.6	31.4	41.3	51.3	58.7	67.3	73.3	74.2	61.0	54.9	44.2	32.5	51.39
1939	28.4	32.2	35.0	46.0	62.6	69.9	72.5	74.2	65.2	52.8	39.4	31.7	50.82
1940	21.2	29.9	31.7	44.6	58.2	65.8	72.1	67.2	62.1	48.0	41.7	33.2	47.98
1941	25.2	28.4	32.8	53.8	60.3	67.0	71.5	68.8	65.3	55.3	45.3	33.7	50.62
1942	24.7	26.6	41.8	52.0	62.2	67.2	72.5	69.8	63.7	53.7	42.2	26.4	50.26
1943	25.8	29.8	35.6	43.2	60.0	72.3	72.9	71.2	62.9	51.0	40.3	27.1	49.34
1944	29.0	29.6	33.4	45.4	64.0	67.2	73.2	71.8	64.7	50.5	40.6	27.3	49.72
1945	18.4	28.9	46.1	51.3	54.6	65.0	69.8	68.2	65.1	51.7	43.0	26.0	49.01
1946	28.1	27.3	46.2*	46.9	57.7	65.1	70.8	67.2	65.4	56.7	46.1	32.2	50.81
1947	31.8	25.5	34.2	47.9	57.0	64.1	71.0	71.9	64.3	57.9	39.0	27.8	49.37
1948	20.0	24.5	37.5	47.6	57.1	65.4	71.7	70.7	64.6	51.5	46.8	31.2	49.05
1949	31.8	32.8	38.6	49.9	58.3	69.5	74.7	72.3	60.8	57.3	40.2	31.7	51.49
1950	34.1	26.0	31.3	43.1	55.4	65.0	69.0	68.3	59.5	55.1	42.5	27.9	48.10
1951	29.4	31.8	38.3	47.9	58.6	63.7	70.5	69.6	61.5	54.6	38.1	32.7	49.72
1952	31.0	32.5	36.7	51.5	56.8	69.3	75.4	70.3	64.7	49.9	43.0	32.6	51.14
1953	32.0	33.6	39.0	47.3	59.5	68.0	71.8	70.1	64.6	54.4	42.8	34.8	51.49
1954	24.0	35.6*	37.3	49.8	55.9	66.7	70.6	69.0	63.0	57.6	41.7	30.2	50.12
1955	26.8	30.1	38.2	51.0	62.0	65.1	76.2*	75.0*	63.9	56.0	40.4	24.4	50.80
1956	27.8	31.9	33.1	44.3	55.4	67.6	69.2	70.9	61.0	54.3	42.7	35.0	49.43
1957	23.5	33.0	38.9	50.5	59.6	70.7	72.3	69.9	65.8	52.7	44.6	35.0	51.29
1958	26.6	24.2	37.6	49.5	55.6	62.8	72.0	72.1	63.6	51.7	43.4	23.3	48.53
1959	26.1	26.8	36.2	49.5	62.5	66.9	72.7	74.1	67.8	55.3	40.5	32.5	50.91
1960	28.4	32.4	29.9	50.7	59.7	67.0	69.6	70.8	63.6	52.2	43.6	24.0	49.32
1961	20.8	29.4	36.4	44.4	55.8	66.8	71.2	70.9	70.0*	56.0	41.9	29.2	49.40
1962	25.7	24.5	36.9	47.0	60.1	67.2	68.1	68.1	59.9	52.4	36.2	23.8	47.49
1963	24.1	22.0	38.4	48.0	58.8	67.2	72.1	69.1	60.2	58.5	47.2	25.2	49.23
1964	29.3	28.0	38.5	45.3	62.6	66.4	72.3	69.5	65.2	52.3	44.7	30.7	50.40
1965	24.3	28.2	35.3	45.4	63.5	66.3	70.1	70.3	64.8	51.9	40.8	33.4	49.52
1966	25.9	29.1	38.3	44.8	55.2	69.0	74.6	73.3	62.3	52.6	44.4	30.6	50.01
1967	32.8	25.1	33.1	46.4	52.1	68.7	71.2	70.2	63.3	53.6	37.7	32.5	48.89
1968	20.9	24.8	39.4	52.0	56.0	65.4	73.1	71.6	66.9	56.1	41.1	27.4	49.56
1969	25.9	27.8	35.5	50.8	59.5	67.4	69.3	72.2	64.5	52.5	41.3	26.9	49.47
1970	19.5	28.7	33.5	47.6	60.0	65.9	72.1	71.5	65.6	55.4	44.2	29.0	49.42
1971	23.3	30.1	35.0	43.8	56.5	69.1	71.1	70.2	66.0	59.0*	40.3	35.2	49.97
1972	30.4	26.1	34.7	44.5	58.5	62.8	71.9	69.0	64.1	47.4	37.7	32.0	48.26
1973	29.3	26.6	43.6	49.3	55.3	69.0	72.4	72.7	64.3	54.7	43.2	33.5	51.16
1974	29.5	26.5	37.9	51.0	56.3	65.1	71.4	70.4	61.0	48.0	41.7	33.2	49.33
1975	31.8	30.5	35.9	43.4	62.3	66.4	70.5	68.0	59.5	55.3	46.8	29.4	49.98
1976	21.9	35.5	41.0	51.2	57.1	68.3	68.8	69.2	61.1	47.7	35.7	23.8	48.44
1977	17.9	27.8	41.6	49.6	61.0	64.7	72.0	71.1	63.8	51.3	43.0	28.7	49.38
1978	23.4	21.2	34.3	46.2	56.9	65.5	69.4	71.8	61.0	51.9	41.6	31.8	47.92
1979	27.4	18.4	41.1	47.0	59.5	64.8	71.1	69.9	62.3	51.2	45.5	34.5	49.39
1980	28.5	25.0	35.6	49.2	61.4	64.5	72.9	73.7	66.3	50.6	38.6	26.0	49.36
1981	20.7	35.1	36.6	49.6	58.8	67.9	72.4	70.6	62.3	49.0	41.7	29.1	49.48
1982	19.3	28.7	35.9	45.2	60.2	62.6	70.2	64.7	59.3	50.9	44.4	37.7	48.26
1983	28.8	29.9	39.7	47.2	55.2	67.6	72.6	73.1	65.6	52.7	41.8	28.4	50.22
1984	23.3	33.9	31.9	46.8	55.8	67.8	69.6	72.2	60.2	56.1	41.5	37.1	49.68
1985	23.4	30.6	40.4	50.0	61.4	63.5	70.8	69.9	65.0	53.0	43.4	27.6	49.92
1986	28.2	26.0	39.5	50.0	61.6	65.2	71.5	68.8	62.0	52.9	38.4	32.6	49.72
1987	26.6	27.2	39.8	49.8	58.7	67.6	73.3	69.8	62.7	48.2	42.3	33.5	49.96
1988	24.3	28.7	38.4	46.4	58.0	66.1	74.1	73.0	61.6	47.3	42.7	30.4	49.25
1989	31.8	28.3	38.2	46.4	58.0	66.6	70.5	70.0	62.4	52.0	41.0	18.5*	48.64
1990	35.4	33.7	40.4	48.7	55.4	65.5	71.3	70.5	62.3	56.0	43.7	35.7	51.55
1991	28.4	34.2	40.3	51.5	63.8	69.0	72.6	72.7	62.0	52.4	42.0	34.0	51.91*
1992	29.7	30.8	34.1	45.7	57.5	64.0	68.6	68.0	62.6	48.2	39.8	30.3	48.28
1993	30.0	23.7	32.3	45.9	58.7	64.3	71.2	69.8	61.5	49.7	41.7	29.2	48.17
1994	18.4	23.9	34.6	50.4	57.0	67.8	73.7	68.3	61.0	50.1	45.3	34.4	48.74
1995	31.9	25.6	39.6	46.3	56.6	67.5	73.0	72.3	62.1	56.3	37.5	26.3	49.58
1996	23.5	27.9	33.3	47.6	57.4	65.8	66.3	70.1	62.5	50.8	36.0	34.0	47.93
1997	24.3	32.7	35.7	44.1	53.3	63.1	67.6	68.0	59.8	54.7	37.4	31.5	47.68
1998	32.2	33.4	39.0	48.4	60.3	61.8	69.3	71.5	60.4	51.7	42.1	37.3	50.62
1999	26.4	30.0	36.4	47.8	57.4	68.1	76.1	70.1	63.7	49.0	44.5	32.8	50.19
2000	24.9	32.2	44.5	47.7	60.7	66.9	70.1	70.1	65.3	54.0	42.4	28.0	50.57

APPENDIX G
PRECIPITATION TOTALS (Inches)
WESTCHESTER ACTIVE RAIN GAUGES

DOBBS FERRY/ARDSLEY

Year	Jan	Feb	Mar	Apr	May	June	July	Aug	Sep	Oct	Nov	Dec	Total
1945										2.59	5.93	6.06	
1946	1.71	2.87	2.75	1.37	14.37*	3.87	5.60	5.44	7.37	1.40	1.38	2.22	50.36
1947	2.89	3.18	3.73	5.35	6.53	4.72	4.68	3.52	2.96	2.03	7.32	5.20	52.11
1948	4.37	1.78	3.90	4.14	7.11	5.23	3.74	3.38	.95*	2.59	4.02	6.18	47.39
1949	6.47	3.77	2.31	4.80	4.73	.37*	3.81	4.36	3.87	1.88	1.21	3.61	41.19
1950	2.95	4.80	4.21	2.37	3.24	1.98	4.47	4.55	1.23	2.02	6.63	6.64	45.09
1951	4.09	4.70	9.10	2.62	4.83	4.40	5.31	5.50	1.91	5.05	8.28	5.71	61.50
1952	5.93	2.32	5.72	8.16	5.92	5.11	4.13	6.59	3.21	.96	4.97	5.58	58.60
1953	6.14	2.46	10.17	6.16	3.30	1.55	4.44	3.54	1.10	2.05	2.64	5.26	51.01
1954	1.93	2.41	4.05	4.33	4.22	1.68	2.07	5.92	7.78	2.05	7.58	3.93	47.95
1955	.74	3.32	4.39	3.13	2.03	3.95	4.27	12.47*	2.61	14.15*	4.80	.59*	56.45
1956	2.77	5.03	5.50	3.83	2.88	4.34	5.41	2.49	4.36	3.23	5.00	5.02	49.86
1957	2.14	2.45	2.96	5.66	2.57	2.93	3.49	3.42	3.80	3.92	4.68	7.83	45.85
1958	6.60	4.76	5.78	7.44	4.58	2.89	2.57	3.95	3.88	6.58	4.21	1.50	54.74
1959	2.82	2.42	5.21	3.19	1.43	5.83	2.64	3.64	3.37	7.31	5.25	5.64	48.75
1960	3.41	5.84	4.32	3.62	3.58	1.60	7.32	5.52	6.92	2.86	2.90	4.04	51.93
1961	3.93	4.02	5.06	6.79	3.64	2.68	5.63	4.73	2.09	2.35	3.45	4.03	48.40
1962	3.43	4.99	3.35	4.43	1.32	6.12	1.57	8.06	4.05	4.54	4.95	3.08	49.89
1963	2.55	2.68	3.75	1.96	3.69	2.23	4.06	3.18	3.92	.34*	8.53	2.95	39.84
1964	4.52	3.08	2.75	5.75	1.28	3.29	5.59	.48*	1.52	1.77	2.18	4.89	37.10
1965	3.75	4.14	2.38	2.78	1.42	1.10	4.68	2.70	2.39	3.50	2.13	2.09	33.06*
1966	3.29	4.15	2.56	2.53	4.85	2.59	1.71	1.62	7.72	4.66	3.91	3.50	43.09
1967	1.19	2.90	7.22	3.13	4.03	3.15	4.11	6.87	1.99	4.11	3.55	6.99	49.24
1968	2.41	1.15	5.92	3.27	7.86	6.35	1.22	3.42	2.16	2.34	5.40	4.88	46.38
1969	2.00	3.31	3.21	4.55	3.23	4.83	6.77	3.59	4.88	1.64	4.03	6.81	48.85
1970	.60*	4.80	4.17	3.54	2.82	1.99	2.50	2.80	1.97	2.15	5.96	3.19	36.49
1971	2.87	5.98	4.06	2.36	4.02	1.18	5.80	8.09	4.83	3.84	5.87	2.64	51.54
1972	2.18	6.12	4.68	4.07	8.56	15.49*	4.49	2.50	2.62	5.15	9.86*	7.24	72.96
1973	4.58	4.61	3.53	7.64	6.03	3.99	5.91	2.31	2.35	3.04	2.31	10.77	57.07
1974	4.80	2.42	5.23	4.26	3.99	2.63	1.64	4.44	9.88	2.09	2.10	5.23	48.71
1975	5.50	3.41	4.05	2.96	3.55	5.36	6.72	3.28	12.64	5.02	4.32	4.29	61.10
1976	6.11	3.42	2.82	3.77	4.25	5.07	4.23	7.42	3.64	6.04	.50*	2.83	50.10
1977	2.34	4.10	8.06	3.75	1.63	4.67	1.06*	4.64	6.67	5.82	8.60	5.22	56.56
1978	8.46	1.98	4.14	2.37	7.66	1.47	5.26	5.05	3.44	1.83	2.74	5.13	49.53
1979	12.28*	4.24	4.18	4.64	5.86	1.80	3.29	6.21	6.23	5.23	4.98	3.10	62.04
1980	1.69	.92	9.82	8.63	2.34	3.59	2.40	1.38	1.98	4.01	4.24	.91	41.91
1981	.71	7.54*	1.13*	3.67	5.14	2.47	5.77	.87	4.86	4.78	1.86	5.04	43.84
1982	5.98	2.79	2.94	6.00	2.46	5.14	2.82	2.49	2.48	1.32	3.67	1.46	39.55
1983	4.53	3.36	10.43*	11.94*	4.15	2.20	3.27	5.57	3.16	8.27	5.29	11.13*	73.30*
1984	2.56	4.67	5.39	8.39	10.44	5.17	10.00*	.90	2.85	4.92	3.73	3.47	62.49
1985	1.34	2.46	1.93	1.01*	7.35	4.78	4.76	4.57	6.02	1.42	6.82	1.99	44.45
1986	5.13	4.19	2.64	3.97	1.10	4.30	5.90	6.05	1.86	1.87	6.98	5.50	49.49
1987	5.87	.86*	4.72	6.36	2.46	4.24	3.62	7.07	5.48	4.76	3.56	2.18	51.18
1988	3.49	4.40	2.34	1.83	4.55	1.30	6.62	2.72	3.34	3.17	9.13	1.55	44.44
1989	2.10	2.93	4.91	3.84	11.70	5.33	4.37	5.49	4.88	7.66	3.74	.90	57.85
1990	4.57	2.34	3.65	4.51	10.01	3.15	2.93	10.33	2.11	7.43	3.50	5.98	60.51
1991	4.03	1.91	4.50	4.12	3.97	1.83	3.23	7.95	4.68	2.14	2.99	4.08	45.43
1992	1.80	2.11	4.12	2.03	4.63	4.15	4.06	5.45	6.33	1.43	6.05	5.52	47.68
1993	3.17	2.88	6.01	4.59	.62*	2.90	1.53	1.11	5.51	4.31	3.57	4.64	40.84
1994	5.82	2.37	6.40	3.15	4.76	2.19	6.11	3.73	2.46	1.29	5.17	3.29	46.74
1995	2.81	2.80	1.14	2.80	2.27	1.95	5.61	1.01	3.29	9.00	5.56	2.30	40.54
1996	6.73	2.67	3.63	7.22	3.34	4.13	8.17	2.04	6.52	8.82	3.23	7.67	64.17
1997	3.49	2.00	5.72	3.67	3.80	4.25	1.96	4.00	2.62	2.02	6.15	4.48	44.16
1998	4.24	5.07	4.91	5.41	6.17	6.15	1.59	2.23	1.46	2.71	1.73	1.27	42.96
1999	8.09	4.19	5.21	2.44	4.90	1.38	1.52	5.49	14.23*	3.36	3.22	3.86	57.87
2000	3.52	1.82	3.80	3.44	4.27	5.44	8.01	6.24	4.63	.55	4.13	4.29	50.14

Dobbs Ferry Monthly Averages 1971 - 2000

	Jan	Feb	Mar	Apr	May	June	July	Aug	Sep	Oct	Nov	Dec	Total
	4.36	3.35	4.54	4.49	4.87	3.92	4.42	4.35	4.77	4.11	4.52	4.26	51.96

APPENDIX H
TOTAL PRECIPITATION (Inches)
KENSICO RESERVOIR

Year	Jan	Feb	Mar	Apr	May	June	July	Aug	Sep	Oct	Nov	Dec	Total
1884	5.23	5.63	4.25	3.12	3.63	5.09	5.92	5.81	.69	3.13	3.61	6.55	52.66
1885	3.92	4.12	1.03	2.82	1.60	.96	4.23	6.28	.86	6.02	4.53	3.38	39.75
1886	3.90	5.38	3.37	3.79	4.18	4.34	4.52	3.36	1.13	2.41	4.35	2.91	43.64
1887	5.31	5.41	3.73	2.98	.20*	8.05	5.49	5.10	2.10	3.81	2.21	5.21	49.60
1888	5.68	4.71	4.16	3.31	5.85	1.65	3.12	9.83	8.56	5.35	3.43	4.94	60.59
1889	4.86	1.68	1.39	6.01	2.53	3.03	13.36*	5.69	7.30	3.68	8.65	2.34	60.52
1890	2.56	4.42	5.15	3.15	4.44	5.91	4.75	3.71	5.08	7.63	.69'	2.32	49.81
1891	6.98	4.98	2.14	2.43	1.97	.65	2.51	2.40	1.27	2.31	3.17	5.02	35.83
1892	4.87	.89	1.94	1.54	5.48	3.90	3.52	4.19	1.70	.55	5.87	1.10	35.55
1893	3.38	5.42	4.01	4.14	5.80	3.45	4.28	7.85	3.14	5.85	3.44	3.89	54.65
1894	2.67	2.32	1.29	1.72	4.93	1.30	1.33	2.48	9.47	5.60	4.88	4.07	42.06
1895	4.16	.33*	2.49	4.10	1.87	3.51	6.40	2.91	1.65	3.19	5.94	3.62	40.17
1896	.93	7.43	9.02	1.26	5.08	5.34	4.64	2.53	5.06	2.10	4.02	1.94	49.35
1897	4.54	4.14	3.39	3.17	7.26	3.16	11.02	2.95	2.20	1.73	5.72	5.25	54.53
1898	4.07	3.90	2.33	4.35	8.74	1.72	5.52	7.27	1.08	7.80	6.90	3.15	56.83
1899	5.10	6.77	6.26	2.61	2.17	5.86	8.08	1.16	4.82	1.82	2.29	2.96	49.90
1900	4.08	7.47	5.16	1.84	4.28	2.48	4.87	2.45	3.21	3.37	6.26	2.64	48.11
1901	1.76	.70	6.78	8.47	6.48	1.33	3.69	8.61	3.28	2.92	1.15	8.02	53.19
1902	3.10	5.01	6.14	4.15	3,56	4.18	3.44	1.97	6.95	5.98	.71	9.26*	54.45
1903	4.80	5.11	4.51	4.35	.59	11.20	1.93	9.05	7.19	8.03	1.29	2.81	60.86
1904	3.17	3.56	3.77	4.23	2.12	2.42	4.91	5.97	5.68	2.94	2.40	3.48	44.65
1905	7.93	2.43	4.60	3.16	.73	4.59	7.49	5.04	5.31	3.82	2.64	4.53	52.27
1906	3.00	3.37	6.18	5.90	5.49	4.70	5.78	2.93	3.30	4.95	1.87	2.88	50.35
1907	4.25	3.01	3.56	4.41	5.11	5.94	1.89	1.92	8.60	6.90	6.58	6.13	58.30
1908	4.36	7.43	3.89	2.34	9.12	1.48	6.95	8.78	1.48	2.53	.95	3.97	53.28
1909	4.27	6.00	5.35	7.95	2.24	4.03	2.78	7.05	4.49	1.61	1.86	5.16	52.79
1910	7.12	5.28	1.07	7.22	4.37	4.70	.97	1.97	1.52	1.53	4.71	2.99	43.45
1911	3.80	4.45	4.60	3.43	1.43	4.60	3.36	5.88	2.34	7.12	5.36	3.72	50.09
1912	2.28	2.63	9.89	3.94	4.17	1.37	1.80	4.78	3.10	3.27	4.11	5.64	46.98
1913	4.55	3.04	6.43	6.03	2.98	1.32	2.13	5.47	2.96	10.11	2.71	2.83	50.56
1914	4.76	1.37	3.51	3.73	3.07	2.05	5.80	1.62	.30*	3.21	3.00	5.45	37.87
1915	7.74	5.73	.90	2.69	2.81	1.72	5.74	11.44	2.27	3.67	2.05	4.49	51.25
1916	1.55	4.30	3.98	2.67	4.04	5.68	6.87	1.76	2.78	1.52	2.15	4.13	41.43
1917	2.85	2.56	4.52	2.69	3.67	3.93	2.13	2.11	5.69	5.69	.70	4.42	37.01
1918	4.12	2.78	1.94	5.16	2.31	2.77	5.98	3.78	2.41	.89	2.22	4.06	38.42
1919	2.84	3.94	6.59	2.05	4.18	2.46	6.60	4.96	5.62	4.15	3.11	2.18	48.68
1920	2.50	2.74	3.07	4.62	2.89	7.18	5.92	6.18	6.62	1.02	3.66	4.95	51.35
1921	3.37	3.22	3.14	4.22	3.49	4.38	4.06	3.59	2.44	.92	3.53	2.51	38.87
1922	2.42	2.88	5.10	1.54	5.06	6.93	9.99	5.19	4.51	1.86	1.11	4.02	50.61
1923	5.54	2.90	3.61	3.53	1.95	3.29	1.76	1.56	2.35	6.07	3.96	4.51	41.03
1924	4.82	3.85	2.55	7.87	5.41	1.47	1.36	5.66	5.51	.31*	2.77	2.78	44.36
1925	4.38	3.73	4.01	1.87	3.85	3.69	8.30	1.05	3.51	4.67	4.50	2.71	46.27
1926	3.09	6.63	3.08	2.47	1.78	2.89	4.03	5.67	3.61	4.26	4.78	4.14	46.33
1927	2.94	4.26	2.04	1.99	4.95	3.16	7.83	9.58	4.36	8.19	5.79	4.26	59.35
1928	2.79	5.89	3.54	5.37	2.32	8.13	6.21	4.58	4.41	1.37	2.71	1.74	49.06
1929	5.04	5.40	3.83	7.36	4.47	1.73	1.18	2.18	2.89	4.41	2.23	5.24	45.96
1930	3.69	2.64	2.90	3.60	3.65	5.05	2.45	5.33	2.57	1.36	5.39	3.72	42.35
1931	2.71	3.28	4.95	5.57	7.82	3.88	2.49	3.37	1.85	2.81	.97	2.70	42.40
1932	4.35	3.32	5.18	2.19	2.11	2.86	2.27	2.94	2.19	6.28	8.39	2.73	44.81
1933	1.95	3.41	5.50	5.92	2.73	2.55	1.39	11.05	6.60	3.39	.60	4.07	49.16
1934	4.11	3.08	5.71	3.63	7.39	5.14	2.59	1.79	13.09	2.72	3.47	4.13	56.85
1935	2.51	2.97	2.73	2.05	2.80	4.25	3.85	1.96	4.36	1.75	4.14	1.41	34.78
1936	7.10	2.36	8.24	4.08	4.15	5.67	1.71	4.93	4.77	2.40	1.44	8.48	55.33
1937	6.69	3.12	3.23	5.39	3.73	4.09	2.01	7.04	4.72	7.07	5.84	2.84	55.77
1938	5.71	2.11	2.29	3.42	4.01	7.28	10.65	3.51	11.65	2.18	3.88	4.34	61.03
1939	4.10	6.53	4.60	4.57	.80	4.66	1.56	6.19	1.82	5.23	2.04	2.29	44.39
1940	3.58	2.39	6.65	7.16	7.66	3.03	3.72	6.47	3.09	3.12	4.79	2.66	54.32

Year	Jan	Feb	Mar	Apr	May	June	July	Aug	Sep	Oct	Nov	Dec	Total
1941	3.32	3.43	2.97	2.42	4.03	4.86	6.05	6.90	.52	2.88	2.93	5.47	45.78
1942	4.04	2.46	8.29	1.46	2.82	2.63	7.85	10.21	3.44	4.96	3.87	6.00	58.03
1943	3.85	2.25	4.05	3.22	5.36	3.98	5.60	2.89	3.45	8.99	3.68	1.54	48.86
1944	3.38	2.77	6.85	5.51	1.87	3.03	1.13	1.20	11.33	2.65	6.80	4.45	50.97
1945	3.05	2.85	3.23	4.09	6.44	3.96	7.94	6.14	5.14	3.25	5.02	5.43	56.54
1946	1.46	3.01	2.63	1.54	11.76	3.80	4.84	4.34	8.14	1.44	1.43	2.06	46.45
1947	2.53	3.11	3.57	5.94	5.19	4.75	4.46	1.05	2.96	1.61	6.89	4.53	46.59
1948	4.05	1.51	5.46	3.30	8.68	5.81	4.14	3.12	1.26	2.65	4.43	6.66	50.07
1949	6.09	3.80	2.03	4.95	5.71	.45*	4.19	4.06	3.70	1.80	1.12	3.17	41.07
1950	2.63	4.03	3.92	2.67	4.06	2.01	4.24	4.15	1.31	1.75	6.09	5.95	42.81
1951	4.47	3.66	8.96	2.49	4.62	3.77	4.31	6.96	2.84	7.53	6.73	5.87	62.21
1952	5.39	2.34	6.33	7.72	7.86	4.08	3.85	8.87	3.27	.89	4.25	6.04	60.89
1953	5.65	2.18	10.61*	7.10	2.46	2.51	4.53	1.69	1.90	3.97	3.45	4.78	50.83
1954	1.90	1.89	3.83	3.17	4.82	1.72	1.45	9.65	7.15	1.87	6.35	3.27	47.07
1955	.51*	2.61	3.20	3.10	1.65	3.60	3.81	11.57*	2.66	14.51*	4.57	.38	52.17
1956	1.94	3.82	4.37	3.70	2.58	2.67	5.16	1.95	3.47	5.70	2.79	3.59	41.74
1957	1.36	1.95	2.12	3.98	2.45	1.10	3.32	3.20	3.79	2.65	2.10	4.39	32.41
1958	4.58	4.05	2.95	4.78	4.59	2.02	3.33	3.67	3.68	4.84	2.48	1.20	42.17
1959	2.00	1.75	3.34	2.58	1.83	5.57	3.72	1.90	2.06	6.39	3.66	3.60	38.40
1960	1.70	3.66	2.58	2.04	3.24	1.67	7.95	3.82	5.64	3.22	1.27	3.57	40.36
1961	3.19	3.05	2.85	4.73	4.02	3.01	4.25	5.18	1.87	3.24	2.78	3.03	41.20
1962	2.65	3.63	2.80	1.52	1.71	1.73	4.13	5.93	3.05	3.79	3.80	2.21	36.95
1963	2.35	1.84	2.69	1.47	3.10	1.50	5.02	2.30	3.69	.36	6.31	1.60	32.23
1964	3.22	1.84	1.74	4.34	3.99	3.12	4.93	1.12	1.27	1.59	1.43	3.60	32.19
1965	3.06	3.02	1.45	2.73	1.48	1.03	5.32	2.77	2.44	3.99	1.96	1.25	30.50*
1966	2.30	3.94	.73	2.83	3.94	1.53	1.61	1.87	7.04	4.44	4.16	3.08	37.47
1967	.76	2.51	5.16	3.05	4.32	3.30	4.87	5.62	2.14	4.28	3.26	6.06	45.33
1968	1.78	1.61	4.62	3.40	7.58	6.16	.67*	4.10	3.19	2.12	5.13	3.63	43.99
1969	1.61	4.33	2.05	4.35	3.13	4.93	6.16	3.03	4.33	1.55	5.56	5.72	46.75
1970	.52	4.76	3.40	3.00	2.30	2.00	2.81	2.49	2.57	1.48	4.41	3.21	32.95
1971	1.70	4.62	3.54	2.28	4.01	.91	6.99	6.86	6.69	3.40	4.82	2.21	48.03
1972	1.64	5.21	5.44	3.96	8.74	12.51*	3.26	2.56	2.45	5.25	10.08	5.05	66.15
1973	3.37	2.58	2.71	5.76	5.27	4.39	6.25	3.36	2.16	1.74	1.66	8.76	48.01
1974	3.50	1.64	4.01	4.12	4.21	2.75	1.28	4.77	8.17	2.78	2.35	4.98	44.56
1975	3.95	2.71	2.82	2.44	3.17	3.97	7.19	4.19	13.10*	4.30	3.72	2.03	53.59
1976	5.02	1.26	3.32	1.42	4.27	5.31	4.21	7.70	4.71	5.77	.40*	2.45	45.84
1977	1.38	3.39	8.14	1.96	1.83	3.68	1.07	4.73	7.24	5.80	10.71*	4.30	54.07
1978	7.52	1.24	3.66	1.89	8.86	1.65	4.55	5.74	2.10	2.01	2.49	4.46	47.00
1979	11.85*	3.51	4.93	5.34	5.29	1.65	1.33	6.67	6.20	3.63	3.88	2.43	56.71
1980	1.35	1.06	7.86	9.32	2.78	2.91	4.96	1.55	1.79	4.54	4.29	.27*	42.68
1981	.67	7.83*	.32*	4.11	4.29	3.47	4.01	.89	6.84	5.43	1.94	4.79	44.59
1982	5.52	2.87	2.32	4.58	2.16	6.63	3.94	2.48	2.38	1.70	3.86	1.47	39.91
1983	4.77	1.90	8.50	11.24*	4.34	2.60	2.80	5.87	2.72	7.79	5.09	9.22	66.84*
1984	1.92	4.30	5.44	7.27	10.57	6.23	10.01	2.15	2.24	3.30	4.34	3.42	61.19
1985	1.17	2.02	1.94	.66*	7.64	4.28	5.05	5.27	6.45	1.53	7.44	1.49	44.94
1986	5.01	3.42	2.52	3.08	1.06	4.34	5.26	6.36	1.69	2.30	7.84	6.48	43.52
1987	5.65	.80	4.90	7.89	1.63	3.58	2.70	7.24	6.04	4.93	4.74	1.90	52.00
1988	3.12	4.09	2.09	1.78	5.42	.91	5.55	1.83	3.06	2.53	9.55	.88	40.81
1989	2.16	2.71	4.82	3.80	11.77*	6.39	4.05	4.76	4.16	9.04	3.56	.98	58.20
1990	4.42	2.89	3.88	4.61	7.80	4.02	2.80	10.45	2.33	7.24	3.62	6.36	57.81
1991	3.81	1.59	3.16	3.30	3.82	2.42	2.34	4.89	4.49	2.57	2.28	3.70	38.37
1992	.74	1.41	3.97	2.37	1.61	3.27	2.96	2.83	2.75	1.65	5.13	4.80	33.49
1993	2.74	2.84	7.66	4.20	1.73	2.59	1.46	2.17	5.17	4.16	3.27	4.46	42.45
1994	5.53	2.43	4.55	3.06	4.88	4.54	8.77	4.83	2.59	2.23	3.67	3.95	51.03
1995	3.82	3.68	1.15	3.51	1.90	1.88	3.49	.36*	2.95	8.54	5.73	1.83	38.84
1996	6.18	2.76	3.06	7.58	2.56	6.95	7.49	1.95	6.82	7.98	3.25	7.51	64.09
1997	4.40	1.85	5.46	2.94	3.40	4.47	5.65	4.47	1.71	1.76	5.82	4.17	41.93
1998	3.97	3.94	4.40	5.33	6.92	4.90	1.41	1.98	2.10	3.55	1.66	1.04	41.20
1999	7.12	4.04	4.89	2.07	4.93	1.29	.68	5.55	11.10	3.05	2.68	3.48	50.88
2000	2.68	2.08	3.96	3.26	3.89	5.11	7.27	2.54	5.63	.42	3.71	3.75	44.30

Kensico Monthly Averages 1961 - 1990

	Jan	Feb	Mar	Apr	May	June	July	Aug	Sep	Oct	Nov	Dec	Total
	3.24	3.02	3.69	3.96	4.69	3.76	4.15	4.33	4.14	3.73	4.51	3.58	46.80

Kensico Monthly Averages 1971 - 2000

	Jan	Feb	Mar	Apr	May	June	July	Aug	Sep	Oct	Nov	Dec	Total
	3.89	2.92	4.18	4.04	4.69	4.02	4.29	4.23	4.598	4.03	4.45	3.75	49.08

APPENDIX I

TOTAL PRECIPITATION (Inches)
PEEKSKILL

Year	Jan	Feb	Mar	Apr	May	June	July	Aug	Sep	Oct	Nov	Dec	Totall
1926			2.21	2.98	2.02	2.22	3.23	10.34	3.03	5.01	5.32	3.25	
1927	2.56	3.44	1.93	2.44	5.21	2.21	5.18	4.31	4.54	7.90	6.81	5.18	51.71
1928	2.36	4.04	3.48	4.56	2.16	9.23*	8.18	7.77	1.78	.78	2.77	.72	47.83
1929	4.55	2.37	3.63	7.76	3.95	2.90	3.27	2.29	3.40	4.65	2.29	2.70	43.76
1930	3.03	2.05	2.80	3.11	3.78	4.70	3.51	5.04	2.53	1.71	5.09	3.03	40.38
1931	2.17	2.30	3.34	4.91	4.93	6.32	3.14	3.24	1.82	1.90	.95	2.90	37.92
1932	3.39	2.78	4.43	3.15	2.63	4.28	3.47	3.40	2.12	5.09	8.21	2.10	45.05
1933	1.91	3.81	4.40	6.09	3.09	1.48	2.30	11.34	4.85	2.88	.72	3.78	46.65
1934	3.46	3.12	2.57	4.98	5.50	3.27	7.88	2.82	11.52	2.66	5.10	3.34	56.22
1935	4.04	2.82	2.60	2.10	1.46	5.61	3.23	1.95	4.48	1.80	3.86	1.07	35.02
1936	7.07	3.37	6.03	4.30	3.40	4.21	2.20	4.04	3.30	3.50	1.40	6.41	49.23
1937	6.25	3.60	2.84	4.37	4.78	3.66	2.26	10.65	4.19	4.80	4.00	2.75	54.15
1938	5.30	2.55	2.12	3.07	3.25	6.01	9.75	2.69	10.62	2.06	3.74	4.22	55.38
1939	3.14	4.19	5.06	5.80	1.07	5.51	4.14	2.24	3.10	3.20	2.60	2.05	42.10
1940	2.87	2.94	6.45	6.07	4.83	4.06	2.81	3.26	2.68	2.94	4.62	3.47	47.00
1941	2.84	2.75	2.23	2.17	1.40	4.04	7.12	3.60	.35*	2.53	3.58	4.27	36.89
1942	2.61	3.85	6.11	1.44	2.92	4.00	3.84	6.39	3.91	3.20	5.01	4.86	48.14
1943	3.36	1.88	3.71	2.96	4.80	3.58	5.78	1.92	3.05	8.12	5.06	.77	44.99
1944	2.91	2.19	5.59	5.22	1.79	3.72	2.02	2.14	5.84	1.60	5.40	3.87	42.29
1945	3.97	3.49	2.20	4.54	6.28	3.94	13.85*	4.45	4.01	2.17	6.43	5.07	60.40
1946	2.08	2.22	1.86	1.45	7.28	3.92	7.87	2.76	5.54	1.86	.97	2.43	40.24
1947	3.07	2.37	3.56	4.27	8.00	4.37	5.28	3.17	1.53	1.56	7.47	4.53	49.18
1948	3.85	1.66	3.69	4.59	6.06	3.80	4.92	2.72	.81	2.36	4.57	6.22	45.25
1949	6.10	3.21	1.69	5.17	6.64	.65	4.56	2.24	3.54	2.36	1.50	3.40	41.25
1950	3.15	4.44	2.91	2.21	4.78	2.63	7.63	4.51	1.98	1.70	6.41	5.01	47.36
1951	3.39	5.01	7.75	3.15	4.78	2.81	5.83	4.14	2.17	4.68	7.06	5.03	55.80
1952	4.78	2.67	3.32	8.75	5.42	5.07	4.17	8.39	4.21	.75	4.18	4.69	58.40
1953	4.87	2.03	9.42*	6.01	5.01	2.40	5.11	1.10	1.87	1.12	3.81	6.54	49.30
1954	2.11	2.10	4.08	3.55	4.69	2.32	1.96	8.74	8.25	1.89	7.37	3.66	50.72
1955	.57	3.53	4.30	4.25	1.24	5.84	3.56	12.97	2.89	12.29	5.79	.92	58.15
1956	2.15	4.12	4.45	5.27	4.11	3.36	5.48	2.41	4.69	2.97	2.60	4.50	46.11
1957	1.46	2.13	2.06	4.76	2.95	1.52	3.71	1.89	2.92	3.36	3.77	8.10	38.63
1958	5.03	3.96	4.75	5.46	4.36	1.77	4.34	2.53	6.55	5.36	3.83	1.00	48.94
1959	2.39	2.25	3.84	3.58	.89*	4.32	4.10	4.91	1.28	7.19	4.36	4.91	44.02
1960	2.89	2.43	2.50	2.89	3.31	3.74	10.19	4.75	6.91	1.88	2.92	2.77	47.18
1961	2.90	3.52	3.98	5.59	4.98	2.76	4.25	7.57	3.26	1.93	3.44	3.65	47.83
1962	3.14	5.25	1.61	5.37	1.83	2.45	2.46	3.49	2.56	4.43	3.73	2.93	39.25
1963	2.46	2.29	3.40	1.17	1.61	3.45	5.33	2.62	3.82	.22*	6.85	2.46	35.68
1964	3.88	2.19	1.94	4.72	2.41	3.13	4.97	2.15	1.54	1.41	1.97	4.08	34.39
1965	3.15	3.49	1.97	2.64	1.45	1.17	1.70	6.01	3.19	3.13	1.91	2.33	32.14*
1966	2.60	4.18	1.71	2.48	2.40	.99	.97*	1.87	7.21	4.74	3.96	3.31	36.42
1967	1.50	2.35	5.88	2.54	4.01	5.26	3.48	6.25	2.01	3.50	2.79	6.43	46.00
1968	2.25	1.11	5.02	3.30	6.78	6.46	1.68	3.91	3.32	2.32	4.36	4.77	45.28
1969	1.90	4.74	2.66	3.95	2.68	5.73	4.86	5.90	3.66	1.95	5.56	6.01	49.69
1970	.39*	4.95	3.70	3.69	2.27	2.82	2.73	2.75	4.14	3.73	5.00	2.45	38.62
1971	2.52	5.79	5.95	3.20	4.15	2.50	3.68	8.45	6.14	3.22	3.49	2.91	52.00
1972	1.90	2.25	3.71	3.58	5.46	9.04	2.97	1.16	1.96	4.06	8.57	5.51	50.17
1973	4.22	4.57	3.14	6.60	5.73	5.87	3.59	2.69	2.68	2.49	2.08	10.44*	54.10
1974	3.87	2.25	4.22	3.94	4.53	4.44	2.19	5.09	7.03	2.25	1.91	4.23	45.95
1975	4.48	3.41	3.81	3.02	3.66	5.07	8.05	3.97	11.41	5.59	5.47	3.86	61.80
1976	5.21	5.49	2.40	3.54	4.68	5.15	4.30	6.79	4.71	7.08	.53*	2.19	52.07
1977	1.59	2.92	4.80	2.11	3.02	4.15	2.55	3.63	8.80	5.96	9.65*	3.37	52.60
1978	7.50	2.36	1.89	1.09	9.85	1.83	4.21	4.32	2.01	1.75	2.43	3.44	46.68
1979	11.34*	1.47	4.47	5.75	6.39	1.53	1.39	5.72	6.30	4.27	5.27	2.68	56.58
1980	1.46	1.11	8.21	7.48	2.26	3.82	3.57	3.20	1.26	4.00	4.56	.12*	44.29

Year	Jan	Feb	Mar	Apr	May	June	July	Aug	Sep	Oct	Nov	Dec	Total
1981	.44	8.66*	.67*	3.71	4.80	2.66	4.08	.53*	2.88	5.93	1.68	4.22	40.26
1982	4.52	2.65	2.59	5.18	4.63	7.25	4.21	3.69	2.94	1.79	3.32	1.66	44.43
1983	2.62	4.56	7.81	11.19*	6.41	3.17	2.37	4.44	3.12	6.79	6.26	8.74	68.48
1984	5.40	4.06	5.61	7.04	11.70*	3.29	5.70	2.28	2.20	2.45	2.38	3.10	55.75
1985	1.44	2.32	2.10	1.05*	6.54	6.07	6.32	3.72	5.06	2.00	6.58	1.80	45.00
1986	4.42	3.57	2.02	3.54	1.44	5.08	8.67	3.17	1.37	2.50	5.16	3.41	44.35
1987	3.92	.31*	4.77	7.10	1.71	3.19	3.71	5.18	8.02	5.62	2.70	1.58	47.83
1988	2.99	4.23	2.51	2.22	5.00	.62*	5.50	3.86	3.12	2.82	8.41	1.08	42.36
1989	2.54	2.78	3.10	3.02	11.53	7.42	2.78	5.59	6.11	9.21	2.70	1.12	57.90
1990	4.44	3.21	4.21	5.79	7.21	3.69	7.18	16.71*	3.43	6.17	4.71	5.00	71.76*
1991	2.03	1.66	5.22	3.76	4.81	4.21	4.54	6.72	7.42	3.82	3.54	3.12	50.85
1992	1.99	2.10	3.93	3.01	4.76	4.28	5.49	3.31	3.08	1.91	6.78	4.63	45.27
1993	3.01	3.55	6.34	5.95	1.65	2.54	1.39	3.78	5.17	5.24	4.49	4.38	47.49
1994	5.55	2.57	5.21	4.05	4.80	7.79	3.96	6.36	3.58	1.61	5.76	3.22	54.46
1995	4.33	1.13	1.68	3.22	2.30	1.83	3.19	1.62	3.75	12.84*	5.69	1.60	43.28
1996	7.02	2.03	2.91	6.28	3.36	6.26	8.50	1.47	7.28	6.62	3.71	7.13	62.57
1997	3.37	1.54	4.74	2.99	3.91	2.94	3.38	7.02	1.83	1.85	6.73	3.96	44.26
1998	3.11	3.47	3.16	4.80	8.44	5.98	1.09	3.63	2.37	4.03	2.19	1.02	43.29
1999	7.80	3.86	5.06	2.02	4.19	1.55	1.81	4.52	15.02*	3.57	4.12	2.41	55.93
2000	2.28	2.99	3.57	3.89	4.92	6.54	5.81	3.89	5.67	.96	3.36	4.75	48.63

Peekskill Monthly Averages 1961 - 1990

	Jan	Feb	Mar	Apr	May	June	July	Aug	Sep	Oct	Nov	Dec	Total
	3.44	3.42	3.69	4.26	4.73	3.98	3.98	4.54	4.19	3.69	4.30	3.71	48.28

Peekskill Monthly Averages 1971 - 2000

	Jan	Feb	Mar	Apr	May	June	July	Aug	Sep	Oct	Nov	Dec	Total
	3.91	3.10	3.99	4.34	5.13	4.33	4.10	4.55	4.86	4.28	4.47	3.56	50.62

APPENDIX J
PRECIPITATION TOTALS
(Inches)
PLEASANTVILLE

Year	Jan	Feb	Mar	Apr	May	June	July	Aug	Sep	Oct	Nov	Dec	Total
1949	6.60	1.73	3.83	4.21	5.42	.21*	3.00	4.95	3.53	1.75	1.16	3.32	39.7
1950	2.64	4.05	3.57	2.25	3.46	3.29	7.39	3.83	1.17*	1.83	6.66	6.26	46.40
1951	3.62	4.81	7.79	2.67	5.35	2.97	4.07	4.27	1.71	4.52	7.97	5.28	55.03
1952	3.66	2.40	5.19	7.21	4.92	5.83	3.51	7.17	4.51	.76	3.74	5.37	54.27
1953	6.06	2.70	9.51	5.58	3.68	3.63	5.15	2.58	1.30	3.97	3.17	5.77	53.10
1954	2.15	2.19	4.30	3.46	4.38	1.50	1.26	6.20	6.17	2.37	5.17	4.29	43.44
1955	1.35	3.71	3.52	4.18	2.31	2.77	2.31	11.51*	2.74	14.56*	5.13	.34*	54.43
1956	2.45	4.48	3.93	5.26	2.29	2.17	5.02	1.40	3.56	1.57	4.60	4.88	41.61
1957	2.17	1.95	1.30	6.72	2.25	2.21	4.06	2.51	3.44	3.31	4.07	7.62	41.61
1958	4.97	4.60	5.90	6.67	5.26	2.62	3.15	4.06	3.99	4.74	3.45	1.21	50.62
1959	3.01	2.42	4.63	3.20	1.15	5.30	3.11	4.84	1.80	6.47	4.79	5.61	46.33
1960	2.92	5.20	3.27	2.72	3.26	2.24	7.87	4.09	7.08	4.21	2.22	3.91	48.99
1961	3.92	3.88	3.90	5.39	4.15	5.38	4.22	6.02	2.10	1.81	4.01	3.79	48.57
1962	3.12	4.78	2.20	4.13	1.02	3.31	1.51	7.79	3.06	3.17	4.88	2.96	41.93
1963	2.67	2.24	3.15	1.60	2.84	2.25	5.31	3.52	3.76	.27*	7.49	2.71	37.81
1964	4.27	2.66	2.13	4.83	1.71	3.07	4.66	.78	1.31	1.11	1.72	4.51	32.76
1965	3.62	3.89	1.75	1.96	1.56	1.01	3.74	3.59	2.63	2.73	1.64	1.51	29.63*
1966	2.71	4.57	1.17	2.13	3.89	1.43	1.27	2.81	5.98	4.56	4.16	3.46	38.14
1967	1.06	2.79	5.08	2.56	3.86	2.80	5.00	4.26	1.87	4.67	2.85	5.54	42.34
1968	2.40	.80*	5.55	4.27	6.52	6.17	1.00*	3.59	2.79	1.77	5.42	4.79	45.07
1969	1.76	3.24	2.48	4.60	3.58	3.98	4.96	3.88	3.80	1.33	5.42	5.69	44.72
1970	.55*	4.69	3.68	3.34	2.50	2.93	1.46	2.55	3.10	2.67	4.22	2.69	34.38
1971	2.12	4.96	3.77	1.99	3.49	.40	6.82	6.87	6.55	2.95	4.21	2.40	46.53
1972	1.65	5.14	5.04	3.90	4.86	13.28*	4.59	3.43	1.64	4.50	8.67	6.04	62.74
1973	4.47	4.59	3.07	6.83	5.21	5.20	5.12	2.29	2.31	2.12	2.06	9.61*	52.88
1974	4.83	1.45	5.34	3.78	3.83	3.92	1.68	5.09	8.40	2.13	2.38	5.05	47.88
1975	5.56	3.28	4.63	2.98	2.99	5.26	7.50	4.18	8.59*	5.10	4.41	4.20	58.68
1976	5.60	3.29	2.67	2.71	4.73	4.64	5.69	8.50	5.10	5.56	.63*	2.80	51.92
1977	2.06	2.58	7.68	3.13	2.42	4.31	1.68	4.18	6.25	6.15	9.47*	5.17	55.08
1978	8.12	1.56	3.41	1.60	8.30	2.44	3.32	4.89	2.45	1.49	2.58	4.70	44.86
1979	11.69*	4.36	4.38	5.36	5.43	1.91	3.95	8.01	5.81	4.43	5.08	2.85	63.26
1980	1.62	.92	10.39	8.58	3.41	4.25	3.19	.95	1.70	3.98	4.13	.67	43.79
1981	.67	7.87*	.93*	4.06	4.22	2.10	4.53	.73*	3.23	5.90	1.90	5.00	41.14
1982	5.28	1.91	2.65	5.74	2.30	7.32	3.41	2.54	2.82	1.65	3.68	1.66	40.96
1983	4.55	3.63	11.06*	11.45*	4.50	2.97	2.34	4.33	2.44	7.22	5.08	9.42	68.99*
1984	2.30	4.74	5.00	8.60	11.54	5.82	9.96*	3.24	1.72	3.53	4.46	3.38	64.29
1985	1.34	2.41	2.13	.67*	7.16	5.14	6.17	3.54	5.53	1.96	7.26	1.52	44.83
1986	4.80	4.10	2.32	3.48	.97	5.26	5.54	9.18	1.77	1.98	8.79	5.41	53.60
1987	6.18	1.16	4.39	7.66	2.00	3.57	3.24	6.93	6.16	4.95	3.69	1.98	51.91
1988	3.05	3.84	2.10	1.90	4.56	1.08	6.58	2.40	3.50	3.17	8.83	1.27	42.28
1989	2.01	2.77	4.72	3.75	12.45*	5.62	2.50	5.40	4.23	9.81	3.13	1.12	58.96
1990	4.05	2.53	3.68	3.98	8.20	4.52	2.00	11.04	2.67	5.86	3.95	5.86	58.34
1991	3.78	1.63	4.23	4.22	3.28	2.98	3.87	6.95	5.21	2.98	3.12	3.34	45.50
1992	1.38	1.89	4.00	2.21	2.32	6.19	3.45	5.25	3.60	1.98	5.67	6.02	43.96
1993	2.58	2.60	6.03	4.92	.25*	4.39	1.87	1.70	6.44	4.33	4.42	4.91	44.44
1994	5.96	2.92	6.02	3.17	5.00	7.66	7.84	5.47	3.00	1.57	5.45	3.19	57.29
1995	4.04	2.75	1.32	2.55	3.22	1.50	3.19	.93	2.60	8.68	5.41	2.20	38.39
1996	6.80	2.90	3.95	6.63	2.85	6.00	9.05	1.57	6.83	6.89	2.62	4.95	61.05
1997	2.85	1.29	3.25	4.99	3.63	3.33	7.09	5.50	1.56	1.96	5.97	3.66	45.08
1998	3.41	3.96	4.64	5.14	6.27	4.40	1.29	2.68	2.93	3.77	2.50	1.09	42.08
1999	5.26		4.70	2.05	4.60	1.05							

Pleasantville Monthly Averages 1961 - 1990

	Jan	Feb	Mar	Apr	May	June	July	Aug	Sep	Oct	Nov	Dec	Total
	3.60	3.37	4.05	4.23	4.47	4.04	4.13	4.53	3.80	3.54	4.53	3.96	48.28

Pleasantville Monthly Averages 1971-1999

	Jan	Feb	Mar	Apr	May	June	July	Aug	Sep	Oct	Nov	Dec	Total
	3.95	3.16	4.40	4.38	4.47	4.31	4.46	4.47	4.06	4.02	4.64	3.93	54.20

APPENDIX K
PRECIPITATION TOTALS
(Inches)

WESTCHESTER AIRPORT

Year	Jan	Feb	Mar	Apr	May	June	July	Aug	Sep	Oct	Nov	Dec	Total
1949	5.36	3.77	2.71	4.58	5.33	.06*	3.93	4.99	4.55	1.95	.84	3.55	41.62
1950	3.63	5.52	4.15	2.85	5.14	2.72	4.28	5.24	1.57	1.63	7.03	5.58	49.34
1951	4.10	5.25	8.69	2.46	5.36	3.70	4.42	6.47	1.94	5.44	7.25	5.96	61.04
1952	5.88	2.32	5.71	9.43	8.36	4.00	4.12	8.14	2.71	.49	3.69	5.39	60.24
1953	5.92	2.56	11.44*	6.53	4.31	1.65	3.86	2.31	1.80	4.17	2.89	5.15	52.59
1954	1.76	2.28	4.25	3.62	4.24	1.27	1.18	8.45	8.12	1.64	7.34	4.69	48.84
1955	.44*	3.79	4.24	4.26	1.57	3.42	4.10	13.13*	3.16	13.85*	6.87	.49*	59.34
1956	2.55	4.99	4.54	4.63	3.07	3.19	5.67	1.71	4.51	6.07	3.29	4.66	48.88
1957	2.86	2.40	3.43	4.79	2.97	1.29	2.92	3.52	3.50	3.99	6.07	7.34	45.08
1958	8.05	4.75	4.64	8.08	5.45	2.61	3.62	5.24	3.98	5.83	3.61	1.31	57.17
1959	2.71	2.30	5.40	2.97	1.73	5.39	2.20	3.87	2.16	6.99	5.44	6.02	47.18
1960	3.16	5.01	4.16	2.81	3.53	1.19	7.38	4.02	5.63	2.77	2.90	3.84	47.30
1961	3.52	6.10	3.46	7.86	4.00	2.78	3.91	5.71	2.35	2.49	3.76	4.02	49.96
1962	2.95	5.75	3.64	3.26	1.18*	4.86	2.36	7.43	4.07	4.28	5.89	2.96	48.63
1963	3.42	2.91	4.21	2.23	2.77	2.21	3.85	1.32	4.28	.19*	8.45	1.99	37.83
1964	4.86	3.23	2.53	5.62	1.80	2.73	5.04	.52	1.37	1.53	1.69	4.69	35.78
1965	3.50	3.53	2.27	2.89	1.55	.97	4.26	3.00	2.06	2.52	2.09	2.52	31.16*
1966	3.22	4.76	1.86	3.04	4.14	1.36	1.48	1.46	7.04	4.54	2.93	3.98	39.81
1967	2.39	3.13	7.67	3.16	4.65	2.54	4.86	4.66	1.49	3.83	3.42	8.23	50.03
1968	1.82	1.23	4.88	3.20	7.08	5.70	.57	3.57	3.44	2.00	5.49	5.58	44.56
1969	1.78	3.70	3.86	5.16	2.73	4.52	7.31	2.97	4.34	1.67	4.73	6.63	49.40
1970	.53	4.81	3.32	3.37	2.72	3.10	2.90	2.33	1.69	2.11	4.57	3.03	34.48
1971	2.49	5.32	4.24	2.51	3.51	.75	5.39	7.35	7.71	3.83	4.49	2.08	49.87
1972	1.57	5.21	5.00	3.84	7.44	4.29	3.62	1.57	1.48	4.86	9.24*	5.55	63.67
1973	4.85	3.90	3.14	8.08	5.56	4.74	5.42	2.06	2.60	2.67	2.15	9.38*	54.55
1974	3.11	1.99	5.70	4.05	4.74	2.69	1.07	3.76	11.07	2.50	2.74	5.57	48.99
1975	5.01	3.26	4.01	3.19	3.00	5.38	7.26	2.53	12.84*	5.10	4.16	4.62	60.36
1976	5.94	3.37	2.63	3.59	4.96	6.39	2.55	6.96	2.87	5.68	.26*	2.52	47.72
1977	2.27	3.81	7.75	4.72	1.73	4.79	1.69	4.37	7.74	5.68	8.89	5.13	58.57
1978	8.17	2.07	4.59	2.19	8.18	1.69	4.51	5.32	2.52	1.98	4.66	4.98	50.86
1979	11.17*	4.76	4.47	5.12	4.70	1.07	1.20	4.55	5.73	4.30	4.62	3.42	55.11
1980	2.01	1.12	11.34	7.46	2.93	4.47	4.57	1.10	1.91	3.84	4.55	.56	45.86
1981	1.19	7.25*	.94*	3.59	5.02	2.19	4.22	.74	5.22	4.82	2.78	4.84	42.80
1982	6.08	2.58	2.42	6.72	2.55	6.85*	3.39	2.54	2.13	1.91	4.24	1.18	42.59
1983	7.60	3.50	11.10	12.11*	4.35	2.40	1.84	3.54	2.07	10.20	5.35	10.09*	74.15*
1984	2.35	4.16	6.77	8.37	11.22	5.14	8.83*	1.43	1.86	4.58	3.31	3.27	61.29
1985	1.34	2.84	1.93	.96*	4.88	4.39	3.34	5.37	6.13	1.43	8.95	2.50	44.06
1986	5.51	4.06	2.36	3.17	.48	3.99	3.63	4.61	1.15*	1.79	5.45	6.41	42.61
1987	5.43	.45	5.31	6.11	1.59	3.25	2.56	6.10	5.14	3.63	3.58	2.62	45.77
1988	4.07	3.96	2.26	1.75	4.90	.64	5.36	2.14	3.87	2.39	6.68	1.30	39.32
1989	3.63	3.39	4.84	3.30	13.29*	4.32	2.50	5.40	4.23	9.81	3.13	1.12	58.96
1990	3.88	2.81	4.29	5.79	6.46	3.15	1.46	10.46	1.23	7.15	4.17	6.86	57.71
1991	4.74	2.27	4.89	3.63	3.51	1.86	3.07	7.57	3.99	1.99	2.87	4.43	44.82
1992	1.59	1.80	3.99	2.11	4.20	6.21	4.17	5.03	6.15	1.83	6.47	6.03	49.58
1993	3.40	3.86	5.27	4.45	.48*	2.45	1.61	2.87	4.92	3.84	1.96	4.52	39.63
1994	2.99	3.35	5.84	2.35	3.41	1.74	5.50	4.49	2.19	.85	5.12	3.20	41.03
1995	4.17	2.21	1.24	2.18	2.34	1.00	4.50	.37*	5.93	8.27	4.33	2.99	39.53
1996	4.28	1.48	4.61	7.64	3.39	4.72	6.11	2.26	8.42	8.12	3.29	7.51	61.83
1997	4.90	2.54	4.08	4.25	4.09	4.85	6.07	4.85	2.77	2.21	5.88	4.44	50.93
1998	4.84	4.47	5.64	4.73	5.56	5.91	2.04	2.30	2.11	3.23	2.04	1.32	44.19
1999	5.97	3.84	6.04	1.21	4.53	1.31	.44*	3.35	10.29	3.18	2.42	3.93	46.51
2000	4.18	2.27	4.06	3.69	4.19	4.28	6.61	4.32	5.32	.64	4.88	4.48	48.92

Westchester Airport Monthly Averages 1961 - 1990

	Jan	Feb	Mar	Apr	May	June	July	Aug	Sep	Oct	Nov	Dec	Total
	3.90	3.63	4.43	4.54	4.47	3.78	3.70	3.83	4.05	3.70	4.55	4.26	48.84

Westchester Airport Monthly Averages 1971 - 2000

	Jan	Feb	Mar	Apr	May	June	July	Aug	Sep	Oct	Nov	Dec	Total
	4.29	3.26	4.69	4.43	4.57	3.56	3.82	3.97	4.72	4.08	4.42	4.23	50.04

APPENDIX L
PRECIPITATION TOTALS
(Inches)
YORKTOWN

Year	Jan	Feb	Mar	Apr	May	June	July	Aug	Sep	Oct	Nov	Dec	Total
1940	2.80	1.79	6.05	5.96	6.86	3.17	4.70	4.12	2.99	3.57	5.22	2.84	50.Q7
1941	2.73	2.97	1.83	1.91	3.20	4.90	9.04	5.19	.50	3.11	4.00	5.12	44.50
1942	3.94	1.76	7.39	1.34	2.77	3.66	8.22	7.95	4.10	3.76	5.71	5.12	58.72
1943	3.01	1.91	3.31	4.31	5.11	5.16	9.16	2.36	2.84	8.65	5.73	1.03	52.58
1944	1.54	2.18	5.91	5.87	2.07	3.22	3.01	2.38	7.83	1.97	6.97	3.92	46.87
1945	2.77	3.42	2.34	5.04	6.16	5.07	11.46*	6.33	4.50	2.98	4.95	5.17	60.49
1946	2.56	2.61	2.56	1.76	7.85	3.93	9.74	5.03	5.82	2.23	1.75	2.23	48.07
1947	3.14	2.12	4.23	4.55	9.54	6.02	4.38	4.39	3.25	1.50	8.90	3.90	55.92
1948	4.21	1.64	3.98	4.93	7.53	5.12	3.86	2.40	.56*	2.12	4.58	6.49	47.42
1949	6.47	2.12	2.53	4.87	5.30	.60*	3.30	4.14	3.40	2.10	1.50	3.20	39.59
1950	3.20	5.23	3.30	2.68	4.57	2.61	6.42	4.80	1.56	.69	5.30	4.66	45.02
1951	3.93	4.24	7.05	3.36	3.94	3.31	3.87	4.00	1.80	4.30	4.57	3.40	47.77
1952	4.87	2.68	5.30	7.92	6.41	5.57	5.27	10.41	4.70	.73	4.15	4.28	62.29
1953	5.30	1.74	9.97*	5.51	5.62	2.96	6.07	2.43	3.81	3.83	2.47	6.04	55.75
1954	2.00	2.34	4.17	4.09	7.19	1.72	1.74	· 8.96	9.42	2.11	7.21	4.62	55.57
1955	.95	4.04	5.06	5.30	2.25	4.19	3.11	14.21*	2.14	15.21*	6.87	.66*	63.95
1956	2.17	4.32	4.45	5.61	3.31	1.76	5.67	2.64	4.29	2.10	4.90	3.59	44.81
1957	2.26	2.50	2.03	5.23	2.85	1.56	3.89	3.09	2.66	3.48	4.04	7.07	40.66
1958	5.02	3.80	5.28	5.60	5.24	4.07	3.94	2.77	5.92	5.62	3.79	.85	51.94
1959	2.36	1.61	4.16	3.80	.1.37	5.88	2.55	4.91	2.14	8.16	4.91	5.13	46.98
1960	3.32	4.77	2.24	4.51	4.19	4.41	11.10	4.00	7.33	2.78	3.31	3.04	55.02
1961	3.78	3.49	3.47	6.62	5.52	4.39	5.88	7.30	3.54	2.94	3.98	4.34	55.25
1962	3.26	4.40	1.89	6.33	1.30	2.90	2.57	3.97	3.14	5.43	4.46	3.08	42.63
1963	3.24	2.42	3.80	1.33	1.42	3.70	6.67	2.53	4.30	.35*	7.39	2.34	39.49
1964	4.62	2.79	2.33	5.04	2.70	2.65	5.55	1.86	1.77	1.26	2.05	4.24	36.86*
1965	3.46	4.34	2.30	3.12	2.92	1.34	2.59	8.33	2.07	3.58	2.00	2.21	38.26
1966	2.52	4.57	1.70	2.51	3.50	.68	1.06*	1.87	6.25	4.57	4.37	3.54	37.14
1967	1.30	2.11	6.31	2.43	4.37	3.61	3.87	7.11	2.24	4.75	2.72	6.90	47.72
1968	2.70	1.00	5.42	3.41	6.73	5.87	1.25	5.34	3.79	1.92	5.09	4.55	47.07
1969	1.88	2.61	2.25	4.78	3.26	4.69	5.34	5.42	3.52	1.98	5.61	4.86	46.20
1970	.43*	4.69	3.80	3.90	1.74	2.99	5.40	2.88	4.12	3.26	4.81	2.94	40.96
1971	2.51	5.23	3.68	1.95	4.06	2.10	5.03	9.04	7.71	3.20	4.11	3.00	51.62
1972	1.97	4.51	4.83	4.03	4.89	13.62*	4.69	1.52	1.04	4.40	8.16	6.84	60.50
1973	4.72	4.42	4.06	6.46	6.26	4.20	6.35	2.81	2.21	2.52	2.04	9.18*	55.23
1974	4.58	2.16	4.41	4.20	4.50	2.49	2.20	3.54	9.00	2.25	2.12	4.62	46.07
1975	5.15	3.23	4.07	2.57	4.49	4.52	6.83	4.07	10.60	5.00	5.23	3.81	59.57
1976	5.57	3.42	2.68	3.48	3.90	5.98	4.99	8.17	3.85	5.84	1.06*	2.58	51.52
1977	1.87	3.16	7.75	4.46	3.20	3.12	2.44	1.96	8.56	6.49	8.59	4.60	56.20
1978	7.74	1.24	3.41	1.44	9.93	2.54	4.52	6.07	2.53	1.47	2.19	4.03	47.11
1979	11.29*	3.58	4.63	5.14	6.00	1.51	2.12	8.77	6.19	5.55	4.19	2.94	61.91
1980	1.97	1.04	8.83	7.68	2.18	2.79	3.89	1.99	1.35	4.19	4.01	.69	40.41
1981	.62	7.60*	.69*	4.24	4.42	1.88	4.26	.45*	3.35	5.92	1.49	4.76	39.66
1982	4.46	2.95	2.11	5.30	3.50	7.10	4.80	2.96	3.06	1.97	3.94	1.77	43.92
1983	4.11	4.17	8.13	10.23*	5.99	2.92	1.84	3.58	2.54	6.41	5.62	8.59	64.13
1984	1.75	4.30	4.73	7.45	10.84	3.50	10.60	3.80	2.11	3.19	3.32	2.89	58.48
1985	1.02	2.24	1.90	1.23*	6.64	4.88	5.14	6.90	5.64	1.95	6.80	1.82	46.16
1986	4.11	4.09	1.84	2.69	.91*	4.09	8.56	4.27	1.22	2.66	7.21	3.77	45.42
1987	5.63	.37*	3.55	8.62	1.92	3.79	3.02	5.49	6.26	5.15	2.79	2.01	48.60
1988	3.23	3.53	2.15	1.91	5.40	.47*	6.50	2.71	2.63	2.79	9.02*	1.26	41.60
1989	1.95	2.63	3.51	3.77	11.04*	7.20	2.25	4.51	6.51	7.42	3.56	.90	55.25
1990	5.02	2.84	3.82	5.16	7.90	2.99	4.43	10.12	2.32	6.06	3.51	6.23	60.40
1991	2.64	1.92	4.11	3.86	3.71	2.91	2.82	6.25	5.23	3.37	4.03	3.46	44.31
1992	1.93	2.24	4.08	2.46	2.08	6.38	4.24	4.27	3.45	1.54	6.73	5.43	44.83
1993	2.91	3.17	6.30	5.46	8.80	3.36	1.77	4.25	5.27	4.33	4.22	4.60	46.52
1994	6.01	3.31	5.87	3.66	5.91	10.07	5.75	5.24	3.07	1.47	6.32	3.85	60.53
1995	5.01	2.42	1.76	2.76	2.47	1.05	2.60	2.77	3.60	9.16	5.70	2.11	41.41
1996	7.41	2.29	3.72	5.91	3.42	5.36	10.37	1.34	6.96	7.26	4.40	7.59	66.03*
1997	3.63	1.71	3.40	4.51	3.96	2.74	6.60	6.53	1.74	2.52	6.74	3.29	47.37
1998	3.12	3.66	5.31	4.69	6.16	5.49	2.54	3.60	2.04	4.17	2.12	1.07	43.97
1999	6.84	3.13	6.15	2.12	4.60	1.93	1.96	4.46	18.00*	2.71	3.18	2.10	54.18
2000	3.00	2.27	3.67	4.16	4.19	5.38	5.68	4.99	4.19	.88	2.98	4.27	45.66

Yorktown Heights 1W Monthly Averages 1971 - 2000

	Jan	Feb	Mar	Apr	May	June	July	Aug	Sep	Oct	Nov	Dec	Total
	4.06	3.09	4.16	4.39	4.84	4.21	4.63	4.55	4.74	4.06	4.51	3.80	51.04

Rain gauges comprising Yorktown precipitation record: Yorktown Heights - 1940 - 1949, ShrubOak- 1950-1964, Yorktown Heights 1W 1964 - 2000

APPENDIX M
TOTAL PRECIPITATION (Inches)
CROTON RIVER WATERSHED - AMAWALK

Year	Jan	Feb	Mar	Apr	May	June	July	Aug	Sep	Oct	Nov	Dec	Total
1903	3.80	3.70	4.80	2.37	.93	9.61	3.39	7.72	2.80	8.30	2.76	4.26	54.53
1904	3.63	3.32	3.45	4.47	4.04	2.79	6.40	9.44	7.22	3.61	2.35	2.90	53.62
1905	6.22	1.58	4.55	3.28	1.64	7.20	3.02	6.34	5.17	3.54	2.29	4.04	48.87
1906	2.70	2.20	6.13	4.59	3.61	4.17	5.84	4.31	3.83	4.55	1.43	3.64	47.00
1907	3.64	3.26	7.84	3.46	5.48	4.12	2.89	1.69	10.95	8.20	6.34	4.91	57.78
1908	4.18	6.39*	3.90	3.26	7.26	2.46	2.23	7.80	1.04	2.00	1.13	3.42	45.06
1909	4.60	5.68	4.87	7.17	1.97	3.20	2.35	5.21	4.15	1.12	3.11	4.72	48.15
1910	7.25	5.19	.84	5.48	3.57	4.48	1.37	2.66	2.21	1.11	5.06	2.67	41.89*
1911	3.34	3.32	4.35	3.76	1.73	3.19	3.37	7.76	3.04	6.38	4.51	3.37	48.10
1912	1.96	2.41	7.80	3.90*	4.03	1.45	2.33	4.35	4.23	3.60	3.04	4.68	43.78
1913	3.94	2.74	6.18	5.95	3.23	.93	3.44	4.26	5.16	8.78	2.99	2.76	50.36
1914	4.20	2.23	4.75	4.40	2.85	3.47	4.84	2.08	.18*	2.99	3.31	3.91	39.21
1915	6.24	6.23	.42	3.72	2.96	2.49	5.65	8.23	3.83	2.99	2.37	5.71	50.85
1916	1.77	5.66	3.41	3.16	3.72	4.92	8.16	3.62	5.74	1.68	3.29	3.29	48.42
1917	3.14	2.27	4.08	2.50	5.43	4.10	2.85	1.73	1.04	6.27	2.25	1.80	37.46
1918	3.77	2.66	1.97	5.63	2.45	3.29	4.01	4.51	4.10	1.44	2.22	4.14	40.15
1919	2.60	4.23	6.67	3.02	5.00	2.70	6.40	4.17	5.35	4.24	4.43	2.69	51.50
1920	2.71	4.39	3.54	5.86	3.18	5.89	5.57	2.52	7.77	1.61	.36*	4.19	47.59
1921	2.81	2.72	4.28	4.91	2.33	3.61	4.62	2.35	3.85	1.58	4.34	2.45	39.89
1922	1.83	2.57	6.53	1.77	5.44	6.37	11.98*	3.15	3.54	2.64	1.59	3.97	51.42
1923	5.19	2.00	3.02	3.43	2.33	3.37	1.93	2.05	3.49	6.69	3.39	3.97	40.86
1924	4.32	2.70	1.27	6.48	5.29	2.28	2.42	6.87	6.11	.22*	3.92*	2.72	44.60
1925	2.95	3.57	4.65	2.32	4.40	4.56	7.34	1.26	4.45	4.04	3.59	2.33	45.46
1926	2.91	3.95	2.66	2.71	1.88	2.17	2.54	6.72	3.33	5.17	5.13	3.50	42.67
1927	2.62	3.48	2.02	2.40	5.77	2.56	9.73	7.72	3.84	7.03	5.29	4.87	57.33
1928	2.73	4.26	2.95	4.77	1.82	7.80	6.18	7.99	3.62	.90	2.94	1.03	46.99
1929	3.89	3.67	3.57	7.09	4.60	2.59	3.09	2.89	5.33	3.81	2.48	3.56	46.57
1930	3.34	2.40	2.82	3.12	3.35	6.81	2.90	4.85	2.64	1.87	5.48	2.59	42.17
1931	2.21	2.82	4.11	4.49	7.15	7.57	3.25	3.80	2.14	2.15	1.16	2.94	43.79
1932	4.37	2.93	4.69	2.71	2.83	3.15	3.76	2.72	1.77	5.22	8.13	2.40	44.68
1933	2.01	4.03	4.72	6.02	2.89	2.92	2.24	11.34	5.76	3.06	.85	3.53	49.37
1934	3.66	2.92	4.55	3.05	6.38	3.24	4.22	2.27	11.10	3.13	4.08	3.55	52.05
1935	2.87	2.81	2.56	1.71	2.19	4.77	3.56	1.67	3.27	1.48	3.26	1.05	31.20*
1936	6.79	3.16	7.02	4.34	2.93	5.17	2.93	3.95	4.78	2.27	1.38	7.08	51.80
1937	6.72	3.24	2.85	4.68	4.22	5.09	4.73	10.61	5.21	6.09	4.63	3.14	61.21
1938	4.69	2.64	2.32	3.31	3.07	6.90	11.33	3.49	12.53	2.54	3.29	4.16	60.27
1939	3.75	5.15	4.52	5.99	1.09	4.75	1.44	3.51	3.58	4.26	1.86	2.12	42.02
1940	2.77	2.20	5.70	6.03	6.45	3.89	3.87	5.00	2.74	3.27	4.82	2.96	49.70
1941	3.25	2.94	2.06	1.58	3.24	3.29	9.43	3.23	.58	3.41	3.04	5.03	41.08
1942	4.26	1.71	6.69	1.30	2.49	3.16	6.27	6.68	3.94	4.52	4.45	5.47	50.94
1943	3.50	1.88	3.58	3.51	5.67	3.62	8.25	2.07	2.84	7.75	5.02	.98	48.67
1944	2.30	2.13	5.72	5.28	2.45	3.32	3.37	2.46	7.45	1.78	6.74	3.74	46.74
1945	3.55	3.50	2.00	4.04	6.32	3.96	11.73	4.65	4.33	2.98	4.01	5.10	56.17
1946	1.66	2.18	2.14	1.56	6.68	4.09	8.26	4.01	4.87	1.63	1.52	2.01	40.61
1947	2.75	2.53	3.41	6.35	5.92	5.29	4.64	2.65	2.86	1.40	7.55	3.79	49.14
1948	4.40	1.64	4.72	3.55	6.02	5.26	3.18	2.60	.68	1.56	3.71	6.42	43.77
1949	5.70	3.05	1.81	4.18	5.48	1.05	3.54	3.06	2.76	2.06	1.23	3.36	37.28
1950	3.09	3.85	2.86	2.83	4.04	2.96	8.68	4.67	1.33	1.54	5.48	4.85	46.18
1951	4.27	3.66	5.91	3.48	4.33	3.63	5.41	4.12	1.83	5.81	6.44	4.44	53.33
1952	4.34	2.19	3.95	7.16	7.92	3.52	4.32	9.32	5.11	.77	3.03	4.50	56.13
1953	6.17	2.21	9.05	6.40	3.48	2.96	6.05	1.24	1.42	1.12	2.39	5.52	48.01
1954	2.23	2.20	4.27	3.50	4.55	4.50	2.19	8.19	8.18	2.48	6.68	3.82	52.79
1955	1.11	4.13	3.85	4.08	2.20	5.20	4.51	15.39*	3.20	13.92*	6.54*	.66*	64.79*
1956	2.04	3.82	3.83	4.47	3.17	2.63	4.57	3.18	4.31	5.04	2.43	3.95	43.44
1957	2.30	2.48	1.69	4.94	4.18	1.19	3.29	2.61	2.52	3.27	3.22	7.45	39.14
1958	4.79	4.13	4.96	5.81	3.77	4.82	3.74	2.85	5.38	4.57	3.84	1.10	49.76
1959	1.93	2.46	4.26	3.31	.80	6.02	2.24	4.60	.96	7.36	4.52	4.65	43.10
1960	3.05	4.69	2.59	2.83	3.67	4.15	8.90	3.77	6.97	2.55	2.59	2.95	48.71

Year	Jan	Feb	Mar	Apr	May	June	July	Aug	Sep	Oct	Nov	Dec	Total
1961	2.40	4.30	3.43	5.01	5.39	4.25	4.74	4.68	2.78	1.57	3.29	3.63	45.47
1962	3.28	4.67	2.91	4.03	1.61	2.70	2.52	3.94	2.94	4.46	4.58	3.25	40.93
1963	2.71	2.29	3.78	1.53	2.41	2.80	4.88	2.00	4.31	.37	7.41	2.59	37.08
1964	4.52	2.59	2.33	5.09	1.81	3.53	4.32	1.89	1.60	1.49	2.30	4.49	35.96
1965	3.59	4.17	2.34	3.27	2.14	2.64	2.27	8.20	2.06	3.65	2.08	1.91	38.32
1966	2.78	4.66	1.61	2.60	3.10	.71	1.03	1.99	5.66	4.76	3.91	3.17	35.98
1967	1.35	2.96	5.69	2.64	4.45	3.50	3.53	6.14	2.37	5.70	2.99	6.88	48.20
1968	2.33	1.85	4.75	3.40	6.70	6.75	1.74	6.01	3.49	1.88	5.43	4.87	49.20
1969	1.75	2.75	2.15	4.86	3.19	4.26	5.33	6.33	3.66	1.82	6.24	6.01	48.35
1970	.39*	4.68	3.55	3.60	1.70	3.37	4.00	2.75	4.24	3.55	4.44	3.19	39.46
1971	2.51	7.55*	3.78	1.65	3.73	1.73	5.56	8.14	8.22	2.15	3.65	2.60	51.27
1972	2.73	5.21	4.65	4.25	6.79	12.31*	4.74	2.39	1.40	4.16	8.99*	6.71	64.33
1973	3.89	4.08	3.32	4.93	6.04	4.50	6.07	2.71	2.42	2.71	2.30	9.07	53.04
1974	4.29	2.20	3.59	4.17	4.82	2.00	1.80	3.19	7.77	2.18	1.90	4.52	42.43
1975	4.63	2.97	3.17	2.53	4.02	4.00	7.26	3.47	11.28	4.53	5.31	3.80	56.97
1976	5.31	3.13	4.23	1.28	3.82	5.85	3.88	7.59	4.13	5.42	.62	2.43	47.69
1977	1.60	2.77	7.28	3.43	2.43	2.88	2.56	2.07	7.66	6.03	8.34	3.39	50.44
1978	7.59	1.83	3.33	1.41	10.11	2.34	4.41	7.30	2.27	1.39	1.79	3.73	47.50
1979	8.97*	3.05	3.90	4.83	6.19	1.70	1.00	8.10	6.47	3.59	4.82	3.00	55.62
1980	1.50	.99*	9.50*	6.01	2.33	3.03	3.27	2.70	2.06	4.01	3.69	.72	39.81
1981	.45	6.44	.32*	1.72	3.35	1.09	2.62	.30*	3.45	5.91	1.27	4.78	31.70
1982	4.73	1.85	2.28	4.58	2.82	6.94	2.73	2.68	3.09	1.63	3.68	1.56	38.57
1983	4.25	3.40	7.51	8.59*	5.46	2.34	1.59	2.46	2.65	5.93	3.88	9.84*	57.90
1984	1.87	3.99	3.80	7.22	9.71	5.16	8.95	1.61	1.62	3.18	3.63	2.40	53.14
1985	1.40	2.35	2.08	.53*	5.82	4.58	6.37	4.52	5.43	1.55	6.50	1.70	42.82
1986	4.23	3.46	2.29	2.09	.57*	4.36	7.42	3.14	.80	2.29	5.75	4.10	36.58
1987	5.12	1.04	3.96	6.74	1.48	3.35	3.05	5.31	5.85	4.81	2.79	1.70	45.20
1988	3.05	3.33	2.13	1.46	4.51	.50*	5.56	2.65	2.63	2.46	7.39	1.23	36.90
1989	1.75	2.61	3.62	3.31	11.03*	7.23	1.89	3.27	5.39	8.05	2.95	1.28	51.22
1990	3.80	3.01	3.92	4.60	7.18	3.42	4.73	12.83	2.21	5.82	3.14	5.85	60.51
1991	3.17	1.90	4.11	3.48	3.09	2.10	2.80	5.88	.97	2.51	3.49	3.20	36.70
1992	1.63	2.70	3.79	2.33	2.91	4.24	4.48	3.86	3.24	1.08	6.49	5.37	41.14
1993	2.77	3.11	6.06	4.11	1.74	1.88	1.43	2.88	5.11	5.02	3.61	4.75	45.20
1994	6.50	3.25	6.02	3.37	6.00	9.68	5.67	4.39	2.68	2.04	4.56	4.50	58.66
1995	4.65	4.00	1.25	3.15	1.70	1.34	2.40	2.66	2.55	9.53	5.30	2.28	40.81
1996	8.61	2.84	3.72	5.82	3.33	.57	9.11	1.65	7.27	6.51	3.63	7.48	60.54
1997	3.51	1.55	6.05	2.64	4.13	2.58	5.05	5.27	1.28	2.07	6.19	3.65	43.97
1998	3.40	3.70	4.80	4.49	7.66	4.37	1.53	2.04	3.52	3.52	2.06	1.02	42.11
1999	5.72	4.15	5.54	1.92	4.27	1.43	.85*	3.73	17.47*	3.15	3.02	2.28	53.53
2000	3.19	2.25	1.78	3.45	5.13	5.23	3.76	3.73	3.93	.82	2.66	3.98	39.81

* = Extremes

Amawalk 1961 - 1990 Monthly Averages

	Jan	Feb	Mar	Apr	May	June	July	Aug	Sep	Oct	Nov	Dec	Total
	3.29	3.34	3.71	3.71	4.49	3.79	4.00	4.34	4.00	3.57	4.17	3.81	46.22

Amawalk 1971 - 2000 Monthly Averages

	Jan	Feb	Mar	Apr	May	June	July	Aug	Sep	Oct	Nov	Dec	Total
	3.89	3.16	3.96	3.67	4.74	3.75	4.08	4.08	4.49	3.80	4.11	3.76	47.49

APPENDIX N
TOTAL PRECIPITATION (Inches)
CROSS RIVER

Year	Jan	Feb	Mar	Apr	May	June	July	Aug	Sep	Oct	Nov	Dec	Total
1907	3.65	2.65	2.26	3.44	4.39	4.12	1.85	1.39	10.79	7.50	6.30	5.80	54.14
1908	4.19	6.57	3.69	3.24	6.17	1.34	2.54	7.97	1.22	2.00	.99	3.34	43.26
1909	3.84	5.90	5.27	7.88	2.00	2.28	2.51	5.09	4.26	1.50	2.66	4.79	47.98
1910	7.52	4.83	.68	5.38	3.54	3.52	1.81	3.39	2.12	1.10	5.10	2.61	41.60
1911	3.06	3.13	3.98	3.39	2.45	3.01	3.28	7.73	2.21	6.74	4.90	3.02	46.90
1912	1.91	2.56	8.00	4.03	4.25	1.37	2.28	4.45	3.88	4.29	3.98	5.00	46.00
1913	4.23	2.70	5.52	5.79	3.44	1.30	2.77	4.95	4.35	10.58	3.19	3.39	52.21
1914	3.78	2.45	4.23	4.33	3.23	3.67	4.90	1.59	.36*	2.78	4.00	4.30	39.62
1915	7.53	6.67	.48	2.76	3.01	2.30	5.07	11.27	3.35	3.28	3.70	7.65	57.07
1916	1.78	5.35	3.67	2.71	2.51	4.29	5.94	2.52	4.59	1.79	2.70	3.26	41.11
1917	2.99	1.71	4.15	2.08	3.65	3.60	2.14	3.06	1.14	6.33	2.12	2.56	35.53
1918	3.97	2.45	1.79	5.28	1.81	4.10	6.76	4.42	3.60	1.82	2.09	3.96	42.05
1919	2.90	4.60	6.77	2.42	4.30	2.55	6.04	3.75	6.81	4.36	4.32	2.70	51.52
1920	2.77	5.10	4.21	5.18	3.14	5.32	5.77	2.30	6.76	1.60	.30*	4.75	47.20
1921	2.48	2.77	3.57	4.25	2.63	4.23	4.79	2.35	3.41	1.51	4.21	2.46	38.66
1922	1.69	2.76	5.61	1.74	5.44	6.24	10.15	2.48	3.66	2.48	1.26	4.25	47.76
1923	5.36	2.01	3.08	.28	2.04	5.36	1.89	1.70	2.69	6.72	2.88	4.02	38.03
1924	5.09	2.76	1.42	7.11	5.00	2.06	1.71	6.35	6.14	.35	4.24	2.35	44.58
1925	3.06	3.75	4.72	2.05	4.14	5.57	7.60	1.32	3.53	3.44	3.95	2.27	45.50
1926	2.92	4.79	2.55	2.59	1.88	2.24	2.25	6.19	3.30	4.51	4.57	3.91	41.70
1927	2.56	3.72	1.64	1.93	4.80	2.57	8.06	8.89	3.47	7.18	5.90	4.56	55.28
1928	2.42	2.47	2.81	4.62	1.81	7.43	6.81	6.75	4.08	.77	2.62	1.37	43.96
1929	4.82	3.44	3.02	6.06	4.09	1.75	2.88	3.84	4.56	3.28	2.15	3.84	43.73
1930	3.00	2.22	2.39	3.06	3.08	7.24	2.90	4.74	2.33	2.17	2.55	2.36	38.04
1931	1.96	2.28	3.57	3.79	5.81	4.51	3.84	2.94	2.37	3.12	.90	2.17	37.26
1932	4.01	2.69	4.48	2.40	2.49	3.77	3.93	2.95	2.05	4.46	7.27	2.32	42.82
1933	2.01	3.56	4.63	5.50	2.47	2.76	1.81	10.98	5.13	3.42	.59	3.54	46.40
1934	3.68	3.38	4.24	2.69	5.97	4.45	4.21	2.24	10.84	3.36	3.22	3.07	51.35
1935	2.88	2.83	2.35	1.39	2.08	5.53	3.91	1.09	3.63	1.39	3.52	1.12	31.72
1936	6.53	3.66	6.34	4.01	2.92	6.72	6.03	3.88	4.53	2.44	1.20	6.85	55.11
1937	6.12	2.92	2.89	3.90	4.34	6.82	3.41	9.79	5.75	6.54	4.19	2.80	59.47
1938	5.65	2.22	2.07	2.75	3.36	8.16	10.37*	4.20	13.21	2.28	3.03	3.52	60.82
1939	3.39	4.90	3.88	5.06	1.57	5.62	2.71	4.50	3.18	2.82	2.25	2.14	42.02
1940	2.68	2.82	5.34	6.52	7.24	4.08	4.20	5.66	2.75	3.06	5.09	2.65	52.09
1941	2.79	3.05	2.30	1.56	3.49	4.13	8.18	4.31	.52	3.36	2.87	4.88	41.44
1942	3.58	1.53	6.58	1.12	3.59	3.61	7.24	6.87	3.70	5.00	4.46	5.09	52.37
1943	3.21	1.64	3.51	3.05	5.40	3.84	5.39	2.29	2.61	7.15	4.31	1.06	43.46
1944	2.31	2.22	5.37	5.52	2.16	3.75	2.38	3.32	7.96	2.33	6.11	3.90	47.33
1945	3.53	3.70	2.13	5.18	5.99	4.01	7.91	4.49	4.94	2.36	5.54	5.23	55.01
1946	1.72	2.20	2.26	1.28	7.42	3.14	6.09	5.81	6.46	1.61	1.42	2.45	41.86
1947	2.27	2.98	3.05	5.25	.54	4.27	4.10	3.79	1.90	1.38	7.49	3.46	40.48
1948	4.19	1.48	5.07	3.28	6.93	4.24	3.60	2.39	.86	1.92	3.86	6.19	44.01
1949	5.03	3.09	1.80	4.23	5.17	.59	3.12	4.64	2.89	2.15	1.21	3.02	36.94
1950	2.85	3.63	2.62	2.57	4.64	2.57	10.00	3.84	1.20	1.72	5.29	4.23	45.16
1951	3.79	3.35	5.03	3.37	4.63	2.70	6.52	4.73	1.19	6.04	5.77	4.25	51.37
1952	4.27	2.31	4.10	7.16	7.48	3.19	4.55	8.50	5.04	.71	2.82	3.17	53.30
1953	5.14	1.96	7.86	6.16	3.03	3.16	4.90	1.33	1.26	4.02	2.35	4.65	45.82
1954	2.31	1.89	3.55	3.58	3.77	1.17	2.18	7.72	7.89	2.38	7.52	3.27	47.23
1955	.76	3.41	3.27	4.29	2.68	2.78	4.36	14.03*	3.15	16.62*	6.81	.52*	62.68*
1956	2.05	3.05	3.86	5.07	3.48	2.60	4.33	3.00	4.26	5.92	3.30	4.10	45.02
1957	2.06	2.32	1.67	4.68	3.49	.61	3.14	2.68	3.29	3.82	3.66	6.38	37.80
1958	4.37	3.77	4.86	5.68	5.41	5.01	3.11	3.14	4.61	3.97	3.36	1.08	48.37
1959	2.02	2.20	3.14	3.52	.83	5.42	3.70	4.39	1.11	6.48	3.92	3.85	40.58
1960	2.57	3.67	2.67	2.57	3.66	2.24	8.99	3.41	5.96	2.81	3.08	3.46	45.08

Year	Jan	Feb	Mar	Apr	May	June	July	Aug	Sep	Oct	Nov	Dec	Total
1961	2.31	3.16	3.49	5.00	4.75	3.25	5.21	4.64	3.27	1.91	3.46	3.43	43.88
1962	3.07	3.48	2.23	2.64	1.32	3.44	2.33	3.73	2.27	3.49	4.06	2.76	34.82
1963	2.64	2.45	3.23	1.54	2.22	2.89	4.30	1.95	3.80	.35*	6.98	2.92	35.27
1964	4.24	2.56	2.19	4.88	1.94	2.77	4.17	1.72	1.47	1.30	1.99	4.57	33.80
1965	3.54	3.69	2.15	3.27	1.99	1.80	2.36	4.61	2.85	3.89	1.64	1.53	33.32
1966	2.60	3.94	1.32	2.11	2.67	1.11	.97	1.63	4.76	4.39	2.90	3.19	31.59*
1967	1.15	2.75	5.57	2.23	3.54	2.85	3.13	4.57	1.71	4.31	2.64	6.08	40.53
1968	1.90	1.69	4.08	2.48	5.02	4.80	.78*	5.74	2.67	1.90	5.07	4.32	40.45
1969	1.43	3.00	1.73	4.26	3.60	3.79	3.97	4.19	2.60	1.32	4.36	5.51	39.76
1970	.40*	4.10	3.64	2.97	1.94	2.82	2.37	2.55	3.60	3.31	3.90	3.15	34.75
1971	2.44	4.02	3.22	2.41	3.06	1.33	5.02	6.12	6.20	3.26	3.37	2.34	42.79
1972	1.85	4.09	4.68	3.03	5.02	11.77*	2.43	2.92	1.04	3.73	7.82	5.64	54.02
1973	3.77	3.81	3.02	5.87	4.79	3.97	3.07	1.49	1.61	2.78	1.50	8.28*	43.96
1974	4.47	1.99	3.57	3.84	3.93	1.72	1.70	5.18	8.06	1.85	1.28	3.45	41.04
1975	3.98	3.00	3.59	2.18	3.16	3.60	6.13	3.39	11.82	4.46	3.21	3.46	51.98
1976	5.56	3.03	4.14	1.13	3.67	5.65	4.00	6.45	3.11	4.95	.46	2.30	44.45
1977	1.90	2.53	6.62	3.36	2.17	2.35	2.79	1.89	5.69	4.20	7.97	3.03	44.50
1978	6.73	1.13	3.40	1.25	9.13	2.36	3.74	6.87	1.61	1.49	1.50	4.99	44.19
1979	10.09*	3.66	4.23	5.07	4.74	1.43	1.70	7.00	6.47	4.96	4.33	3.05	56.73
1980	1.28	.92*	9.56*	6.15	2.45	3.08	2.68	1.94	1.28	3.45	3.69	.75	35.45
1981	.46	7.32*	.46*	1.93	3.29	1.22	3.44	.44*	2.08	6.13	1.31	4.78	32.86
1982	4.09	1.66	2.11	4.59	2.49	6.45	3.23	2.96	3.44	1.35	3.87	1.31	37.65
1983	4.57	4.82	8.32	9.12*	4.53	2.83	1.81	2.88	1.92	6.25	4.11	7.54	58.70
1984	2.15	4.23	4.11	5.76	9.62	5.25	7.87	2.38	1.29	2.52	3.75	2.13	45.31
1985	1.27	1.78	1.53	.23*	5.92	4.80	5.36	4.67	4.02	1.39	6.11	1.22	38.30
1986	3.27	3.20	2.15	1.78	.40*	3.80	6.61	5.03	.73	2.24	5.52	2.99	37.72
1987	5.73	1.00	3.72	6.69	1.62	2.79	2.20	4.33	4.58	5.27	2.46	1.55	41.94
1988	3.03	3.14	2.05	1.53	5.52	.48*	5.53	2.13	1.76	2.47	8.54*	1.13	37.31
1989	1.81	2.42	3.50	3.11	9.80*	5.54	2.63	3.32	4.57	8.02	2.81	1.18	48.71
1990	3.87	2.61	3.05	3.78	6.78	2.99	3.43	9.81	2.09	4.73	3.03	5.58	51.75
1991	2.98	2.15	4.08	3.70	3.61	1.63	3.92	8.49	.75	2.30	3.44	3.43	40.48
1992	1.54	2.71	3.07	1.90	2.97	4.19	5.31	5.06	4.03	2.13	5.85	5.94	44.70
1993	2.62	2.76	6.58	3.44	1.71	2.21	1.56	2.58	4.68	5.05	3.49	4.01	40.69
1994	6.43	3.63	5.57	2.94	4.62	8.78	7.26	4.56	3.07	2.08	4.09	4.31	57.41
1995	4.56	4.00	1.35	3.33	1.57	1.08	3.19	1.96	2.31	9.74	5.59	2.43	41.11
1996	8.55	3.12	3.89	5.96	2.78	6.03	9.15	1.65	7.08	6.70	3.07	6.93	58.59
1997	3.54	1.41	5.69	2.30	4.20	2.80	5.59	4.88	1.13	1.75	6.46	3.65	43.40
1998	3.46	3.83	4.99	4.21	7.05	4.23	2.02	3.05	3.15	3.56	2.06	1.07	42.68
1999	7.96	3.57	5.53	1.94	4.07	.78	1.24	2.67	16.54*	3.47	2.97	2.26	53.00
2000	3.65	2.25	1.84	3.03	2.60	4.88	4.25	2.76	3.10	.65	3.20	3.87	36.08

Cross River 1961 - 1990 Monthly Averages

	Jan	Feb	Mar	Apr	May	June	July	Aug	Sep	Oct	Nov	Dec	Total
	3.19	3.04	3.56	3.47	4.04	3.44	3.50	3.88	3.41	3.38	3.79	3.47	42.17

Cross River 1971 - 2000 Monthly Averages

	Jan	Feb	Mar	Apr	May	June	July	Aug	Sep	Oct	Nov	Dec	Total
	2.92	2.99	3.99	3.52	4.24	3.67	3.96	3.96	3.97	3.76	3.90	3.49	45.37

APPENDIX O
TOTAL PRECIPITATION (Inches)

CROTON FALLS

Year	Jan	Feb	Mar	Apr	May	June	July	Aug	Sep	Oct	Nov	Dec	Total
1907	4.19	2.98	2.61	3.75	5.00	3.94	1.63	2.53	11.07	7.49	5.12	3.42	53.73
1908	3.56	4.62	2.40	2.66	5.56	1.87	2.40	6.10	.81	1.45	.94	2.64	36.01
1909	4.25	5.77	3.90	6.14	2.00	2.99	3.00	5.74	3.72	1.50	3.39	4.50	46.90
1910	7.48	4.65	.86	4.23	3.90	4.07	2.64	3.05	1.82	1.00	4.59	1.44	39.73
1911	2.88	2.45	3.84	3.29	2.47	3.16	2.50	8.62	2.12	6.29	4.03	2.82	44.47
1912	1.94	2.44	7.34	3.70	5.19	1.23	3.03	4.20	3.38	4.00	3.61	4.32	44.38
1913	3.67	2.50	5.73	5.07	3.67	.90	2.58	4.34	3.64	9.60	2.81	2.84	47.35
1914	3.38	3.07	4.49	3.92	2.51	2.83	5.46	1.81	.40*	2.96	2.89	3.79	37.51
1915	6.80	5.72	.28*	3.35	3.01	2.93	4.64	8.31	3.31	2.69	2.47	5.78	49.29
1916	1.57	4.51	3.32	3.08	3.35	4.30	5.62	2.31	5.67	1.21	2.89	2.88	40.71
1917	2.88	2.55	3.63	1.85	3.80	3.25	4.17	2.18	1.00	6.57	2.20	1.76	35.84
1918	3.72	2.80	1.75	5.69	2.21	3.03	4.85	3.86	3.96	1.08	2.67	3.75	39.37
1919	2.77	4.42	6.01	2.55	4.22	2.30	6.46	4.11	5.63	3.65	4.76	2.39	49.27
1920	2.59	4.53	3.72	5.40	2.94	5.70	6.37	1.91	7.55	1.40	.26*	4.39	46.76
1921	2.48	2.26	3.71	4.07	2.19	3.39	4.68	2.17	3.35	1.45	3.94	2.10	35.79
1922	1.66	2.31	6.27	1.60	4.50	7.34	10.40*	3.51	2.69	2.95	1.21	3.71	48.15
1923	5.41	1.72	2.92	3.18	2.24	3.13	1.86	2.84	3.95	6.62	2.82	3.80	40.49
1924	4.46	2.66	1.47	6.40	4.24	1.80	3.01	5.03	5.90	.12*	4.06	2.75	41.90
1925	2.63	3.67	4.43	2.18	3.88	4.27	6.70	1.06	3.19	3.38	3.22	2.04	40.65
1926	2.94	4.09	2.40	2.68	1.71	2.24	3.59	7.91	3.30	5.03	4.96	3.32	44.17
1927	2.31	3.29	1.90	2.02	5.26	3.10	6.50	8.41	4.07	7.01	5.64	4.87	54.38
1928	2.44	3.72	3.25	4.66	2.14	7.43	6.43	9.56	3.23	.97	2.85	1.00	47.68
1929	3.84	3.00	3.30	6.74	3.98	2.93	2.16	3.39	4.51	3.09	2.16	3.79	42.89
1930	3.08	2.18	2.28	2.91	2.57	7.33	3.46	3.49	2.65	1.66	4.77	2.40	38.78
1931	1.93	2.38	3.63	3.75	6.46	6.14	4.35	5.20	3.31	2.39	1.14	2.84	43.52
1932	4.30	2.58	4.41	2.66	3.09	3.50	4.14	3.92	2.32	4.58	7.71	2.08	45.29
1933	2.07	3.79	4.63	5.24	2.99	1.93	2.51	9.02	5.18	3.00	.89	3.35	44.60
1934	3.62	3.63	3.58	2.95	6.02	4.38	4.56	2.54	10.55	2.87	4.18	3.25	52.13
1935	3.18	2.98	2.62	1.74	2.52	4.67	4.74	1.47	3.44	1.38	3.25	1.07	33.06
1936	6.60	3.19	6.55	3.87	2.74	5.79	3.37	6.62	4.93	2.36	1.30	6.36	53.68
1937	6.63	2.67	2.79	3.77	4.60	5.47	2.14	9.51	5.52	5.77	3.83	2.51	55.11
1938	4.54	2.64	2.08	2.98	3.32	5.61	8.54	5.37	13.78	2.59	3.86	3.61	58.92
1939	3.49	4.72	4.63	5.82	1.09	3.40	2.58	4.56	4.36	4.61	1.83	2.19	43.28
1940	2.56	3.14	5.57	5.67	5.55	4.32	3.43	4.25	2.30	2.71	4.48	2.82	46.90
1941	2.86	2.95	1.94	1.22	2.28	5.01	8.22	4.08	.84	3.85	2.85	4.61	40.71
1942	3.54	1.71	6.78	1.03	2.98	3.37	5.42	5.80	4.02	4.51	4.05	4.98	48.19
1943	3.22	1.88	3.29	3.55	5.02	3.43	4.55	2.16	2.56	6.44	5.30	.96	42.36
1944	2.10	2.09	5.13	4.84	1.75	3.41	3.65	1.89	6.24	2.07	6.13	3.89	43.19
1945	3.22	3.32	1.88	4.59	6.51	4.16	10.19	4.15	4.31	2.91	3.46	4.47	53.17
1946	1.63	2.08	2.14	1.32	6.06	5.06	7.70	2.50	5.99	1.43	1.47	2.10	39.48
1947	2.49	2.94	3.34	5.63	5.43	4.63	3.73	4.93	2.27	1.72	6.63	3.59	47.33
1948	3.80	1.58	4.68	3.53	5.19	4.84	4.32	3.17	.91	1.60	3.28	6.02	42.92
1949	4.92	2.82	1.68	3.49	6.11	.54	2.35	4.03	2.60	2.07	.82	3.52	34.95
1950	2.63	3.15	2.45	2.25	4.69	2.83	7.39	5.72	.95	1.30	3.75	3.79	40.90
1951	3.75	3.03	4.44	2.57	4.85	2.88	4.85	4.74	2.34	5.30	5.54	3.98	48.27
1952	4.06	1.80	3.20	6.66	7.17	2.99	4.02	8.11	4.54	.76	2.78	3.16	49.25
1953	5.68	1.93	8.03	5.72	3.33	1.87	5.55	.70*	1.31	4.14	2.54	5.20	46.00
1954	2.16	2.09	3.77	3.61	3.91	1.14	1.11	6.42	6.00	1.86	7.43	3.10	42.60
1955	.73	4.06	3.64	4.04	2.44	3.33	3.98	16.93*	3.22	15.72*	5.59	.53*	64.21*
1956	1.80	3.27	3.97	3.92	3.27	2.33	4.18	1.69	4.58	5.24	2.36	3.85	40.46
1957	1.94	2.21	1.15	4.71	3.30	1.78	3.51	3.41	1.68	3.43	3.79	5.66	36.57
1958	3.65	3.41	3.62	5.06	4.38	3.13	2.75	3.73	6.82	4.68	3.73	.97	45.93
1959	2.24	2.44	3.70	3.52	.67	5.19	2.60	3.89	.64	7.27	4.29	3.85	40.30
1960	2.76	4.22	2.43	2.66	3.50	3.34	8.08	3.32	6.42	2.72	2.12	3.76	45.33

Year	Jan	Feb	Mar	Apr	May	June	July	Aug	Sep	Oct	Nov	Dec	Total
1961	2.51	3.78	3.56	4.67	5.10	3.12	4.63	4.09	2.65	1.57	3.18	3.41	42.27
1962	3.44	4.18	2.39	3.31	1.42	5.32	2.46	2.90	2.91	4.24	4.02	3.13	39.72
1963	2.10	2.48	3.19	1.50	1.92	4.00	3.63	2.21	4.58	.20	7.03	2.60	35.44
1964	3.60	2.12	2.15	4.25	2.43	4.21	3.52	2.00	1.54	1.52	1.83	4.05	33.22
1965	3.01	3.40	2.10	2.67	1.84	1.57	1.55	5.15	2.55	3.36	2.07	1.97	31.24*
1966	2.24	3.97	1.47	2.11	3.20	.79	.91	1.18	5.69	4.77	3.22	3.12	32.67
1967	1.20	2.33	4.76	2.64	3.43	3.34	3.83	6.31	1.75	5.28	2.55	5.32	42.74
1968	1.93	1.75	4.16	3.06	6.24	5.80	1.55	5.10	3.77	2.18	5.15	4.40	45.09
1969	1.45	2.07	2.03	4.37	3.41	3.84	5.00	6.27	2.98	2.02	5.54	5.08	44.06
1970	.33*	4.36	3.15	3.47	2.33	2.22	3.08	3.01	3.47	3.39	3.91	2.74	35.46
1971	1.59	4.04	3.31	2.11	3.97	1.73	5.71	7.28	6.27	3.34	3.35	2.93	45.73
1972	1.71	3.96	4.43	3.16	5.51	10.53*	3.72	1.65	1.44	4.27	8.07*	5.86	54.31
1973	3.69	3.97	3.91	5.45	5.03	4.73	6.55	3.58	2.37	3.17	1.63	8.76*	52.84
1974	4.21	1.92	4.13	4.42	4.51	1.85	2.69	3.05	8.34	2.61	1.79	4.58	44.10
1975	4.04	2.92	3.77	2.28	3.34	5.19	7.02	4.68	11.49	5.22	5.03	2.80	57.78
1976	5.76	3.23	3.66	1.63	3.56	5.39	2.92	9.66	4.94	5.55	.48	2.24	49.02
1977	1.44	1.82	5.82	2.89	1.95	2.85	2.36	1.40	6.52	5.22	6.83	2.91	42.01
1978	6.44	.79*	2.49	.74	5.87	1.89	3.97	6.39	1.88	1.46	1.75	4.41	38.08
1979	9.21*	3.57	4.63	4.74	5.52	1.37	.58*	7.23	5.35	3.63	4.21	2.65	52.69
1980	1.38	1.05	8.25*	5.47	2.72	2.62	2.64	1.60	1.52	4.02	3.86	.56	35.67
1981	.52	6.77*	.38	1.63	3.45	1.97	2.64	1.26	2.08	5.72	1.55	4.57	32.54
1982	4.89	1.94	2.10	4.71	2.67	6.92	3.16	3.72	2.14	1.93	3.46	1.81	39.45
1983	3.96	3.15	7.17	9.10*	4.06	2.43	1.87	3.83	2.53	4.94	4.11	7.26	54.41
1984	1.85	2.93	3.57	5.84	10.85*	4.60	6.72	2.84	1.28	2.48	3.76	2.59	49.31
1985	1.15	2.32	2.07	.42*	4.24	4.62	7.09	4.63	5.50	1.78	6.32	1.45	41.59
1986	3.52	3.54	1.72	1.31	.43*	4.78	7.69	2.11	1.34	2.28	5.97	3.89	38.58
1987	4.74	.77	3.72	6.28	2.06	2.99	2.63	5.00	5.37	5.16	2.70	1.85	43.27
1988	2.72	3.59	2.06	1.76	4.39	.44*	5.83	2.34	2.66	2.10	7.65	.96	36.50
1989	1.61	2.52	3.56	3.26	9.86	7.57	1.76	4.08	5.17	7.82	2.80	1.24	51.25
1990	4.46	3.08	3.63	4.61	7.17	4.42	3.11	13.27	2.57	5.14	2.82	5.07	59.35
1991	2.80	2.12	3.78	3.74	4.90	1.40	6.02	6.59	1.01	2.60	3.78	3.42	42.26
1992	1.98	2.77	4.00	2.53	2.83	6.30	6.50	3.48	3.21	1.90	6.63	5.31	47.44
1993	2.69	2.86	6.76	3.71	1.77	1.39	1.20	3.54	5.31	4.75	4.56	4.61	43.15
1994	5.73	2.74	3.46	3.38	4.40	7.85	4.75	4.59	2.53	1.94	4.51	4.54	50.42
1995	4.32	3.74	1.16	2.76	1.41	1.13	2.85	3.02	2.85	9.13	4.73	2.25	38.85
1996	7.45	2.26	2.47	5.95	2.90	4.73	9.55	1.41	6.87	6.05	4.07	7.52	61.23
1997	3.76	1.60	5.52	2.72	3.90	2.81	4.66	4.65	.91	1.85	6.75	3.70	42.83
1998	3.42	3.81	4.70	4.28	8.62	4.49	1.34	3.98	3.08	4.03	2.12	1.16	45.03
1999	7.40	3.78	5.13	1.96	4.00	1.68	2.06	2.88	15.54*	3.41	3.39	2.12	52.72
2000	3.49	2.41	1.65	3.09	3.50	5.50	3.59	3.08	3.03	.60	2.89	4.25	37.06

Croton Falls 1961 - 1990 Monthly Averages

	Jan	Feb	Mar	Apr	May	June	July	Aug	Sep	Oct	Nov	Dec	Total
	2.98	2.94	3.44	3.46	4.08	3.90	3.69	4.05	3.76	3.54	3.89	3.47	43.20

Croton Falls 1971 - 2000 Monthly Averages

	Jan	Feb	Mar	Apr	May	June	July	Aug	Sep	Oct	Nov	Dec	Total
	3.73	2.87	3.77	3.53	4.31	3.87	4.10	4.23	4.17	3.80	4.05	3.58	46.01

APPENDIX P
TOTAL PRECIPITATION
(Inches)

CROTON LAKE

Year	Jan	Feb	Mar	Apr	May	June	July	Aug	Sep	Oct	Nov	Dec	Total
1860	1.01	1.86	2.06	2.54	2.52	3.03	6.60	5.63	4.63	2.96	6.75	3.12	42.71
1861	2.79	2.19	4.44	6.75	5.75	2.88	3.62	5.18	6.29	4.46	6.30	1.13	51.78
1862	4.75	2.88	2.17	.55	2.83	4.86	5.42	2.18	2.35	3.37	5.35	.68	37.39
1863	4.08	.15*	3.16	3.86	3.54	.52	10.27	4.38	1.39	5.02	4.37	4.10	44.84
1864	1.84	1.49	2.16	3.09	4.86	1.76	2.42	6.40	3.66	2.97	3.48	3.01	37.14
1865	3.43	2.86	5.12	2.95	7.38	3.41	8.12	3.08	2.23	4.56	3.15	3.87	50.16
1866	.59	5.58	2.15	2.69	4.98	4.41	5.27	5.50	6.16	4.44	3.87	4.14	49.78
1867	.72	4.18	2.46	3.13	7.26	7.19	5.22	8.79	3.66	4.74	3.42	1.71	52.48
1868	3.23	1.52	3.91	5.47	8.79	4.53	3.65	6.98	9.33	.63	4.65	2.50	55.19
1869	5.40	3.64	5.48	3.38	4.52	3.59	2.06	1.97	2.64	8.93	2.43	5.74	49.78
1870	3.70	6.37	3.80	4.95	2.71	3.50	2.75	5.10	2.36	4.73	3.74	1.20	44.91
1871	1.18	3.81	5.62	4.92	5.74	5.73	5.33	5.24	1.47	7.89	4.35	2.59	53.87
1872	.76	1.29	3.57	3.04	3.93	3.65	5.11	5.99	3.17	1.80	4.51	3.68	40.50
1873	2.96	3.09	1.90	3.17	3.02	.71	4.44	5.73	5.36	4.85	2.16	4.13	41.52
1874	5.98	2.78	.54	3.49	1.59	2.26	5.96	4.22	4.32	1.90	2.68	.99	36.71
1875	2.01	3.83	5.87	3.78	1.36	2.78	3.10	10.33	1.36	4.27	4.61	1.86	45.56
1876	1.68	4.91	6.33	3.82	3.87	4.34	3.42	2.51	4.37	2.13	3.39	2.35	43.12
1877	3.22	1.21	8.98	2.72	.57	5.58	6.48	3.18	1.09	10.69	7.54	1.35	52.61
1878	4.30	4.06	2.87	3.00	4.11	3.13	3.86	2.63	7.83	4.10	6.27	7.62	53.78
1879	4.56	4.98	5.76	4.17	2.74	4.81	5.15	6.95	2.88	.60	2.99	5.64	51.23
1880	2.96	3.33	4.59	3.28	1.10	1.47	6.56	4.05	2.64	2.86	2.54	3.16	38.54
1881	5.32	6.70	6.54	.86	2.74	5.27	1.82	2.75	.41	1.76	5.60	7.54	47.31
1882	4.68	5.27	3.71	1.46	6.44	2.57	3.19	3.82	16.26*	2.77	1.71	3.17	55.05
1883	3.40	7.11	2.22	3.94	2.45	3.38	5.80	2.55	2.47	5.53	1.13	4.84	45.27
1884	4.87	6.23	3.31	3.15	3.92	3.30	5.56	8.87	.34	2.92	5.23	6.58	54.28
1885	6.18	4.44	1.62	2.51	1.87	.99	4.87	7.33	.87	5.96	6.43	3.38	46.45
1886	5.42	6.52	4.48	5.09	4.02	3.35	4.46	3.58	1.43	2.51	5.13	3.19	49.18
1887	6.44	7.08	3.59	3.02	.18*	6.80	10.72	4.37	1.47	3.77	2.17	4.99	54.60
1888	4.91	4.63	3.32	2.46	6.73	2.76	2.80	6.49	8.19	4.47	3.33	5.59	55.68
1889	5.15	2.40	1.79	5.48	2.21	3.18	8.39	5.21	5.67	3.39	8.44	2.92	54.23
1890	2.51	3.30	7.19	3.71	5.57	3.75	4.70	4.41	4.48	6.29	.81	2.78	49.60
1891	8.11	4.58	3.53	2.66	2.30	2.42	4.59	4.21	2.31	2.24	3.31	4.99	45.25
1892	5.96	1.28	2.92	1.29	4.99	4.28	4.92	5.19	2.18	.77	6.46	1.16	41.40
1893	3.93	5.78	3.85	2.99	6.31	2.94	3.97	7.36	3.09	4.54	2.99	4.56	52.31
1894	2.48	4.23	1.34	2.23	4.73	2.20	1.73	3.01	6.96	4.33	5.21	3.77	42.22
1895	3.74	1.67	2.00	3.97	1.60	2.05	6.11	3.55	3.16	3.58	4.84	4.72	40.99
1896	.89	5.94	7.71	1.05	3.02	4.65	6.50	2.81	4.89	1.93	3.70	1.21	44.30
1897	3.49	2.16	3.03	3.10	6.52	2.51	10.99*	5.04	2.00	1.49	4.49	3.55	48.37
1898	4.82	4.36	3.66	3.83	8.60	1.54	5.57	9.19	2.17	5.38	5.80	2.40	57.31
1899	4.73	4.19	5.65	1.92	2.13	4.93	6.04	1.57	5.08	1.28	1.85	2.30	41.67
1900	3.90	7.70	3.97	1.95	3.46	2.55	4.16	2.43	2.79	4.32	5.24	2.08	44.55
1901	1.60	.55	6.37	8.97	6.62	1.47	4.97	9.03	4.75	2.75	1.38	7.74	56.20
1902	3.06	4.28	5.96	3.68	4.47	4.12	4.16	1.73	6.47	5.92	1.10	6.56	51.51
1903	3.65	3.77	4.59	3.46	.57	9.22	3.07	7.70	3.17	7.61	2.44	4.09	53.44
1904	3.25	2.81	2.29	3.39	3.08	1.62	4.00	8.11	7.56	3.82	2.63	4.00	46.56
1905	7.37	1.67	3.99	2.70	.55	5.96	3.83	6.41	4.37	3.27	2.14	2.81	45.07
1906	1.90	2.50	5.47	4.88	4.43	3.85	5.10	4.66	3.71	4.82	1.49	5.29	48.10
1907	4.66	4.20	3.51	3.57	5.30	4.92	1.35	1.74	11.85	9.16	6.60	4.88	61.74
1908	4.95	6.45	4.23	3.45	7.60	2.74	2.92	4.68	1.15	2.15	.75*	3.68	44.76
1909	4.67	6.57	5.11	7.51	1.62	3.46	1.93	6.33	4.43	1.20	3.27	5.00	51.10
1910	7.20	5.70	.78	6.59	3.39	5.35	1.23	2.69	1.98	1.62	5.00	3.19	44.72

Year	Jan	Feb	Mar	Apr	May	June	July	Aug	Sep	Oct	Nov	Dec	Total
1911	3.07	3.30	4.39	4.00	1.91	3.57	2.32	6.67	2.80	6.30	4.59	3.22	46.14
1912	2.65	2.43	7.97	3.56	3.93	1.83	2.50	4.20	3.74	3.26	4.33	5.03	45.43
1913	3.98	2.94	6.18	6.14	3.76	1.14	2.35	3.47	4.34	9.00	2.88	2.97	49.15
1914	4.10	1.98	4.22	4.33	3.15	3.13	4.78	1.73	.21*	2.97	4.12	4.83	39.55
1915	6.24	6.25	.42*	3.72	2.96	2.49	5.65	8.23	3.38	2.99	2.37	5.71	50.86
1916	1.57	4.51	3.32	3.08	3.35	4.30	5.62	2.31	5.67	1.21	2.89	2.88	40.71
1917	3.24	2.63	4.83	2.54	5.15	4.84	2.75	2.49	1.53	7.20	2.30	2.42	41.92
1918	4.72	3.09	2.28	7.38	2.98	4.63	5.96	4.49	3.42	.92	3.36	4.41	47.64
1919	3.26	4.98	5.65	2.92	6.17	3.25	6.88	5.14	5.98	5.31	5.02	3.66	58.22
1920	3.29	4.67	4.26	5.86	3.51	6.46	6.56	2.84	6.67	2.27	4.46	4.87	55.72
1921	3.78	3.61	4.13	4.21	2.61	4.71	5.32	2.09	3.34	1.77	5.18	2.79	43.54
1922	1.90	3.00	6.96	1.98	6.03	6.31	9.51	2.91	4.24	2.22	1.64	5.11	51.81
1923	5.74	3.12	3.41	3.04	2.70	4.43	1.90	1.29	4.75	6.59	3.86	4.83	45.66
1924	4.87	3.00	2.05	7.93	5.77	2.54	1.58	5.88	6.66	.30*	3.68	3.18	47.38
1925	3.97	4.21	5.39	2.60	4.83	6.74	9.73	1.34	3.38	3.78	4.17	3.30	53.44
1926	3.59	5.10	3.40	3.29	2.24	2.91	2.87	6.98	3.97	5.56	5.50	3.71	49.12
1927	2.83	4.09	2.36	2.74	6.70	3.34	9.65	9.72	4.53	7.33	5.39	5.47	64.15*
1928	3.30	4.73	3.19	5.30	2.30	9.09	7.46	8.76	4.34	.97	3.09	1.25	53.86
1929	4.34	3.75	3.48	6.47	4.88	2.01	3.01	4.08	5.44	4.13	2.35	4.22	48.16
1930	3.28	2.52	3.13	3.09	3.68	5.83	4.01	4.98	2.67	2.17	5.17	2.87	43.42
1931	2.34	2.83	4.36	4.46	6.74	5.56	3.32	3.65	1.88	2.44	1.16	2.85	41.59
1932	4.60	2.87	4.94	2.54	2.76	3.48	5.16	2.47	1.41	5.89	7.91	2.56	46.60
1933	2.06	4.15	5.41	6.20	2.81	3.56	1.77	11.13	5.21	3.39	.78	3.62	50.09
1934	3.99	2.63	4.85	3.47	6.61	3.68	4.48	1.89	10.08	3.40	4.04	4.00	53.12
1935	2.51	3.24	2.66	1.97	2.49	4.88	4.05	2.79	3.94	1.91	3.40	1.38	35.22
1936	6.30	2.92	7.14	4.52	2.84	5.93	3.02	4.07	4.80	2.40	1.34	6.70	51.98
1937	6.50	3.46	3.03	4.34	4.37	5.64	3.38	13.05	4.59	6.40	4.65	3.19	62.62
1938	4.66	2.53	2.15	3.08	3.86	7.54	10.13	3.30	10.98	2.45	3.24	4.74	58.66
1939	3.66	5.45	4.81	6.23	1.32	4.69	1.36	3.08	2.84	4.26	1.92	2.39	42.01
1940	2.94	3.13	6.23	6.43	6.80	5.02	4.66	4.39	3.16	3.83	5.41	2.85	54.85
1941	4.24	3.17	2.28	1.78	3.61	3.87	8.16	4.91	.69	3.43	2.81	5.29	44.34
1942	3.97	1.76	7.08	1.34	2.68	3.59	8.51	8.12	3.47	4.37	4.85	5.58	55.32
1943	3.65	2.00	3.91	3.92	4.51	4.31	8.50	2.57	3.14	8.70	5.25	.99	51.45
1944	2.52	2.43	6.35	5.69	1.92	3.00	2.09	1.75	7.20	2.00	7.09	4.13	46.17
1945	3.70	3.69	2.12	4.28	5.68	4.83	10.52	5.11	3.98	2.36	5.18	5.88	57.33
1946	1.63	2.68	2.25	1.71	7.94	3.77	8.55	5.06	4.89	1.75	1.63	2.74	44.60
1947	3.25	3.33	3.59	6.72	6.32	4.89	3.88	3.61	1.65	1.46	8.21	5.71	52.62
1948	4.54	1.80	4.69	3.70	7.98	4.69	4.49	2.50	.76	2.11	4.43	6.57	48.26
1949	5.47	3.31	2.12	4.51	5.59	.65	4.05	4.97	3.21	2.16	1.30	3.28	40.62
1950	3.19	4.23	3.10	2.74	4.50	2.68	10.24	3.70	1.11	1.78	6.90	5.69	49.86
1951	4.02	3.57	6.65	3.56	4.48	3.57	5.87	4.11	1.61	6.11	6.70	4.42	54.66
1952	4.19	2.25	4.17	7.23	8.48	3.98	3.96	9.96	5.95	.84	3.17	4.70	58.88
1953	5.80	2.19	9.59	6.01	3.97	2.98	6.20	2.16	1.30	4.20	2.35	5.01	51.76
1954	2.07	1.97	3.60	3.70	4.54	1.21	1.79	7.21	7.89	2.18	7.43	3.75	47.34
1955	.89	4.10	3.38	3.95	1.95	3.31	5.50	14.45*	3.27	14.08*	6.01	.67*	61.56
1956	2.38	3.65	4.17	5.31	4.08	2.52	5.10	2.20	4.42	4.66	4.90	4.23	47.62
1957	2.27	2.40	1.92	4.72	2.73	1.61	3.19	1.73	2.97	3.58	4.40	7.17	38.69
1958	5.12	4.49	5.62	6.06	5.54	4.71	4.12	4.08	4.90	4.88	3.91	1.14	54.57
1959	2.30	2.26	4.20	3.74	.72	6.61	2.90	5.66	.97	7.89	4.96	4.58	46.79
1960	2.78	4.46	3.09	2.90	3.41	2.77	8.75	4.55	7.26	2.63	2.39	4.00	48.99
1961	3.02	3.44	3.98	4.98	4.96	3.23	5.28	5.97	2.66	1.54	3.19	3.55	45.80
1962	3.20	4.60	2.70	3.79	1.79	3.66	2.56	7.07	4.02	4.55	4.25	2.70	44.89
1963	2.65	2.30	3.65	1.51	2.22	2.52	5.98	2.33	4.06	.41	7.98	2.50	38.11
1964	4.02	2.46	1.93	5.16	2.11	3.19	5.93	2.05	1.37	1.22	2.08	3.99	35.51*
1965	3.37	4.14	1.99	2.81	2.80	1.30	2.55	8.59	2.45	3.26	1.94	1.66	36.86
1966	2.72	4.17	1.48	2.66	3.68	.77	1.02*	1.94	6.35	4.69	4.19	3.65	37.32
1967	1.22	2.53	5.99	2.75	4.46	3.46	4.44	5.88	2.15	4.75	3.06	6.91	47.60
1968	2.15	1.99	4.78	3.48	6.73	4.78	1.13	4.40	3.77	2.04	5.21	4.68	45.14
1969	1.56	3.41	2.09	4.63	2.87	5.08	5.42	5.65	3.24	1.84	5.32	5.81	46.92
1970	.51*	4.30	3.72	3.46	1.33	3.43	4.53	2.89	3.84	2.99	5.62	3.13	39.75

Year	Jan	Feb	Mar	Apr	May	June	July	Aug	Sep	Oct	Nov	Dec	Total
1971	2.17	4.84	2.50	2.13	4.12	1.65	4.82	8.44	8.18	3.64	3.53	2.31	48.33
1972	1.97	4.58	4.81	3.91	6.30	13.10*	3.49	2.00	1.59	4.33	8.96	5.98	61.02
1973	4.14	3.91	3.63	5.74	6.33	3.61	5.99	2.46	2.79	3.82	1.38	8.99*	52.79
1974	4.25	2.00	4.25	3.91	4.62	2.10	2.29	3.92	8.72	2.22	1.94	4.46	44.68
1975	4.38	3.07	3.80	2.70	4.60	4.62	5.49	3.96	10.77	5.02	4.76	3.54	56.71
1976	5.25	3.14	3.89	1.66	3.75	6.44	2.95	7.26	3.60	5.62	1.10	2.50	47.16
1977	1.79	3.15	7.32	4.05	2.66	3.15	2.19	2.30	6.68	6.20	9.95	3.09	49.44
1978	6.39	2.05	3.23	1.19	9.53	2.35	4.50	7.49	1.40	1.18	1.93	4.96	46.20
1979	10.77*	3.63	4.16	4.95	6.89	1.56	2.93	8.02	5.30	6.44	4.36	2.64	61.65
1980	1.58	1.20	10.27*	6.84	2.32	2.81	3.49	1.51	1.69	4.13	3.94	.79	40.57
1981	.61	7.18	.46	1.97	4.45	1.16	4.52	.19*	3.74	5.61	1.23	5.04	36.16
1982	4.96	1.98	2.11	4.68	3.27	5.78	4.43	2.82	3.15	1.15	4.30	1.30	39.93
1983	3.96	4.84	7.94	9.76*	5.46	2.85	1.57	3.10	2.98	5.80	5.35	8.10	61.71
1984	1.81	4.54	4.24	7.37	10.16	5.00	9.82	1.43	1.86	3.13	3.40	2.32	55.08
1985	.94	2.45	1.74	.26*	5.39	3.89	6.95	4.36	5.10	1.49	7.04	1.57	41.18
1986	5.06	3.64	2.08	2.41	.61	4.52	7.65	5.02	.99	2.31	6.51	4.15	44.95
1987	5.42	1.08	3.76	7.17	1.58	3.62	2.46	6.43	5.38	5.11	2.77	1.70	46.48
1988	3.25	3.43	2.04	1.54	5.37	.47*	6.73	2.54	2.41	2.31	9.09	1.36	40.54
1989	1.73	2.85	3.62	3.40	10.53*	7.64	2.27	3.39	5.76	7.86	2.61	1.16	50.77
1990	3.86	2.12	3.12	5.07	7.54	2.97	4.08	9.83	2.39	5.06	3.27	5.97	55.28
1991	3.15	1.85	4.35	3.51	4.01	1.82	2.20	6.26	.96	2.60	3.42	3.30	37.44
1992	1.45	2.97	3.77	2.29	3.55	3.39	4.70	3.50	3.53	1.36	5.85	5.55	41.91
1993	2.52	2.85	6.89	3.72	1.54	2.73	1.04	2.99	3.76	4.66	2.93	4.47	40.10
1994	6.32	3.18	5.85	2.85	4.10	9.71	4.54	4.13	2.20	2.03	4.18	4.00	53.09
1995	4.28	3.68	1.78	2.65	1.23	.81	2.58	4.38	2.48	7.05	4.23	1.45	36.60
1996	5.72	2.16	2.82	5.54	2.39	5.49	8.70	.97	4.88	5.18	3.24	5.80	52.89
1997	3.29	1.01	5.64	2.20	3.09	2.46	7.28	5.04	.77	1.35	5.57	2.70	40.40
1998	2.36	3.93	4.32	4.39	6.50	3.70	1.40	2.47	3.12	3.57	1.73	.97	38.46
1999	7.21	3.51	5.42	1.83	4.38	1.64	1.29	4.20	13.60	3.17	3.63	2.47	52.35
2000	3.26	2.34	2.04	3.34	2.93	4.01	4.69	3.73	4.19	.74	2.97	3.82	38.06

Croton Lake 1961 - 1990 Monthly Averages

	Jan	Feb	Mar	Apr	May	June	July	Aug	Sep	Oct	Nov	Dec	Total
	3.29	3.30	3.71	3.86	4.61	3.69	4.25	4.44	3.83	3.66	4.34	3.58	46.56

Croton Lake 1971 - 2000 Monthly Averages

	Jan	Feb	Mar	Apr	May	June	July	Aug	Sep	Oct	Nov	Dec	Total
	3.80	3.11	4.06	3.77	4.64	3.84	4.23	4.14	4.13	3.80	4.17	3.55	47.24

Note: during the period of 1868 through 1884, one to five months in some years had missing precipitation on some days

APPENDIX Q
TOTAL PRECIPITATION (Inches)

TITICUS

Year	Jan	Feb	Mar	Apr	May	June	July	Aug	Sep	Oct	Nov	Dec	Total
1903	4.83	5.72	6.88	4.24	.60	13.57*	3.46	6.80	4.04	7.78	2.81	5.61	66.34*
1904	5.37	3.51	4.67	5.35	4.24	2.59	4.78	7.38	7.17	3.87	2.65	3.47	55.05
1905	7.28	1.70	3.77	3.62	1.39	7.28	3.28	6.49	5.34	3.82	2.48	4.03	50.48
1906	2.95	3.29	6.50	4.93	4.79	5.14	6.01	3.49	4.91	4.98	1.79	4.03	52.81
1907	4.43	3.23	3.07	3.61	5.60	4.70	2.33	2.07	13.36	9.39	7.41	6.22	65.33
1908	4.93	7.01	4.37	4.11	7.58	1.98	2.25	7.25	1.23	1.93	1.17	3.63	47.44
1909	4.97	7.48*	5.81	8.79	*2.22	3.25	3.11	6.72	4.39	1.18	3.10	5.56	56.58
1910	7.73	4.53	.74	4.55	4.52	3.65	2.24	2.56	2.12	1.12	4.96	2.62	41.24
1911	3.24	3.07	3.76	3.60	3.26	3.47	2.44	7.37	2.80	6.28	4.26	3.37	46.92
1912	2.47	2.44	7.33	3.85	4.59	1.14	2.36	3.68	3.64	3.74	3.70	4.84	43.78
1913	3.77	3.17	5.55	5.18	4.03	1.10	2.74	4.88	4.18	9.24	3.18	2.77	49.79
1914	3.96	3.02	4.66	4.00	2.88	2.90	5.17	2.02	.37*	3.23	3.47	4.41	40.09
1915	6.95	5.63	.41*	3.12	2.92	2.46	4.68	8.52	3.09	2.88	2.70	7.78	51.14
1916	1.66	5.05	3.88	3.31	3.60	4.46	5.56	1.55	4.60	1.49	3.06	3.27	41.49
1917	3.05	2.07	3.92	2.16	3.90	4.08	2.99	2.92	.99	6.80	2.26	2.24	37.38
1918	4.64	2.91	1.88	5.51	2.16	3.22	5.44	3.58	4.07	1.07	2.54	3.75	40.77
1919	2.87	4.49	6.35	2.66	4.32	2.22	5.67	3.19	5.38	3.89	4.79	2.89	48.72
1920	2.80	5.18	3.24	5.39	3.18	5.04	4.68	1.49	7.22	1.55	.26*	4.38	44.41
1921	2.75	3.53	3.87	4.09	2.39	3.62	3.06	2.50	3.53	1.39	4.60	2.44	37.77
1922	2.05	2.50	6.01	1.64	4.61	6.05	11.06*	2.91	3.17	1.87	1.18	3.90	46.95
1923	5.35	1.90	2.95	2.65	2.13	3.40	1.38	2.41	3.34	5.72	2.62	3.88	37.73
1924	4.73	2.58	1.64	6.36	4.22	2.22	1.85	5.55	5.77	.19*	4.12	2.51	41.94
1925	3.00	3.88	4.06	2.00	4.08	4.14	7.41	1.14	3.07	3.33	3.10	2.19	41.40
1926	2.89	5.00	2.63	2.57	1.80	2.05	2.74	5.98	3.53	4.62	4.58	3.73	42.12
1927	2.60	3.55	1.77	2.10	5.56	2.05	8.67	8.16	3.70	6.81	5.91	4.64	55.52
1928	2.68	3.95	3.10	4.45	1.63	7.93	6.91	6.63	2.99	.74	2.69	1.18	44.88
1929	3.83	3.33	3.23	6.81	4.77	2.75	1.87	2.88	5.14	3.26	2.28	3.99	44.14
1930	3.02	2.16	2.61	2.90	2.88	7.32	2.28	4.12	1.87	1.82	5.18	2.32	38.48
1931	1.87	2.36	3.54	3.85	6.07	5.66	3.29	3.92	3.09	2.67	1.16	2.66	40.14
1932	4.13	2.43	4.36	2.43	3.15	3.50	3.68	3.66	1.83	5.01	8.43	2.07	44.68
1933	1.85	3.50	4.59	5.17	2.81	2.01	2.14	10.27	4.96	2.92	.87	3.37	44.46
1934	3.49	3.72	3.84	2.71	5.39	3.26	3.66	2.05	10.32	3.06	3.66	3.46	48.62
1935	2.77	3.06	2.47	1.78	2.08	4.52	4.32	1.54	3.34	1.42	3.68	1.11	32.09*
1936	6.67	3.06	6.60	4.02	2.53	5.54	3.79	4.81	4.27	2.34	1.28	6.49	51.40
1937	6.38	2.85	2.65	3.89	3.98	5.98	3.62	8.85	5.30	5.83	4.06	2.67	56.06
1938	4.83	2.37	1.89	2.86	2.92	6.10	9.70	4.83	11.86	2.32	3.53	3.50	56.71
1939	3.39	4.61	4.23	4.60	.93	3.61	2.53	5.90	3.52	4.69	1.94	2.09	42.04
1940	2.48	3.17	5.46	5.62	6.15	4.08	3.11	4.05	3.43	2.61	4.18	2.67	46.01
1941	2.55	2.90	2.03	1.36	2.59	3.85	9.00	3.68	.59	3.33	2.53	5.01	39.42
1942	3.50	1.64	6.43	.97	3.11	5.07	5.17	6.09	3.72	4.51	3.90	5.22	49.33
1943	3.42	1.68	3.50	3.83	5.35	3.31	5.07	1.80	2.48	6.07	4.74	1.06	42.31
1944	2.54	2.01	4.86	4.56	1.92	3.88	3.55	2.35	6.83	2.14	6.54	3.73	44.91
1945	3.30	3.81	1.86	4.46	6.27	4.58	8.06	4.17	3.75	2.88	4.52	5.01	52.67
1946	1.77	2.12	2.26	1.46	6.69	3.77	6.28	3.39	5.77	1.39	1.58	2.15	38.63
1947	2.79	3.10	3.00	5.81	5.28	5.38	2.85	4.78	2.97	1.56	7.59	3.90	49.01
1948	4.17	1.55	4.76	3.47	6.55	5.08	4.31	2.37	.91	1.79	3.64	5.95	44.55
1949	5.30	3.75	1.85	3.42	5.46	.55	2.37	4.15	2.61	1.95	1.56	3.47	36.44
1950	3.24	3.20	2.64	2.18	4.54	2.84	8.33	6.77	.88	1.35	5.16	4.22	45.35

Year	Jan	Feb	Mar	Apr	May	June	July	Aug	Sep	Oct	Nov	Dec	Total
1951	3.75	3.38	4.33	2.59	4.58	2.55	4.28	5.36	1.85	5.89	5.82	3.83	48.21
1952	4.07	1.96	3.22	6.68	6.92	2.51	4.46	8.23	4.35	.75	3.35	3.40	49.90
1953	5.39	2.21	8.04	5.76	2.79	1.94	4.86	.95	1.30	3.92	2.94	5.34	45.44
1954	2.34	1.89	3.51	3.03	3.42	1.08	1.42	6.09	6.83	2.22	6.92	2.98	41.73
1955	.65	3.69	3.19	4.37	2.16	2.84	5.32	14.90*	3.02	14.59*	6.12	.59*	61.44
1956	2.26	3.46	4.05	4.50	3.53	3.11	3.89	2.41	4.37	5.31	2.87	4.10	43.86
1957	2.28	2.22	1.50	5.09	3.96	.87	2.91	2.73	2.15	3.46	3.21	6.52	36.90
1958	4.37	3.48	4.86	5.34	4.48	3.48	3.87	2.25	6.79	4.43	3.40	1.08	47.83
1959	1.99	2.13	2.89	3.48	.73	4.80	3.02	4.37	1.22	6.75	4.11	3.16	38.65
1960	2.38	3.86	2.52	2.78	3.61	4.04	7.72	3.54	6.00	3.41	3.05	3.14	46.05
1961	2.81	2.76	3.29	4.23	5.49	2.65	5.46	4.72	2.85	1.79	3.45	3.29	42.79
1962	3.24	4.41	2.43	3.65	1.38	4.14	2.55	3.17	2.90	3.98	3.93	2.85	38.63
1963	2.57	2.44	3.34	1.61	1.87	3.47	3.92	1.93	4.22	.32	7.25	2.73	35.67
1964	4.08	2.53	2.18	4.54	2.15	3.87	3.48	1.82	1.64	1.45	7.23	4.81	34.78
1965	3.44	3.79	2.57	3.00	2.27	1.54	1.91	6.01	2.26	3.67	1.95	1.69	34.10
1966	2.60	4.14	1.18	2.33	2.91	.68	1.15*	1.65	5.90	4.89	3.30	3.41	34.14
1967	1.22	3.05	5.77	2.55	4.18	3.32	3.02	6.18	1.68	4.98	2.97	6.71	45.63
1968	2.27	1.91	4.43	3.43	6.12	5.94	1.54	4.87	3.49	1.97	6.14	4.76	46.87
1969	1.79	2.62	2.07	4.88	3.87	4.24	4.76	5.32	3.47	1.63	6.31	5.93	46.89
1970	.53	4.78	4.27	3.62	2.82	2.53	3.15	3.35	3.96	3.42	3.89	3.68	40.00
1971	2.14	5.07	3.49	2.94	4.07	1.82	5.62	7.57	7.13	3.50	4.46	3.12	50.93
1972	1.91	4.52	5.14	4.09	5.52	11.70	3.15	2.33	1.62	4.30	8.80*	5.92	59.00
1973	4.40	4.34	3.27	5.52	5.87	4.21	3.46	3.23	2.78	3.31	1.71	9.15*	51.25
1974	4.78	2.27	4.00	4.33	4.79	2.22	2.09	3.97	7.99	2.28	1.80	4.84	45.36
1975	4.66	3.07	4.08	1.80	5.08	3.76	7.63	3.57	13.11	5.02	4.95	3.88	60.61
1976	5.21	2.64	3.85	1.36	3.89	5.97	4.03	8.18	3.26	5.48	.52	2.75	47.14
1977	1.71	3.35	8.17	3.47	2.14	2.47	3.19	1.08	7.94	5.21	6.71	2.79	48.23
1978	7.53	1.11	3.07	1.22	8.98	2.53	4.09	7.25	1.91	1.54	1.41	5.04	45.68
1979	10.25*	3.37	4.15	5.04	4.94	1.62	1.45	7.93	6.55	4.08	4.69	3.31	57.38
1980	1.19	.97*	9.54*	6.35	2.58	2.62	3.09	1.79	2.25	3.77	3.38	.66	38.19
1981	.44*	6.65	.43	1.75	3.28	1.10	3.50	.43*	2.76	6.18	1.46	5.07	33.05
1982	4.73	1.41	2.06	4.66	2.83	6.79	2.76	3.40	3.67	1.55	3.58	1.67	39.11
1983	4.25	4.64	7.92	8.76	4.00	2.42	1.98	3.71	1.78	6.30	5.14	8.64	59.54
1984	2.07	4.06	4.03	5.71	9.63	5.35	9.03	1.61	.98	2.89	4.57	2.52	52.45
1985	1.32	2.11	2.07	.43*	4.95	5.16	6.28	5.07	5.36	1.84	6.55	1.34	42.48
1986	4.17	3.95	2.20	1.78	.41*	4.37	6.34	3.23	1.01	2.05	5.75	4.19	39.45
1987	5.19	.98	2.75	6.15	1.64	2.72	3.50	5.29	5.18	5.11	2.64	1.73	42.88
1988	3.14	3.36	1.93	1.75	4.31	.46*	6.29	2.11	2.33	2.36	8.13	1.66	37.83
1989	1.67	2.56	3.79	3.65	9.74*	7.44	1.99	4.11	4.59	8.01	3.05	1.11	51.71
1990	4.41	2.80	3.66	4.75	7.12	3.41	3.60	11.09	2.24	5.44	3.22	5.99	57.75
1991	2.99	1.99	4.19	3.91	3.75	1.81	5.84	7.30	.93	2.48	3.82	3.32	42.33
1992	1.83	2.70	4.05	2.52	2.88	4.90	6.58	4.83	4.41	1.92	6.70	4.86	48.18
1993	2.77	2.44	5.85	4.04	1.90	2.15	1.20	2.83	6.45	4.58	4.36	3.95	42.52
1994	5.28	2.90	5.88	3.16	4.82	8.74	4.26	4.41	2.58	1.70	3.90	4.23	51.86
1995	4.26	3.65	1.12	3.04	1.51	1.47	2.48	2.20	2.48	8.01	4.23	2.16	36.61
1996	8.64	2.84	3.20	5.84	2.68	6.03	8.09	1.61	6.01	5.37	3.41	7.16	60.88
1997	3.47	1.38	3.49	2.28	2.92	2.52	4.22	4.12	.76	1.94	6.25	3.65	37.00
1998	3.11	3.99	4.83	4.11	7.92	4.19	1.25	3.27	2.93	3.63	2.12	1.05	42.40
1999	7.80	3.52	5.40	1.91	4.11	1.22	1.68	2.92	15.24*	3.41	3.39	2.12	52.72
2000	3.49	2.25	1.74	3.10	3.50	4.92	3.19	3.18	3.20	.70	2.39	4.27	35.93

Titicus 1961 - 1990 Monthly Averages

	Jan	Feb	Mar	Apr	May	June	July	Aug	Sep	Oct	Nov	Dec	Total
	3.32	3.19	3.70	3.64	4.29	3.68	3.80	4.20	3.89	3.61	4.30	3.84	45.46

Titicus 1971 - 2000 Monthly Averages

	Jan	Feb	Mar	Apr	May	June	July	Aug	Sep	Oct	Nov	Dec	Total
	3.96	3.03	3.48	3.65	4.39	3.87	4.06	4.12	4.31	3.81	4.10	3.74	47.02

APPENDIX R
CROTON RIVER WATERSHED- PUTNAM COUNTY GAUGES
TOTAL PRECIPITATION
(Inches)
BOYD'S CORNERS

(Elevation - 560 feet)

Year	Jan	Feb	Mar	Apr	May	June	July	Aug	Sep	Oct	Nov	Dec	Total
1866						4.45	4.01	6.56	4.92	5.09	3.80	3.27	
1867	2.11	3.00	1.49	3.74	6.86	5.28	5.25	10.04	3.62	3.66	3.10	2.62	50.77
1868	2.90	1.38	2.55	3.87	8.79	4.53	2.13	6.98	9.33	.87	4.65	2.35	50.33
1869	3.79	3.64	5.48	2.11	4.52	3.59	2.26	1.92	3.20	9.46	2.43	5.96	48.36
1870	4.51	6.40	3.80	5.45	2.30	2.06	3.43	5.10	2.85	4.73	2.51	1.49	44.63
1871	3.80	3.81	4.27	3.01	3.45	5.73	5.07	5.24	1.44	6.18	4.35	2.58	48.93
1872	1.44	1.22											
1887	5.68	5.95	3.60	3.47	.32*	7.70	13.55*	6.85	1.90	3.12	2.69	6.71	61.54
1888	5.56	5.07	6.44	2.68	6.17	2.19	2.24	6.87	10.77	4.80	4.49	6.13	63.41
1889	5.14	2.33	1.86	4.42	3.22	4.76	7.19	2.90	6.13	5.09	8.01	2.94	53.99
1890	1.97	4.94	5.66	3.03	5.74	3.56	5.46	4.70	6.86	7.63	1.12	3.69	54.36
1891	9.76	6.00	3.36	3.77	1.36	1.81	3.03	5.61	1.87	2.21	3.86	5.65	48.29
1892	5.95	1.22	3.92	1.08	5.74	3.84	5.05	6.13	2.65	.92	7.85	1.15	45.50
1893	4.03	8.05											
1894								1.45					
1895									1.06	3.55	2.98	4.85	
1896	1.09	8.41*	8.30	1.13	3.48	3.47	3.98	4.60	6.54	2.21	3.96	2.72	49.89
1897	4.07	3.14	3.68	2.78	5.56	3.41	12.51	5.63	1.74	2.01	6.31	6.56	57.40
1898	4.68	5.21	2.64	3.84	7.37	1.50	4.78	7.66	2.17	4.84	6.81	3.17	54.67
1899	3.37	5.54	7.56	2.99	1.80	5.38	5.99	.48*	8.86	1.49	2.05	2.75	47.26
1900	4.18	7.97	6.39	1.92	6.34	2.63	4.36	1.54	3.27	4.27	4.91	2.58	50.35
1901	1.69	.94	7.24	8.48	7.91	1.61	7.07	8.21	4.68	3.30	2.15	9.53	62.81
1902	2.77	6.81	7.49	4.47	3.44	4.68	3.81	2.91	6.13	5.38	.91	7.59	56.39
1903	4.52	5.70	6.30	2.68	1.25	11.81*	3.54	9.10	2.61	8.59	2.48	4.67	63.25
1904	4.52	3.22	3.77	4.23	4.99	2.40	6.73	5.16	7.21	4.00	1.78	3.48	51.49
1905	6.54	1.82	3.98	2.74	1.05	4.87	3.73	5.09	5.67	3.25	2.63	4.04	45.41
1906	2.55	2.74	6.85	5.41	4.50	4.19	6.92	3.60	2.92	5.24	1.57	4.09	50.58
1907	3.85	2.86	1.95	4.25	4.39	5.64	1.64	1.96	9.77	8.16	5.87	5.66	56.60
1908	3.97	6.27	3.46	2.13	7.37	2.22	2.50	4.59	1.04	2.09	.90	3.57	40.11
1909	4.78	6.04	4.47	6.67	2.49	3.85	3.17	7.55	4.31	1.23	2.83	4.06	51.55
1910	7.21	4.45	1.32	5.59	3.41	4.38	2.46	3.03	2.37	.99	3.97	2.97	42.15
1911	2.82	2.83	4.69	3.74	2.61	4.14	2.60	9.71	4.19	7.54	4.34	3.67	52.88
1912	2.05	3.15	7.64	4.82	6.44	1.29	2.87	5.02	3.12	4.85	4.61	4.46	50.32
1913	3.84	2.59	8.30	5.50	3.11	.93	2.21	4.17	4.88	9.72	2.87	3.05	51.17
1914	3.59	2.13	4.43	5.15	3.26	3.40	4.99	2.50	.33	3.96	3.64	4.26	41.64
1915	7.21	6.47	.19*	3.46	3.51	1.84	6.27	10.11	3.87	3.67	2.20	7.13	55.93
1916	1.50	4.56	3.45	3.16	4.40	3.90	4.52	2.23	5.82	1.40	4.17	3.46	42.57
1917	2.98	1.99	4.20	1.66	4.00	3.21	2.92	2.93	.89	6.60	.66	3.23	35.27
1918	4.38	3.11	1.52	4.58	3.78	3.26	5.35	4.88	3.85	1.64	3.35	4.37	44.07
1919	2.91	3.12	7.08	3.01	5.37	1.88	7.12	4.51	4.94	3.34	5.93	2.85	52.06
1920	2.61	4.89	3.45	5.45	2.81	5.86	6.74	4.97	9.19	1.21	4.02	5.72	56.92
1921	2.82	2.95	4.97	5.14	3.00	4.02	5.92	2.58	3.31	1.74	5.50	2.64	44.59
1922	1.88	2.15	5.80	2.88	5.85	7.34	7.61	4.56	2.08	2.89	1.24	3.72	48.00
1923	5.87	1.83	2.77	3.81	2.77	2.72	2.69	2.24	4.65	7.83	4.75	4.63	46.56
1924	4.69	2.42	1.75	7.56	4.71	2.65	2.80	4.66	8.28	.19*	3.44	2.96	46.11
1925	2.51	4.18	5.22	2.25	3.21	3.78	6.51	2.00	4.85	3.95	3.82	2.16	44.44
1926	3.45	4.28	2.49	2.64	1.98	2.86	3.37	5.87	3.70	5.33	5.63	3.18	44.78
1927	2.43	3.03	1.83	2.58	7.11	3.63	7.50	7.42	3.72	8.24	6.31	5.71	59.51
1928	2.74	4.11	3.10	5.01	2.45	8.05	8.70	8.88	2.71	1.19	3.00	1.15	51.09
1929	4.24	3.19	3.03	7.28	4.35	2.93	2.53	1.56	2.89	5.02	2.73	3.99	43.74
1930	2.47	1.96	2.70	3.12	3.02	5.08	3.04	3.90	1.36	1.65	5.15	2.06	35.51

Boyd's Comers precipitation averages through 1930

Year	Jan	Feb	Mar	Apr	May	June	July	Aug	Sep	Oct	Nov	Dec	Total
	3.82	3.94	4.27	3.86	4.16	3.92	4.85	4.92	4.26	4.10	3.72	3.98	49.80
1931	1.34	2.41	3.09	2.47	6.06	4.05	3.37	2.91	1.57	2.53	.96	3.19	33.95
1932	4.25	2.28	4.47	2.31	3.72	3.28	4.02	4.83	1.60	6.52	9.13*	1.77	48.21
1933	1.90	3.40	4.54	5.50	2.77	2.02	2.74	11.45	5.90	3.11	1.15	3.33	47.81
1934	3.79	3.78	3.77	3.90	6.15	3.44	2.92	3.32	10.55	2.90	4.15	4.02	52.69
1935	4.54	2.68	2.40	1.56	2.59	5.17	2.99	1.18	3.20	1.55	3.18	1.18	32.22
1936	6.07	4.47	6.79	2.90	3.21	5.83	3.77	4.54	4.17	3.22	1.45	6.19	52.61

Year	Jan	Feb	Mar	Apr	May	June	July	Aug	Sep	Oct	Nov	Dec	Total
1937	6.82	2.64	2.75	3.74	5.15	5.82	2.63	6.70	4.23	6.82	5.00	2.84	55.14
1938	5.29	2.48	1.99	2.83	3.92	6.71	12.22	5.57	11.73	2.48	3.56	4.44	63.22
1939	3.42	4.65	4.21	5.73	1.09	5.54	1.33	4.17	3.52	5.03	1.79	2.35	42.83
1940	3.06	2.16	5.75	5.69	5.72	3.72	3.07	4.01	3.53	2.45	5.31	3.46	47.93
1941	2.29	2.74	1.85	1.10	2.13	4.28	6.93	4.11	.69	2.45	3.34	5.01	36.92
1942	4.26	1.95	6.07	1.13	4.11	3.55	9.22	6.00	5.01	4.56	5.78	5.12	56.70
1943	3.61	1.67	3.01	3.11	5.52	2.61	3.71	3.34	2.76	6.99	5.96	.83	43.12
1944	2.44	2.25	5.45	3.03	2.53	3.99	5.49	3.80	6.52	1.96	5.94	3.64	47.04
1945	3.53	3.38	1.60	4.52	8.38	4.83	8.10	4.68	3.12	2.61	5.51	5.49	55.75
1946	1.40	2.25	1.94	1.77	8.34	5.10	6.53	3.07	5.36	2.07	1.44	2.28	42.02
1947	3.03	2.31	3.34	5.47	9.71	4.30	4.19	3.27	2.86	1.91	7.60	3.84	51.86
1948	4.02	1.85	4.86	4.01	6.85	5.09	4.95	2.77	.25*	2.35	3.99	5.82	46.81
1949	5.28	2.82	2.55	4.47	6.69	.99	2.73	4.28	3.49	2.37	1.90	4.40	41.97
1950	3.78	3.59	2.89	2.34	4.66	4.71	6.21	4.98	1.53	1.54	7.01	4.17	47.41
1951	3.86	4.63	6.64	3.36	3.96	3.60	4.63	2.27	2.23	4.54	6.58	5.15	51.45
1952	5.17	2.53	4.12	7.64	5.40	6.27	4.14	10.46	5.49	.90	4.77	4.17	61.06
1953	6.60	2.22	9.19*	6.97	4.14	2.01	6.11	1.39	2.62	4.81	2.41	5.83	54.30
1954	2.13	1.90	3.92	3.78	4.87	1.28	1.59	6.19	8.61	2.08	7.71	3.90	47.96
1955	.63	3.58	4.34	4.45	2.36	3.82	1.62	16.01*	3.54	16.68*	6.46	.55*	64.04
1956	1.91	3.76	4.73	4.81	2.85	4.29	6.16	1.74	4.86	1.79	4.72	4.41	46.03
1957	1.83	2.03	1.84	4.59	2.53	1.75	4.30	2.13	2.44	4.00	3.36	8.37	39.17
1958	5.02	3.44	4.81	5.78	5.17	3.53	2.28	2.39	6.30	6.13	4.25	1.03	50.13
1959	2.47	2.35	4.09	3.46	.92	4.84	2.90	3.46	3.19	8.11	4.87	4.56	45.22
1960	3.08	4.65	2.61	3.40	4.10	4.61	8.79	3.86	7.53	2.44	3.38	3.17	51.62
1961	2.70	3.34	3.83	5.47	6.13	3.40	3.18	5.42	3.10	1.79	3.81	3.68	45.85
1962	3.39	4.85	2.72	2.73	1.05	2.40	2.02	3.65	2.29	4.16	3.16	2.96	35.38
1963	2.57	2.28	3.07	1.75	1.89	5.15	7.25	3.00	4.18	.23	6.93	2.06	40.36
1964	3.54	2.15	2.14	3.97	1.64	4.33	3.09	1.59	1.63	1.52	1.43	3.97	31.00*
1965	2.83	3.03	2.00	2.31	1.93	2.53	3.29	5.78	3.21	3.97	1.98	2.04	34.90
1966	2.37	4.36	1.82	2.43	3.12	1.08	1.09*	1.75	6.18	4.85	4.06	3.22	36.33
1967	1.48	2.36	5.28	3.12	4.00	6.20	7.15	7.73	2.58	5.32	2.34	5.81	53.37
1968	1.88	1.31	4.78	3.67	7.12	5.05	2.39	2.55	3.86	2.93	5.47	4.80	45.82
1969	1.48	2.69	2.72	5.09	3.30	7.25	4.27	5.05	3.50	2.44	8.37	6.76	50.62
1970	.35*	4.78	3.29	3.36	2.86	3.31	2.38	3.15	4.26	4.28	3.95	3.03	39.00
1971	1.80	4.43	2.88	1.83	3.99	1.49	6.25	8.75	5.32	3.45	3.69	3.16	43.74
1972	2.32	3.84	4.39	3.60	7.50	8.39	3.05	1.95	1.94	5.38	8.30	5.89	56.55
1973	4.39	3.98	3.80	5.91	5.52	5.53	6.82	2.29	2.60	2.89	1.93	10.37*	56.03
1974	4.20	2.11	4.36	5.02	4.20	3.24	2.39	4.54	7.62	2.23	3.16	4.29	44.41
1975	5.31	2.76	3.76	2.74	3.34	4.80	5.78	4.22	9.41	4.46	4.97	3.56	51.90
1976	5.54	3.10	4.42	1.30	4.37	4.04	3.60	11.40	4.01	5.99	.51*	1.92	50.20
1977	1.70	3.50	7.35	3.75	2.53	4.62	2.85	1.72	9.38	6.14	8.09	3.80	55.43
1978	8.20	1.17	2.78	1.67	7.02	2.18	3.67	6.03	1.86	1.59	2.11	4.53	36.81
1979	10.75*	3.49	4.15	4.97	6.28	.83	1.21	5.24	5.69	4.32	4.57	2.88	54.38
1980	1.22	1.00	7.55	5.67	2.12	3.76	3.42	3.47	1.64	3.38	4.29	.65	38.17
1981	.69	7.33	.40	2.76	3.76	1.49	3.01	1.44	2.04	4.95	.80	5.28	33.95
1982	5.16	1.99	2.49	4.24	2.60	8.50	3.67	3.92	2.99	1.31	3.61	1.91	37.74
1983	4.01	4.20	7.21	9.64*	4.08	3.73	1.49	3.71	2.54	5.60	4.83	8.24	59.28
1984	1.73	3.22	4.28	3.90	9.14	3.77	5.85	1.83	1.54	1.69	3.75	3.43	44.13
1985	1.38	2.27	2.31	.64*	4.25	3.76	4.48	1.97	5.99	1.93	6.17	1.43	36.58
1986	3.45	3.70	2.50	1.71	.49	5.18	6.38	3.05	1.31	2.40	6.19	3.66	40.02
1987	4.85	.78	4.71	6.25	2.17	4.14	3.73	6.35	8.55	6.13	2.93	1.73	52.32
1988	2.84	3.62	1.88	1.48	4.69	.50*	6.76	2.37	4.12	2.26	7.95	1.06	39.53
1989	1.74	2.51	3.24	2.87	11.55*	8.35	1.98	5.71	4.64	8.24	2.65	1.33	54.81
1990	4.61	3.16	3.98	5.04	7.01	4.04	4.05	14.85	2.06	6.33	3.32	6.60	65.05*
1991	2.62	1.94	4.17	3.24	4.17	1.42	3.23	4.20	1.59	2.75	3.08	3.41	35.82
1992	1.99	2.89	4.06	2.80	3.21	5.11	7.04	3.06	2.89	1.86	6.01	5.22	46.14
1993	3.08	3.02	6.90	3.90	1.74	2.16	1.34	2.98	5.29	4.16	3.59	4.35	42.51
1994	5.81	3.26	4.64	3.06	2.77	4.01	3.93	5.37	3.67	1.86	3.56	3.71	45.65
1995	4.20	3.48	1.26	2.81	2.25	.89	5.41	2.55	2.86	10.77	5.03	2.41	43.92
1996	9.49	2.38	2.07	6.36	2.63	5.26	7.67	2.78	7.19	5.76	3.89	7.44	60.52
1997	3.42	1.50	6.00	2.45	3.17	1.37	4.21	4.83	1.07	1.71	6.57	3.42	39.72
1998	3.40	3.68	3.98	4.14	6.70	6.30	1.64	3.30	2.69	3.64	2.46	.86	42.79
1999	7.23	3.55	5.27	1.52	4.28	.80	1.20	2.47	14.17*	3.17	3.47	2.23	49.36
2000	2.95	3.17	1.88	2.12	3.86	6.36	3.35	3.43	2.99	.88	2.82	4.82	38.63

Boyd's Corners monthly averages (1960-1990)

	Jan	Feb	Mar	Apr	May	June	July	Aug	Sep	Oct	Nov	Dec	Total
	3.28	3.11	3.67	3.63	4.32	4.10	3.88	4.48	4.00	3.74	4.14	3.80	46.15

Boyd's Corners monthly averages (1971-2000)

	Jan	Feb	Mar	Apr	May	June	July	Aug	Sep	Oct	Nov	Dec	Total
	4.00	3.03	3.96	3.58	4.38	3.87	3.98	4.33	4.32	3.91	4.14	3.79	47.29

APPENDIX S
TOTAL PRECIPITATION (Inches)
EAST BRANCH (Sodom)
Elevation - 340 feet

Year	Jan	Feb	Mar	Apr	May	June	July	Aug	Sep	Oct	Nov	Dec	Total
1895									.78	3.74	5.06	4.12	
1896	1.30	7.18	6.80	1.48	2.93	4.00	4.28	3.74	5.17	2.39	3.38	2.03	44.68
1897	3.55	2.66	3.49	3.05	6.03	4.18	11.15	5.21	1.79	.93	5.72	4.78	51.54
1898	4.60	4.18	2.89	3.50	7.89	1.39	3.52	13.94	2.23	4.63	6.34	3.17	58.28
1899	3.78	5.84	6.46	1.58	2.10	5.52	6.17	.32*	7.10	11.39	1.32	2.37	44.45
1900	3.73	7.77*	4.52	2.27	6.40	2.08	3.91	2.33	3.52	3.98	5.98	2.47	48.96
1901	1.78	.79	6.99	7.61	6.78	2.27	8.30	7.98	5.88	5.24	2.06	8.64	64.32
1902	3.12	3.63	7.01	4.68	3.75	5.95	4.74	3.24	6.73	6.55	1.17	7.34	57.91
1903	4.83	4.96	5.19	2.69	1.16	11.35*	2.45	6.88	3.67	6.90	2.89	3.68	56.65
1904	3.73	3.10	3.82	4.03	4.45	2.25	5.32	6.43	4.64	3.61	1.98	3.37	46.73
1905	6.53	1.84	4.29	3.22	1.08	6.78	2.62	5.43	3.51	3.14	2.33	3.57	44.34
1906	2.44	2.93	6.36	4.11	3.95	4.87	5.34	2.74	3.02	4.99	1.58	4.21	46.54
1907	4.40	2.80	1.92	3.95	5.77	4.64	2.14	3.09	10.58	8.95	5.57	5.61	59.42
1908	4.21	5.63	4.00	2.13	7.38	2.26	3.03	6.12	.83	1.92	1.09	3.32	41.92
1909	4.80	6.50	4.39	7.41	2.93	2.95	2.83	6.61	4.41	1.17	3.54	4.01	51.55
1910	8.09	5.13	1.52	4.09	4.19	4.54	3.24	3.34	1.77	.97	5.07	2.48	44.43
1911	3.34	2.66	3.74	3.40	2.48	3.03	1.95	9.27	2.12	6.17	3.93	3.15	45.24
1912	2.15	2.33	6.93	3.84	4.37	1.37	3.15	4.23	3.67	3.38	3.82	4.65	43.89
1913	3.32	2.99	5.15	4.87	3.69	1.14	2.47	4.31	3.42	10.49	3.29	2.74	47.86
1914	3.90	2.26	4.85	4.41	2.81	2.70	5.15	2.44	.35*	3.26	2.96	4.27	39.36
1915	6.19	5.05	.19*	3.31	2.76	1.23	6.25	8.95	3.59	2.43	2.44	5.88	48.27
1916	1.47	4.47	3.25	3.06	3.63	4.42	5.00	2.18	5.20	1.13	2.90	3.03	39.74
1917	2.59	2.34	3.63	2.09	3.91	3.12	3.57	2.22	.98	6.62	.70	3.99	35.70
1918	3.97	2.85	1.64	4.79	3.21	3.01	5.03	3.62	3.66	1.96	2.40	2.96	39.10
1919	2.96	3.02	6.93	2.77	4.49	2.12	5.29	3.95	5.08	3.73	4.99	2.66	47.99
1920	2.72	4.70	3.62	4.82	2.76	5.39	6.31	2.72	7.11	1.23	3.61	4.53	49.52
1921	2.76	3.02	3.46	4.55	2.37	3.39	5.79	2.16	3.69	1.25	4.52	2.25	39.21
1922	1.86	2.21	5.41	2.67	4.24	6.94	8.79	3.69	2.56	3.34	1.26	3.79	46.76
1923	5.95	1.64	2.70	2.97	2.29	2.70	2.23	2.28	3.97	6.23	2.78	3.91	39.65
1924	4.42	2.65	1.21	6.31	4.13	2.41	2.74	4.25	5.72	.14*	3.91	2.60	40.49
1925	2.56	3.78	4.47	2.20	3.76	3.83	6.28	1.31	3.45	3.25	3.28	2.55	40.72
1926	2.83	3.58	2.60	2.66	1.68	2.21	3.42	7.80	3.25	5.06	5.17	3.34	43.60
1927	2.33	3.48	2.14	2.35	6.58	3.80	6.20	8.12	4.58	6.33	6.10	4.82	56.83
1928	2.23	3.73	3.34	4.26	2.66	7.50	7.79	7.47	3.36	1.03	2.71	1.06	47.14
1929	4.29	3.22	3.39	6.79	5.04	2.08	2.96	3.04	2.53	5.00	2.43	4.31	45.08
1930	3.17	2.15	2.93	3.01	2.97	7.01	4.03	3.56	3.88	1.80	4.77	2.51	41.79
Average East Branch precipitation through 1930													
	3.49	3.63	4.04	3.74	3.90	3.81	4.67	4.71	3.83	3.73	3.43	3.73	46.71
1931	2.18	2.61	3.78	4.63	5.77	8.34	3.03	4.13	2.57	2.54	1.32	3.05	43.95
1932	4.36	2.56	4.57	3.39	2.83	3.52	3.56	5.12	2.62	5.11	8.83*	2.11	48.58
1933	1.86	3.49	4.11	5.53	2.70	1.84	3.39	10.29	5.85	3.05	1.12	3.34	46.57
1934	3.99	3.67	4.20	3.47	5.44	4.83	3.66	1.83	10.48	2.82	3.91	2.48	50.78
1935	3.82	2.78	2.70	2.07	1.98	5.08	4.14	1.33	2.88	1.26	3.22	1.12	32.38
1936	6.57	3.65	6.75	2.58	2.93	5.75	3.86	4.28	5.15	2.48	1.35	6.05	51.40
1937	6.87	2.41	2.73	3.83	4.20	5.25	1.92	7.74	4.89	5.43	4.19	2.44	51.90
1938	4.00	2.31	1.96	2.92	3.32	5.15	7.80	5.63	12.60	2.18	3.04	3.66	54.57
1939	3.58	4.37	4.39	5.70	.71	3.02	1.87	4.64	4.58	4.67	1.98	2.23	41.74
1940	2.51	2.41	5.29	4.91	5.85	3.29	2.80	3.82	2.48	2.15	4.46	2.53	42.50
1941	2.36	2.68	1.82	1.12	2.34	4.64	12.03*	2.79	.85	2.69	2.63	4.69	40.64
1942	3.23	1.69	5.89	.86	3.64	3.53	4.34	6.00	3.65	3.84	5.04	4.52	46.23
1943	3.36	1.63	3.15	3.35	5.12	3.97	4.48	2.63	2.00	6.22	4.97	.86	41.74
1944	2.63	1.71	4.51	4.43	2.45	3.47	3.15	1.47	6.36	2.15	6.25	3.73	42.31
1945	3.11	3.05	1.50	4.52	6.54	4.42	9.71	3.69	3.39	2.28	4.51	4.84	51.56
1946	1.50	2.22	1.91	1.43	6.07	4.69	5.76	2.22	4.87	1.31	1.53	2.21	35.72
1947	2.48	2.29	3.48	5.68	5.49	4.47	3.28	4.26	4.81	1.80	6.72	3.45	46.62
1948	3.96	1.51	5.02	3.47	5.99	4.73	4.56	2.75	.88	1.77	3.71	6.50	38.85
1949	5.35	2.86	1.71	3.55	5.97	.79*	2.87	6.55	1.65	1.95	1.23	3.93	39.41
1950	3.12	2.91	2.77	2.33	4.16	2.50	6.43	7.10	1.32	1.21	6.55	4.78	45.18

Year	Jan	Feb	Mar	Apr	May	June	July	Aug	Sep	Oct	Nov	Dec	Total
1951	3.79	3.20	4.86	2.74	4.55	3.23	4.98	3.97	2.25	5.39	6.04	4.14	49.14
1952	4.66	2.33	3.95	7.91	6.64	2.59	4.50	8.92	3.87	1.13	4.49	4.15	55.14
1953	6.11	2.43	8.48	5.96	3.86	2.05	7.05	1.15	1.34	4.64	2.94	5.73	51.74
1954	2.20	2.18	4.16	3.99	4.41	1.23	1.49	5.87	7.45	2.03	7.54	3.78	46.33
1955	.72	4.18	3.92	4.65	2.23	2.93	2.23	16.94*	2.98	16.54*	6.55	.66	64.53*
1956	2.22	3.60	4.02	4.18	3.91	2.89	4.30	1.69	5.00	5.09	2.70	4.30	43.90
1957	2.29	2.20	1.35	5.02	2.93	2.11	5.52	3.53	2.35	3.41	3.86	7.07	41.64
1958	4.78	4.27	4.62	5.09	4.01	2.13	3.00	4.11	6.40	4.95	3.23	1.13	47.72
1959	2.03	2.80	3.68	3.18	.73	5.50	2.92	4.24	.83	6.96	3.98	5.12	41.97
1960	2.98	4.50	2.77	2.78	3.07	3.19	7.85	3.10	6.41	2.91	2.14	3.58	45.28
1961	2.37	3.77	3.65	5.27	5.41	2.71	3.14	3.66	3.09	1.95	3.44	3.20	41.66
1962	3.20	4.44	3.06	3.89	1.73	4.22	3.91	3.05	2.90	4.79	3.88	2.84	41.91
1963	2.28	2.35	3.16	1.79	2.11	4.70	4.84	1.91	4.51	.23	6.62	2.44	36.94
1964	3.26	2.34	2.04	3.98	2.58	3.73	3.50	2.32	1.49	1.65	2.08	3.70	32.67
1965	3.16	3.25	2.09	2.62	1.85	2.17	1.60	4.06	2.83	3.06	1.87	1.90	30.46*
1966	2.45	3.61	1.31	2.21	2.52	.62	.83*	1.37	5.49	4.58	3.36	3.14	31.49
1967	1.02	2.76	4.85	2.96	3.36	3.20	3.71	5.60	1.83	4.42	2.75	5.67	42.13
1968	2.19	1.76	4.19	3.01	6.42	5.28	2.05	5.07	4.45	1.75	4.63	4.56	45.36
1969	1.37	1.97	1.99	4.38	2.90	3.20	4.54	6.91	3.33	1.86	6.26	5.61	44.32
1970	.28*	4.81	3.44	3.41	3.02	2.82	2.81	3.03	3.35	2.71	3.72	3.23	36.63
1971	1.65	3.80	3.37	2.55	4.35	2.10	4.78	7.26	7.59	3.24	3.51	3.02	47.22
1972	1.55	4.69	4.80	3.36	5.17	9.53	3.11	1.45	1.35	4.93	8.60	6.10	54.64
1973	3.62	4.25	3.57	5.81	4.85	5.51	4.35	5.37	2.48	3.44	1.66	8.77*	53.68
1974	4.35	1.77	3.82	4.01	3.98	2.85	2.15	2.62	7.44	2.25	1.66	5.11	42.02
1975	4.53	2.63	3.55	2.26	3.07	3.20	6.79	4.75	12.75	4.99	4.45	3.04	56.01
1976	5.55	3.04	3.25	1.37	3.22	5.60	3.00	7.90	2.86	5.22	.47*	2.54	44.02
1977	1.68	2.36	6.84	4.61	1.78	2.77	1.54	2.16	5.76	4.94	6.33	3.51	44.28
1978	7.40	1.27	2.91	1.22	7.06	1.98	4.12	5.25	1.55	1.50	1.38	4.52	40.16
1979	10.68*	3.24	4.65	4.84	5.24	1.40	.90	5.81	5.08	3.26	3.93	2.61	51.64
1980	1.22	.95	8.66*	5.46	2.47	2.90	2.41	2.75	1.94	3.68	3.94	.50*	36.88
1981	.54	6.32	.36	1.50	3.06	1.20	2.99	1.44	2.28	5.68	1.59	4.59	31.55
1982	4.96	1.92	1.93	4.16	2.46	6.83	2.86	3.89	2.22	1.32	3.11	1.56	37.20
1983	4.14	3.39	8.26	9.33*	4.20	2.67	2.20	3.51	2.34	5.66	4.83	7.29	57.82
1984	1.85	3.49	4.44	5.51	10.73*	4.59	7.04	2.15	1.13	2.86	4.66	2.67	51.12
1985	1.09	2.16	2.39	.42*	4.38	3.86	6.37	4.29	5.99	1.70	6.34	1.50	40.49
1986	3.50	3.19	2.42	1.60	.36*	4.57	7.54	1.79	1.09	2.49	5.83	3.22	37.60
1987	4.29	.74*	3.48	6.27	2.38	3.65	3.76	6.05	6.49	4.72	2.55	1.67	46.05
1988	3.09	3.62	1.91	1.67	4.27	.44*	6.98	2.18	3.05	2.28	8.19	1.50	39.18
1989	1.65	2.46	3.64	3.46	10.46	5.39	1.46	4.50	4.70	8.61	3.01	1.24	50.58
1990	4.43	3.31	3.63	4.86	7.19	3.94	3.05	9.68	2.18	6.11	3.24	5.53	57.15
1991	2.66	2.03	3.68	3.54	4.63	1.12	3.57	9.40	1.21	2.74	3.51	3.46	41.56
1992	1.72	2.89	4.58	2.71	2.88	5.54	7.47	4.15	2.82	1.94	5.98	5.23	47.91
1993	2.35	2.79	6.39	4.17	1.54	1.70	.98	2.07	6.07	4.91	4.07	4.52	41.56
1994	5.55	2.84	2.28	2.88	3.56	5.64	3.52	4.64	2.78	1.68	3.57	3.64	42.58
1995	3.96	3.70	1.17	2.60	1.06	.84	3.87	2.52	2.20	9.98	4.78	2.19	38.87
1996	5.92	2.51	1.74	5.74	2.43	3.88	9.19	3.81	5.67	6.97	3.99	6.96	58.81
1997	3.56	1.50	5.30	2.68	4.01	2.46	4.66	5.61	.97	2.70	6.56	3.80	43.81
1998	3.31	4.04	4.42	4.39	7.66	5.23	2.06	3.75	3.60	4.59	1.88	.99	45.92
1999	6.94	3.63	5.00	1.78	4.29	2.00	1.03	2.24	15.14*	3.50	3.23	2.17	50.95
2000	3.44	2.65	1.86	3.10	3.81	5.67	3.59	2.85	2.59	.79	2.58	3.94	36.87

East Branch Monthly Precipitation Averages 1961 - 1990

	Jan	Feb	Mar	Apr	May	June	July	Aug	Sep	Oct	Nov	Dec	Total
	3.11	2.99	3.59	3.56	4.09	3.59	3.61	4.06	3.78	3.53	3.93	3.56	43.30

East Branch Monthly Precipitation Averages 1971 - 2000

	Jan	Feb	Mar	Apr	May	June	July	Aug	Sep	Oct	Nov	Dec	Total
	3.71	2.91	3.81	3.60	4.22	3.64	3.91	4.19	4.11	3.96	3.98	3.58	45.62

APPENDIX T
TOTAL PRECIPITATION (Inches)
MIDDLE BRANCH

Year	Jan	Feb	Mar	Apr	May	June	July	Aug	Sep	Oct	Nov	Dec	Total
1924	4.42	2.65	1.39	6.31	4.13	2.41	2.74	4.25	5.72	.14*	3.91	2.60	40.67
1925	2.56	3.78	4.47	2.23	3.79	3.80	6.28	1.31	3.45	3.25	3.31	2.04	40.27
1926	2.83	3.58	2.60	2.74	1.68	2.21	3.42	7.80	3.25	5.06	5.17	3.42	43.76
1927	2.25	3.35	1.90	2.10	5.92	3.27	6.03	8.27	3.93	6.36	5.75	4.85	53.98
1928	2.33	3.68	3.12	4.73	2.17	7.53	7.29	8.46	3.44	1.00	2.66	1.01	47.42
1929	3.89	2.90	3.08	6.79	3.99	1.94	2.46	2.67	2.62	5.01	2.16	3.65	41.16
1930	2.95	1.99	2.69	2.70	2.50	6.85	2.81	3.13	2.64	1.60	4.91	2.16	36.92
1931	2.01	2.29	3.90	4.09	6.59	5.68	3.37	5.69	2.82	2.14	1.10	2.99	42.67
1932	4.23	2.39	4.59	2.33	3.02	3.22	2.87	4.21	2.69	4.95	8.41	2.04	44.95
1933	1.80	3.63	4.53	5.19	2.72	2.14	3.29	9.58	5.37	3.32	1.10	3.22	45.89
1934	3.54	3.47	3.40	2.95	5.34	4.35	3.45	2.27	10.68	3.10	3.75	2.94	49.24
1935	3.27	2.71	2.56	1.99	2.10	4.29	3.92	1.32	3.40	1.26	3.06	.94	30.82
1936	6.21	3.10	6.35	3.30	2.17	5.88	4.37	5.02	4.22	2.15	1.35	6.01	50.13
1937	6.85	2.41	2.73	3.91	4.20	5.24	2.15	7.74	4.89	5.43	4.20	2.44	52.19
1938	4.00	2.31	1.96	2.93	3.34	5.15	7.23	5.63	12.30	2.44	3.18	3.64	54.11
1939	3.58	4.37	4.39	5.70	.73	3.28	1.85	3.35	4.58	4.55	1.98	2.18	40.54
1940	2.41	2.40	5.29	5.30	5.31	3.65	2.80	4.36	2.35	2.26	4.19	2.43	42.75
1941	2.64	2.82	1.94	1.10	2.34	4.64	8.79	2.70	1.02	2.98	2.85	4.34	38.16
1942	3.36	1.89	6.56	.95	3.96	3.51	4.91	5.12	3.63	4.38	4.11	4.96	47.34
1943	3.23	1.63	3.44	3.49	5.44	3.36	4.52	2.29	2.15	6.18	5.07	.86	41.66
1944	2.20	2.10	5.60	4.30	2.75	4.20	2.66	1.41	6.30	1.99	6.22	4.04	43.77
1945	3.12	3.39	1.54	4.65	6.70	4.27	8.92*	4.03	4.02	2.59	4.46	4.78	52.47
1946	1.53	2.16	1.87	1.39	5.81	5.25	7.39	2.49	5.65	1.22	1.34	1.85	37.95
1947	2.47	2.82	3.38	5.87	5.37	4.58	3.42	5.08	2.11	1.79	6.68	3.95	47.52
1948	4.16	1.59	4.72	3.54	5.24	4.76	5.21	2.51	.86*	1.60	3.49	6.29	43.97
1949	5.49	3.40	1.73	3.24	5.87	.59	2.81	6.09	2.56	1.96	1.19	3.96	38.89
1950	3.32	3.33	2.76	2.28	4.30	2.96	6.99	5.84	1.14	1.24	5.85	4.77	44.78
1951	4.41	3.69	5.17	2.80	4.62	3.09	5.04	3.60	2.10	5.60	6.01	4.46	50.59
1952	4.37	2.27	4.13	7.36	7.25	2.72	4.13	8.67	4.63	.83	3.87	3.75	53.98
1953	6.38	2.10	9.01*	6.02	3.31	1.89	5.64	1.00	1.30	4.57	2.70	5.48	49.40
1954	2.16	1.94	3.88	3.80	4.89	1.07	.88	6.30	7.65	1.86	6.86	3.95	45.24
1955	.64	4.23	4.14	4.51	2.42	3.20	2.91	17.75*	2.82	14.65*	6.30	.60	64.17*
1956	2.09	3.62	4.70	4.48	3.57	2.57	4.76	1.67	4.82	5.37	2.79	4.61	45.05
1957	2.18	2.34	1.39	5.07	3.12	1.60	4.39	2.71	1.97	3.56	3.80	7.00	39.12
1958	5.07	4.05	4.96	5.83	4.91	3.17	3.04	3.31	6.07	4.84	3.76	1.07	50.08
1959	2.35	2.70	4.00	3.59	.68	5.33	2.89	4.63	1.01	7.07	4.07	4.61	42.93
1960	2.64	3.90	2.81	3.08	2.94	3.29	8.32	2.87	6.45	2.78	2.19	3.33	44.60
1961	2.55	3.81	3.66	5.27	4.75	2.86	3.81	4.17	2.71	1.67	3.25	3.53	42.04
1962	3.42	4.56	2.19	3.19	1.47	4.00	2.92	2.79	2.56	4.42	3.87	2.84	38.23
1963	2.57	2.26	3.28	1.40	2.05	4.07	3.96	2.11	4.61	.24	6.70	2.53	35.78
1964	3.81	2.53	1.97	4.02	2.65	3.87	2.64	1.78	1.45	1.39	1.78	3.90	31.70
1965	3.23	3.51	2.13	2.28	1.39	1.49	1.28	4.44	2.30	2.92	1.90	2.17	29.04*
1966	2.62	3.99	1.46	2.24	2.69	.58	1.02	1.42	5.25	4.74	3.13	3.47	32.61
1967	1.19	2.64	5.12	2.84	3.64	2.77	5.69	6.35	1.62	5.16	2.75	5.50	43.27
1968	2.19	1.92	4.05	3.08	6.14	5.28	1.60	3.95	3.75	1.90	5.23	4.84	43.93
1969	1.48	2.46	2.07	4.53	3.14	3.52	4.88	6.64	3.66	2.02	5.87	5.84	46.11
1970	.32*	4.66	3.89	3.51	2.53	2.82	4.11	3.26	3.39	2.62	3.93	3.34	38.38
1971	1.65	4.17	2.98	2.58	4.25	1.77	4.45	6.71	6.69	3.28	3.42	2.84	44.79
1972	1.80	4.28	4.57	3.10	5.54	9.47*	3.13	1.50	1.74	4.68	7.62	6.01	53.44
1973	3.82	3.79	3.83	5.79	5.13	4.29	6.05	4.25	2.32	3.14	1.50	7.65	51.56
1974	4.49	2.13	4.14	4.42	4.32	2.25	1.93	3.10	7.84	2.26	1.59	4.82	43.29
1975	4.12	2.65	3.56	2.40	2.87	3.74	6.87	4.60	9.50	4.80	4.42	3.11	52.64
1976	5.55	3.29	4.06	1.51	3.34	5.13	2.72	9.37	4.09	4.94	.48*	1.75	46.23
1977	1.68	2.95	6.97	3.01	1.84	2.68	1.73	1.42	6.09	4.73	6.28	3.12	42.50
1978	6.86	1.11	2.75	1.03	7.45	2.08	4.56	5.86	1.79	1.76	1.55	4.12	40.92
1979	9.48*	3.47	4.24	4.59	5.43	1.55	.71	5.47	4.42	3.89	3.87	2.29	49.41
1980	1.25	1.03	7.87	5.47	2.81	2.98	2.74	2.75	1.65	3.15	3.88	.55*	36.13

Year	Jan	Feb	Mar	Apr	May	June	July	Aug	Sep	Oct	Nov	Dec	Total
1981	.57	6.18*	.42*	1.51	3.28	1.52	2.61	.84*	2.01	5.08	1.43	4.28	29.73
1982	5.35	1.77	2.06	4.29	2.62	7.23	3.30	2.74	2.25	1.17	3.05	1.35	37.18
1983	3.50	2.98	7.21	8.61*	3.62	2.81	1.38	3.69	2.29	4.88	5.13	7.00	53.10
1984	1.75	3.76	4.52	4.75	9.54	4.64	5.35	2.19	1.36	2.43	3.82	2.78	46.89
1985	1.01	2.28	2.39	.46*	4.82	3.81	6.62	3.44	4.95	1.69	6.16	1.72	39.35
1986	3.38	3.40	1.56	1.82	.45*	4.68	5.08	1.32	.93	2.55	5.74	4.04	34.95
1987	5.38	.71*	3.40	6.40	2.26	4.14	4.08	7.32	6.36	5.45	2.57	1.69	49.76
1988	3.21	3.51	2.00	1.63	4.52	.50*	7.60	2.28	2.66	2.34	7.93*	1.38	39.56
1989	1.66	2.37	3.40	3.26	10.06*	5.87	.65*	5.17	5.02	7.65	2.21	1.28	47.10
1990	3.99	2.12	3.47	4.98	7.29	3.87	3.16	12.01	2.25	5.28	2.63	4.90	55.95
1991	2.35	1.58	3.64	3.37	4.72	1.06	3.89	5.63	1.33	2.58	3.42	3.04	36.61
1992	1.57	2.91	3.91	2.63	3.04	5.33	6.49	3.62	2.30	1.62	5.82	4.70	43.94
1993	1.80	2.18	6.97	3.82	1.70	1.86	1.13	2.38	5.45	4.96	3.78	4.29	40.32
1994	6.38	2.90	4.64	3.50	4.08	6.76	4.84	5.07	2.85	1.87	4.00	4.72	51.61
1995	3.99	3.38	.99	2.96	1.24	.90	3.62	2.63	2.85	8.20	4.84	2.45	38.05
1996	7.98	2.38	1.91	5.94	2.79	4.76	8.48	3.32	6.51	6.22	3.80	7.67*	61.76
1997	3.77	1.53	6.08	3.07	4.03	2.81	4.48	5.58	1.08	1.98	7.09	3.59	45.09
1998	3.54	4.16	4.57	4.55	8.13	5.58	1.58	3.60	3.92	3.89	2.22	.99	46.73
1999	6.92	3.76	5.20	1.86	4.08	1.55	2.01	2.33	15.92*	3.42	3.16	2.03	52.24
2000	3.44	2.63	1.73	3.10	3.37	5.50	3.47	3.51	2.90	.73	2.75	4.60	37.73

Middle Branch Average Monthly Precipitation 1961 - 1990

	3.13	3.01	3.51	3.46	4.06	3.54	3.55	4.10	3.62	3.41	3.79	3.49	42.67

Middle Branch Average Monthly Precipitation 1971 - 2000

	3.74	2.88	36.83	3.55	4.29	3.70	3.82	4.12	4.04	3.69	3.87	3.49	44.99

APPENDIX U
TOTAL PRECIPITATION
(Inches)
WEST BRANCH (Carmel)
Elevation 500 feet

Year	Jan	Feb	Mar	Apr	May	June	July	Aug	Sep	Oct	Nov	Dec	Total
1888						2.33	2.22	6.49	10.92	4.39			
1889	5.28	2.08	2.89	3.91	3.04	4.06	9.52	3.69	6.03	4.19	8.74		
1890	2.76	4.56	5.59	2.96	6.06	3.26	5.05	4.44	7.80	6.76	1.33	3.99	54.56
1891	9.71	5.91	3.39	3.14	1.30	1.83	3.65	4.80	1.67	2.23	3.57	5.14	46.34
1892	6.12	1.12	3.81	.95	5.41	3.22	6.46	7.41	2.33	1.10	7.37	.79	46.09
1893	3.51	7.59											
1894								2.53					
1895									.81	3.60	4.95	4.62	
1896	1.10	7.69	6.90	1.20	2.79	3.32	3.54	4.32	5.18	2.63	3.43	2.10	44.20
1897	3.45	2.76	3.34	3.05	5.96	3.23	16.64*	4.90	1.74	.89	6.22	5.22	57.40
1898	4.97	4.64	2.43	3.78	7.13	1.23	3.80	12.87	2.38	4.69	6.51	3.31	57.74
1899	3.59	5.76	7.02	1.66	1.68	6.73	5.28	.53*	7.78	1.02	2.02	2.67	45.74
1900	4.06	8.39*	5.44	2.13	6.51	2.60	3.87	2.30	3.54	3.83	5.26	2.77	50.70
1901	1.65	.81	7.89	7.93	7.49	1.33	8.52	7.74	5.81	4.15	2.08	9.46	64.86
1902	2.92	5.13	5.93	4.66	3.49	4.98	5.21	2.76	6.79	6.32	.89	7.30	56.38
1903	4.81	5.55	5.90	2.63	1.80	12.70*	2.44	8.29	2.69	8.45	3.35	4.91	63.52
1904	3.82	3.39	4.08	4.80	3.79	2.44	6.11	6.50	7.73	3.64	2.04	3.26	51.60
1905	6.30	1.77	4.51	3.18	.97	5.93	3.79	6.38	5.03	3.12	2.42	3.96	47.36
1906	2.59	2.74	6.85	5.41	4.50	4.19	6.92	3.60	2.92	5.24	1.57	4.09	50.61
1907	3.68	2.84	1.96	4.07	4.77	4.84	2.06	3.03	10.27	9.43	5.69	5.26	57.90
1908	3.50	5.16	3.22	1.81	6.33	2.25	2.56	6.32	.84	1.76	1.05	3.72	38.52
1909	4.79	6.72	4.16	7.22	3.02	3.42	3.43	6.76	4.40	1.08	2.84	4.06	51.91
1910	7.44	5.03	1.28	5.13	3.81	5.03	2.46	3.48	2.37	1.07	4.81	3.00	44.91
1911	3.32	2.87	4.34	3.10	2.75	3.93	2.79	9.66	2.82	7.04	4.19	3.29	50.10
1912	1.88	2.75	7.60	3.99	5.91	1.34	3.21	4.90	3.50	4.48	4.25	4.39	48.20
1913	3.43	2.77	7.52	5.35	3.05	.88	1.65	4.73	4.46	9.93	3.14	2.70	49.61
1914	3.92	2.06	4.18	4.91	2.78	3.40	4.68	2.29	.25	4.11	2.82	3.31	38.71
1915	6.50	6.26	.13*	3.28	2.80	1.35	5.73	9.58	3.87	3.12	2.39	5.59	50.60
1916	1.36	4.10	2.97	3.20	3.86	4.08	4.81	1.90	5.58	1.41	3.51	3.04	39.82
1917	2.51	2.10	3.49	1.63	3.87	2.95	2.46	1.98	.94	6.25	.70*	2.90	31.78
1918	3.48	2.74	1.62	4.74	3.33	2.82	4.82	3.94	3.53	1.55	2.61	3.40	38.58
1919	3.10	2.81	7.59	2.88	4.42	2.45	6.62	4.67	4.86	3.50	5.65	2.98	51.53
1920	2.47	4.43	3.13	5.40	2.89	5.45	6.88	4.66	7.83	1.28	3.85	4.92	53.19
1921	2.68	2.55	4.20	5.09	2.23	3.62	4.47	3.40	3.47	1.31	5.09	2.38	40.49
1922	1.52	2.02	2.56	5.35	4.77	8.23	10.79	4.07	2.23	4.74	1.20	3.31	50.79
1923	5.41	1.62	2.47	2.98	2.43	2.77	2.81	2.31	3.65	6.56	3.74	4.09	40.84
1924	4.12	2.24	1.25	5.91	5.24	2.62	3.28	4.66	6.87	.15*	3.70	2.57	42.61
1925	2.11	3.80	4.70	2.03	3.71	3.10	5.87	1.56	3.89	3.56	3.29	2.14	39.76
1926	2.87	3.25	2.51	2.73	1.62	2.55	3.93	7.02	3.12	5.29	5.32	2.88	43.09
1927	2.39	2.88	1.88	2.36	7.51	3.57	6.40	8.41	3.98	7.14	5.42	5.27	57.21
1928	2.61	3.75	2.99	4.67	2.19	7.26	7.59	10.14	2.78	1.05	2.62	1.07	48.72
1929	3.72	2.92	2.95	6.86	4.10	2.91	2.49	2.11	2.73	4.31	2.30	3.70	41.10
1930	2.69	2.05	2.84	2.64	2.55	6.37	2.72	3.76	1.64	1.63	5.19	2.30	36.38
Averages through 1930													
	3.70	3.74	4.11	3.74	3.89	3.76	4.94	5.00	4.17	3.85	3.68	3.74	48.32
1931	1.95	2.33	3.28	4.86	6.38	8.35	4.02	4.85	2.08	2.21	.86	2.84	44.01
1932	4.20	2.25	4.36	2.06	3.61	3.24	3.29	4.28	2.56	5.65	9.08*	1.95	46.53
1933	1.92	3.73	4.49	5.71	2.85	2.03	3.15	10.55	6.34	3.17	1.16	3.08	48.18
1934	3.58	3.57	3.56	3.34	6.11	3.83	4.00	3.27	11.10	3.14	3.83	3.12	52.45
1935	3.71	2.67	2.36	1.62	2.04	4.73	3.15	1.08	3.70	1.36	3.13	.85	30.40
1936	6.04	3.34	6.25	3.57	2.82	5.93	4.20	4.19	4.17	2.36	1.19	6.15	50.21
1937	6.61	2.20	2.62	3.51	5.83	5.27	2.49	9.19	5.12	6.44	3.77	2.49	55.54
1938	4.76	2.29	1.72	2.78	4.00	5.81	11.54	5.67	12.35	2.60	3.10	3.66	60.28
1939	3.13	4.42	3.74	5.20	.79	4.07	2.14	3.68	3.41	5.11	2.27	2.29	40.25
1940	2.90	1.71	5.49	5.24	5.06	4.76	2.88	3.47	2.57	2.35	4.87	2.98	44.28

Year	Jan	Feb	Mar	Apr	May	June	July	Aug	Sep	Oct	Nov	Dec	Total
1941	2.29	2.82	1.59	1.11	2.32	4.18	7.15	2.83	.89	3.27	3.08	4.36	35.89
1942	2.32	2.96	5.78	.94	4.18	4.12	5.60	6.35	4.13	3.32	5.07	4.91	49.68
1943	2.72	1.49	3.39	3.28	6.08	2.47	3.86	2.36	2.15	6.58	6.77	.79	41.94
1944	2.06	2.04	5.15	4.17	2.58	3.98	4.39	2.57	6.81	1.83	5.39	3.87	44.84
1945	3.33	2.94	1.54	4.79	6.86	4.88	7.87	4.64	5.05	2.57	5.07	4.31	53.85
1946	1.48	1.91	1.92	1.47	7.69	4.91	8.41	2.43	5.20	1.82	1.34	2.12	40.70
1947	2.47	2.06	3.20	3.87	7.20	4.08	6.57	4.62	2.20	1.72	6.99	3.48	48.46
1948	3.72	1.52	3.53	3.69	6.49	4.37	4.55	3.35	.23*	2.18	3.42	5.94	42.99
1949	4.90	2.49	2.63	3.43	6.63	.72	2.98	4.35	2.99	2.22	1.57	3.90	38.81
1950	3.57	3.30	2.70	1.92	4.47	3.64	6.30	6.49	1.18	1.47	5.60	4.56	45.20
1951	3.64	4.57	5.64	2.98	4.14	3.27	5.52	2.99	2.77	4.71	6.82	4.80	51.85
1952	4.87	1.80	4.05	7.43	5.17	4.89	3.66	9.33	4.12	.74	4.01	3.94	54.01
1953	6.62	2.16	9A5*	5.03	5.10	2.61	6.08	1.11	1.86	4.59	2.18	6.13	52.92
1954	2.36	2.19	3.89	4.08	4.32	1.11	1.32	6.42	8.35	1.96	7.26	3.72	46.98
1955	.64	3.86	4.53	4.42	2.17	3.71	1.77	14.87	3.03	15.34*	5.85	.67	60.83
1956	2.10	3.75	4.15	4.24	3.51	3.14	5.11	1.56	4.63	1.87	5.13	4.34	43.53
1957	1.87	2.16	1.78	4.72	3.04	1.64	4.13	2.50	2.55	3.56	3.09	8.50	39.54
1958	5.20	3.25	3.94	5.92	4.55	2.97	3.66	1.96	5.77	5.25	3.89	1.11	47.47
1959	2.54	2.63	3.88	3.28	.86	5.00	2.85	2.46	3.84	7.40	4.75	4.13	43.62
1960	2.56	3.98	2.14	3.19	3.66	3.17	8.52	4.94	6.05	2.18	3.03	2.73	46.15
1961	2.48	3.43	3.50	5.31	5.36	2.73	3.09	4.51	2.73	1.70	3.29	3.41	41.54
1962	3.33	4.25	1.13	4.88	.91	3.71	3.69	3.94	2.62	4.59	3.32	3.16	39.53
1963	2.64	2.47	3.46	1.20	2.58	4.51	5.16	2.78	4.40	.16	6.80	2.35	38.51
1964	3.52	2.37	2.25	4.18	2.17	2.96	2.57	1.14	1.59	1.34	1.58	4.53	30.20*
1965	3.43	3.79	2.42	2.64	1.57	1.33	2.08	4.47	2.76	3.38	2.20	2.71	32.78
1966	2.87	3.91	2.62	1.66	3.90	.66	.90*	1.45	4.87	4.41	3.33	3.56	34.14
1967	1.35	2.66	5.44	3.27	3.86	3.54	6.30	6.56	1.93	4.91	2.73	6.82	49.37
1968	2.40	.93	5.50	3.18	6.23	5.00	2.90	3.76	3.78	2.40	4.93	4.92	45.93
1969	1.62	2.41	2.48	4.91	3.27	6.49	4.56	5.73	3.61	1.95	6.19	5.81	49.03
1970	.43*	4.75	3.38	3.73	2.41	2.70	2.45	3.04	4.14	2.48	4.11	2.79	36.41
1971	2.30	4.67	3.41	2.48	3.68	1.84	4.28	6.50	5.37	3.31	3.92	3.46	45.22
1972	2.14	4.21	4.75	3.64	4.52	10.39	4.24	1.85	1.81	4.77	7.34	6.07	55.73
1973	4.72	4.39	3.97	6.34	5.71	5.22	5.91	1.93	2.49	2.51	1.81	9.47*	54.47
1974	5.07	1.96	4.59	4.31	4.53	3.36	2.38	5.66	8.04	2.41	1.69	4.04	48.04
1975	4.71	2.88	3.94	2.72	3.15	4.03	7.23	4.91	10.92	4.97	5.27	3.94	58.67
1976	5.92	3.15	2.45	3.45	3.95	2.33	4.35	9.18	3.44	5.28	.71	2.86	47.07
1977	1.67	3.09	8.32	4.29	2.42	3.39	2.52	2.06	9.72	6.43	7.08	4.84	55.83
1978	8.04	1.15	3.48	1.49	8.05	2.20	5.30	4.68	2.57	1.66	1.75	4.09	44.46
1979	11.76*	3.17	4.56	5.32	5.83	1.54	.98	6.94	5.77	4.58	4.70	3.11	58.26
1980	1.31	1.05	7.35	6.23	1.95	3.73	3.47	2.24	1.73	3.94	4.45	.48*	37.93
1981	.60	7.11	.43	2.34	3.67	1.74	3.51	1.49	1.89	5.03	.84	5.81	34.46
1982	5.31	2.06	2.40	4.46	3.17	7.73	3.38	4.21	2.33	1.28	3.40	3.04	41.77
1983	4.43	4.22	7.91	9.22*	4.31	3.11	2.94	3.92	2.64	5.81	5.02	7.80	58.93
1984	1.70	3.46	4.62	5.11	11.33*	4.35	7.64	2.90	1.69	1.67	3.70	2.97	48.02
1985	1.18	2.44	2.46	.63*	4.64	4.09	4.62	2.97	5.60	2.11	6.35	1.49	34.38
1986	3.39	3.55	2.25	1.64	.42*	4.47	6.26	2.18	1.23	2.14	5.26	3.53	36.32
1987	4.42	.75*	3.65	6.10	2.10	3.48	3.92	7.08	7.87	6.05	2.72	1.49	49.63
1988	3.13	3.63	1.98	1.59	4.58	.53*	5.93	1.99	2.77	2.28	8.13	1.33	37.87
1989	1.66	2.48	3.17	3.08	10.83	6.93	2.01	5.70	6.91	9.61	3.01	1.38	56.77
1990	4.49	3.20	4.01	5.60	6.58	3.44	3.02	14.88*	2.25	6.73	3.75	6.33	64.58
1991	2.79	2.06	4.16	3.67	4.89	1.12	3.27	5.09	1.65	2.75	3.67	3.54	38.66
1992	2.07	2.99	4.37	2.80	3.31	5.68	7.30	3.06	2.68	1.85	6.57	5.76	48.47
1993	3.23	3.31	6.93	4.09	1.68	1.88	1.55	.3.11	5.58	5.23	3.95	4.23	44.80
1994	6.14	3.20	4.43	3.77	3.62	3.93	8.34	4.69	3.31	2.25	4.18	4.50	52.36
1995	4.26	3.56	1.06	3.01	1.30	1.21	5.93	2.33	3.06	11.14	5.01	2.31	44.18
1996	9.49	2.44	1.44	6.36	2.64	5.04	9.33	3.42	6.94	6.00	3.87	8.18	65.15*
1997	3.78	1.65	6.79	2.95	3.43	2.06	5.32	5.88	1.09	1.65	6.35	3.77	44.72
1998	3.59	3.85	4.07	4.40	8.20	6.19	1.82	3.68	3.69	4.12	2.30	.91	46.82
1999	7.67	3.74	5.27	1.65	4.37	1.03	1.37	2.14	16.44*	3.02	3.34	2.15	52.19
2000	2.95	2.63	2.14	3.33	3.65	5.88	4.12	3.71	2.86	.69	2.86	5.37	40.19

West Branch Average Monthly Precipitation 1961 - 1990

	Jan	Feb	Mar	Apr	May	June	July	Aug	Sep	Oct	Nov	Dec	Total
	3.40	3.13	3.73	3.96	4.25	3.72	3.92	4.36	3.98	3.66	4.01	3.88	45.99

West Branch Average Monthly Precipitation 1971 - 2000

	Jan	Feb	Mar	Apr	May	June	July	Aug	Sep	Oct	Nov	Dec	Total
	4.13	3.07	4.01	3.87	4.42	3.73	4.41	4.35	4.48	4.04	4.10	3.94	48.55

APPENDIX V

WHITE POND
1924 - 1983

	Jan	Feb	Mar	Apr	May	June	July	Aug	Sep	Oct	Nov	Dec	Annual
1951 - 1980 precipitation averages													
	3.42	3.05	4.11	3.98	3.88	3.64	3.84	4.46	4.44	4.05	4.15	4.01	47.03

	Jan	Feb	Mar	Apr	May	June	July	Aug	Sep	Oct	Nov	Dec	Annual
Wettest Months													
	10.51	7.00	8.93	9.47	8.56	8.31	13.11	14.92	12.33	15.07	8.75	10.26	63.47
	1979	1981	1953	1983	1945	1972	1938	1955	1938	1955	1932	1973	1938

	Jan	Feb	Mar	Apr	May	June	July	Aug	Sep	Oct	Nov	Dec	Annual
Driest Months													
	.31	.94	.39	1.14	.70	.57	1.12	1.14	.75	.22	.47	.49	32.06
	1970	1980	1981	1941	1959	1949	1966	1935	1948	1963	1976	1980	1964

APPENDIX W
PRECIPITATION TOTALS (inches)
ROCKLAND COUNTY - SUFFERN

Year	Jan	Feb	Mar	Apr	May	June	July	Aug	Sep	Oct	Nov	Dec	Total
1940							2.97	4.22	1.84	3.39	4.23	3.85	
1941							6.28	4.64	.38*	1.99	3.97	5.45	
1942	3.55	2.80	6.73	1.18	3.23	2.78	6.73	7.00	5.59	3.75	4.75	5.22	53.31
1943	3.27	2.29	3.07	4.17	4.06	4.17	5.83	2.68	2.91	8.44	3.27	.99	45.15
1944	3.74	2.49	5.74	5.80	2.06	4.17	2.22	2.48	5.59	1.34	6.74	3.55	45.92
1945	4.18	3.47	2.38	4.61	7.81	4.18	18.08*	4.82	7.45	2.01	6.78	5.69	71.46*
1946	1.38	2.52	2.66	1.37	7.29	5.39	7.16	5.70	6.22	2.11	1.40	2.20	45.40
1947	3.25	2.41	4.40	4.78	8.34	5.02	4.98						
1948													
1949											1.65	3.01	
1950	2.83	4.25	3.76	2.37	4.07	2.42	3.88	6.37	3.00	2.60	5.23	5.81	38.82
1951	3.01	4.98	7.96	2.28	4.49	3.11	5.70	4.40	1.72	4.19	7.00	7.33	56.17
1952	5.72	2.88		7.80		1.40							
1953							2.71	3.31	.77*	1.63	3.24	2.57	5.72	47.25
1954	1.95	2.71	4.06	4.17	5.41	1.01*	2.34	11.34	7.49	1.96	7.27	4.15	53.86
1955	.78	3.43	4.63	3.20	1.54	3.88	3.70	15.68*	2.38	12.00*	5.00	.80	57.02
1956	2.00	4.50	4.40	5.30	2.42	3.47	5.11	3.04	4.56	1.19	5.55	4.34	45.88
1957	2.21	2.61	1.19	5.30	1.36	2.27	2.49	1.95	3.48	3.66	2.53	7.63	36.68
1958	5.92	3.79	3.61	6.29	3.99	5.44	3.27	4.69	5.78	3.79	3.47	1.01	51.05
1959	1.88	2.39	3.96	3.94	.60	5.83	4.72	5.11	2.21	7.93	4.19	5.45	48.21
1960	3.64	3.83	2.10	3.68	4.83	2.31	7.79	5.14	7.20	1.89	1.80	2.07	45.56
1961	3.26	4.25	5.41	6.21	4.62	2.39	4.10	3.42	2.94	1.81	3.15	3.01	44.57
1962	3.45	4.99	2.18	5.45	1.00	2.90	2.38	7.34	3.29	5.85	4.24	2.81	45.88
1963	3.03	2.44	3.80	1.10*	3.39	2.64	6.18	2.23	3.51	.80*	7.58	2.42	39.12
1964	4.98	2.70	2.55	5.10	.38*	3.31	2.98	1.37	1.40	.96	2.92	4.65	33.30*
1965	2.28	3.61	1.50	2.73	2.03	1.40	3.04	6.50	5.49	5.72	2.20	2.47	38.97
1966	1.07	1.44	1.28	2.40	3.04	1.62	1.13	2.07	7.61	4.36	5.42	3.05	34.49
1967	1.24	1.99	2.15	2.58	2.83	3.06	8.26	4.48	1.41	4.04	1.12	3.94	37.10
1968	2.62	.99	4.23	3.26	8.84	5.50	1.46	2.99	3.98	2.46	4.85	3.94	45.12
1969	1.53	2.58	2.96	4.51	3.01	5.82	6.77	4.76	4.63	1.76	5.21	6.10	49.64
1970	.30*	4.24	2.88	4.49	4.17	2.41	1.96	4.32	2.99	4.90	6.13	2.39	41.18
1971	1.97	6.03	3.47	3.85	4.31	2.60	5.49	10.44	6.42	3.90	4.86	2.21	55.55
1972	1.84	5.14	4.33	4.31	9.89	10.06*	4.83	3.35	1.34	5.04	9.78	6.38	66.29
1973	4.89	3.94	3.72	6.75	6.34	6.54	4.64	1.87	5.15	3.84	1.62	9.66*	58.96
1974	3.04	2.08	5.70	3.56	4.71	4.99	1.99	4.79	8.82	1.16	1.91	3.61	46.36
1975	4.31	2.95	4.43	3.42	3.78	5.29	9.35	5.55	10.09*	5.53	4.43	2.39	61.52
1976	5.22	2.68	2.60	3.01	4.12	5.97	5.54	5.08	4.70	7.13	.37*	2.54	48.96
1977	1.38	3.00	9.01*	3.86	1.25	4.05	1.81	3.46	7.78	4.85	11.20*	2.43	54.08
1978	7.74	.68*	3.74	1.60	7.81	3.90	3.60	6.23	3.32	1.67	3.34	4.31	47.94
1979	9.48*	3.92	4.44	5.18	7.53	2.38	1.00	5.01	8.30	4.60	5.09	2.47	59.40
1980	2.35	1.10	8.80	10.57*	2.57	3.55	3.00	1.13	.88	4.11	3.11	.43*	41.60
1981	.48	7.99*	.54*	3.92	5.88	2.57	4.59	1.01	2.82	5.06	1.44	4.78	41.08
1982	4.46	3.04	2.17	5.98		7.98							
1987	4.50	1.15	3.72	9.39	1.37	2.90	3.93	7.95	7.60	7.42	4.35	2.32	56.60
1988	2.55	2.93	2.50	3.24	6.85	1.02	8.02	5.25	3.62	2.26	7.56	1.40	47.20
1989	3.20	3.14	3.75	3.75	12.40*	7.98	3.41	6.06	7.35	7.76	4.32	.86	63.98
1990	5.64	2.70	3.31	3.09	8.40	3.29	5.37	8.94	2.00	5.83	3.43	6.53	58.53
1991	2.84	1.83	5.33	3.77	3.51	2.15	4.16	4.63	5.55	2.58	2.33	3.60	42.28
1992	2.21	2.28	4.50	2.45	5.66	5.42	5.67	4.66	3.43	1.92	6.06	5.34	49.60
1993	3.08	2.09	6.57	5.47	.88	3.22	1.88	1.90	4.90	4.51	4.89	4.38	43.77
1994	6.38	4.39	6.20	3.07	4.92	6.51	3.93	5.54	3.38				
1995												2.66	
1996	6.15	2.15	3.53	6.00	3.65	6.36	8.88	1.93	5.54	6.09	2.75	6.58	69.61
1997	3.08	1.22	3.00	4.00	3.12	2.35	3.65	5.20	2.54	1.77	4.92	3.29	38.14
1998	1.87	4.22	3.33	2.31	5.66	7.00	.91*	3.26	2.17	3.374	1.72	1.05	36.84
1999	8.35	2.24											

Total Precipitation is estimated from neighboring gauges for one to three months in years: 1950, 1951, 1955, 1956, 1960, 1980, 1987, 1990, and 1997

APPENDIX X
PRECIPITATION TOTALS
(Inches)
WEST POINT

Year	Jan	Feb	Mar	Apr	May	June	July	Aug	Sep	Oct	Nov	Dec	Total
1840	2.50	2.50	3.41	4.50	3.35	2.80	2.73	5.18	3.08	8.33	3.10	6.25	47.82
1841	9.95	2.00	5.25	6.60	4.37	5.97	3.40	2.80	3.05	2.10	3.35	5.10	53.94
1842	2.00	2.60	.75	4.95	4.80	3.23	5.19	9.92	5.60	4.20	2.98	4.40	50.62
1843	2.70	3.02	5.05	3.40	2.28	1.95	3.00	11.33	3.62	6.95	4.60	2.70	50.60
1844	5.25	3.10	4.20	.50*	5.10	3.45	7.90	5.28	3.50	4.92	1.05	4.12	48.37
1845	5.15	2.88	3.40	1.80	4.10	1.82	2.38	7.72	2.60	2.93	5.36	3.24	43.98
1846	3.42	2.78	3.90	3.04	6.62	2.30	6.14	2.93	.17*	2.46	10.02*	2.80	46.58
1847	4.01	6.22	3.49	.79	2.70	2.27	2.52	2.20	3.58	1.97	1.80	3.50	35.05
1848	1.87	3.98	2.71	2.90	7.05	7.37	4.42	.49	3.67	4.43	6.76	5.04	50.79
1849	1.03	2.07	4.55	.90	6.10	1.08	3.15	4.84	.48	7.63	2.31	4.11	38.25
1850	6.06	3.33	4.84	4.30	8.26	3.83	5.89	5.13	8.14	2.34	2.17	5.65	59.94
1851	.82	5.09	2.56	7.24	4.34	1.53	4.44	2.58	1.22	4.02	4.31	2.45	4.06
1852	1.80	3.80	2.68	4.66	1.85	2.30	4.67	6.39	2.39	2.99	4.47	5.31	43.31
1853	3.27	5.45	3.23	5.84	7.99	3.77	10.48	7.87	3.95	3.85	5.60	2.26	63.56
1854	3.52	5.04	2.81	10.53*	5.08	1.62	3.73	.46	4.00	1.08	5.65	2.64	47.06
1855	3.63	4.23	.83	2.52	4.16	4.50	6.26	3.10	.97	10.25	3.69	5.14	49.29
1856	2.81	.63	1.68	3.76	6.50	4.13	2.42	11.96	4.52	1.35	2.50	5.76	47.41
1857	2.25	1.79	1.88	5.32	5.70	6.38	2.04	3.97	4.46	5.40	2.75	5.25	47.19
1858	3.83	1.65	.92	4.48	6.17	4.30	3.17	3.52	2.05	3.65	6.30	3.90	43.94
1859	4.00	2.30	5.85	4.00	2.89	5.45	1.65	6.70	5.20	1.85	2.70	1.40	43.69
(CIVIL WAR YEARS)													
1864	2.60												
1865	3.20	1.25	5.25	4.55	7.75	4.80	4.35	1.65	3.05	3.60	2.70	3.25	45.40
1866	1.00	4.50	3.65	3.20	4.25	5.60	3.80	5.30	7.20	2.10	3.45	1.30	45.15
1867	1.05	4.40	1.25	3.40	10.50	6.00	6.15	11.70	.90	2.00	3.50	.83	51.78
1868	1.55	1.60	3.86	4.80	11.66*	3.45	1.15	11.75	11.22	.90	3.85	.92	56.71
1869	2.40	3.55	4.25	3.07	4.75	5.33	2.45	1.90	3.35	7.80	3.82	4.90	47.66
1870	4.91	6.15	4.65	5.15	3.82	3.15	2.53	2.95	2.40	3.52	1.11	2.00	42.34
1871	1.48	2.77	5.24	3.97	3.85	7.36	8.55	6.60	1.63	4.96	4.40	2.73	52.94
1872	1.70	1.00	2.40	1.70	2.41	3.18	1.10	4.57	2.78	2.18	4.73	2.89	30.64
1373	4.81	4.60	2.79	3.82	3.46	.76	2.46	5.11	3.52	5.75	2.77	5.00	44.85
1874	5.70	1.56	1.68	6.49	2.15	2.17	7.99	2.60	3.86	1.79	2.93	2.01	40.93
1875	2.52	4.24	4.22	2.83	1.13	2.98	3.69	8.32	1.98	3.58	4.06	1.82	41.37
1876	1.47	5.88	8.71	3.89	3.40	1.29	5.80	.05	2.47	2.00	3.90	2.75	41.61
1877	2.77	.92	7.40	3.30	1.02	5.15	4.02	2.46	1.65	8.54	6.06	1.26	44.55
1878	4.64	2.16	3.38	2.98	5.37	3.20	3.37	1.85	2.61	3.96	4.28	6.97	44.97
1879	1.71	2.10	3.79	3.04	2.40	6.50	4.60	5.76	3.20	.70	2.00	5.12	40.92
1880	3.72	3.40	3.55	3.50	1.26	1.66	5.70	2.90	1.90	2.50	3.00	2.80	35.87
1881	5.80	4.60	5.40	1.60	4.82	4.80	3.50	3.00	1.00	5.20	3.50	5.80	49.02
1882	5.40	2.80	4.90	1.94	6.00	3.60	2.90	1.40	13.50*	2.40	2.00	2.40	49.80
1883	2.50	4.40	1.70	3.40	2.60	4.10	3.80	4.50	3.40	5.30	1.40	2.70	39.80
1884	3.00	4.00	4.50	2.30	3.80	2.50	8.40	5.50	1.00	3.00	5.00	6.20	49.20
1885	4.09	3.60	2.40	3.30	2.10	3.60	3.60	7.50	.90	5.80	5.70	4.60	47.19
1886	6.80	4.24	3.98	3.70	4.16	3.60	4.40	4.60	1.70	2.10	4.30	3.00	46.58
1887	4.40	5.60	3.10	3.30	1.50	6.30	7.44	2.20	1.90	3.30	2.86	5.38	47.28
1888	4.58	3.78	3.62	2.68	6.22	1.04	2.18	6.40	8.34	3.94	3.10	5.42	51.29
1889	5.08	2.88	1.50	4.56	3.00	3.32	9.92	4.09	6.42	4.85	8.08	3.06	56.76
1890	1.96	5.12	5.91	3.90	5.07	4.60	7.00	4.10	6.80	4.30	1.00	3.00	58.94
1891	8.20	4.68	2.83	2.70	1.90	2.46	4.16	4.88	1.66	.93	2.83	5.03	42.26
1892	6.93	1.07	4.15	1.09	4.84	3.61	5.97	3.67	3.53	T	6.02	1.33	42.21
1893	4.43	7.29	3.94	3.16	8.24	1.83	4.53	6.62	2.84	4.25	3.63	2.66	53.42
1894	3.05	3.94	1.33	2.86	4.45	2.08	1.04*	1.86	6.30	6.25	4.08	2.92	40.26
1895	5.49	1.60	1.10	6.81	3.55	2.63	6.86	3.42	1.16	4.22	5.58	4.20	46.62
1896	.83	4.46	12.02*	1.98	2.89	4.07	2.50	1.96	5.74	2.36	5.10	1.63	45.54
1897	3.05	3.35	3.35	3.17	4.70	3.20	13.05*	5.15	2.90	1.43	5.40	5.60	54.35
1898	4.80	3.60	2.48	3.72	7.51	1.85	3.80	9.08	1.37	4.82	6.29	2.41	51.73
1899	3.50	3.73	7.45	1.70	2.31	4.85	5.78	1.90	6.39	1.64	3.24	2.23	44.72
1900	4.15												

Year	Jan	Feb	Mar	Apr	May	June	July	Aug	Sep	Oct	Nov	Dec	Total
1901													
1902													
1903													
1904													
1905	6.00	1.70	3.40	2.53	1.00	5.83	4.01	4.00	5.90	3.00	1.80	2.30	41.47
1906	1.00	1.00	3.00	4.45	4.71	2.75	5.55	1.80	2.83	4.10	1.45	4.00	36.64
1907	2.33	2.20	2.30	3.14	3.11	3.53	2.21	.82	10.68	7.51	4.61	3.90	46.34
1908	2.05	2.40	1.35	2.59	7.59	2.40	4.11	4.35	1.50	1.70	.67	2.70	33.41
1909	1.66	4.31	3.43	5.83	1.83	4.46	2.00	4.50	2.57	.69	2.07	4.68	38.03
1910	6.10	3.50	1.50	9.45	5.60	4.77	1.87	2.81	2.45	1.35	4.46	2.01	45.87
1911	4.25	3.07	4.02	3.98	.57	6.01	2.97	7.10	4.50	8.49	5.37	1.56	51.89
1912	1.75	2.73	6.14	3.99	4.24	1.56	2.52	5.26	3.25	3.38	3.03	5.00	42.85
1913	4.09	4.32	10.32	5.14	4.11	1.34	1.96	4.03	6.52	8.66	2.16	3.89	56.54
1914	5.15	2.30	4.53	3.75	3.01	4.70	4.87	2.34	1.09	2.19	4.31	2.93	41.17
1915	4.59	3.69	.52	*2.98	3.03	2.50	6.29	6.53	2.28	2.28	3.60	5.11	43.40
1916	2.64	2.56	3.06	.88	2.78	4.05	2.71	1.00	3.61	1.83	2.44	3.92	31.48
1917	2.12	2.31	6.21	1.32	3.34	2.38	3.70	4.35	1.36	5.94	.43	3.07	36.53
1918	3.38	1.54	1.27	3.91	3.55	1.54	3.45	2.90	2.39	.98	2.10	4.04	31.05
1919	2.61	1.97	4.28	4.74	4.30	3.83	7.21	4.74	4.59	2.37	6.19	3.71	50.54
1920	1.42	2.43	4.20	4.40	1.63	5.35	3.30	4.55	2.73	3.73	3.47	5.39	42.60
1921	6.05	4.85	2.80	5.54	1.84	3.07	4.00	2.43	4.40	2.95	5.55	3.40	46.88
1922	2.27	3.05	5.60	2.00	2.10	6.09	5.34	1.20	2.85	1.50	.25*	1.94	34.14
1923	3.80	2.48	2.33	.91	2.50	3.20	1.54	.70	5.35	3.50	3.25	2.35	31.91
1924	3.20	2.22	.93	5.57	3.65	2.25	2.31	3.76	9.33	0*	3.40	2.52	39.14
1925	2.22	4.75	5.10	1.66	1.50	1.88	4.64	1.22	3.59	2.82	1.01	1.25	31.64
1926	2.41	4.16	1.48	1.10	.72	1.36	2.74	4.84	2.30	3.99	3.75	2.96	31.81
1927	3.11	3.43	2.36	2.06	3.49	1.65	3.27	7.08	4.38	6.89	6.83	5.84	50.39
1928	1.91	4.00	1.77	4.15	1.52	6.52	7.30	7.24	2.88	1.43	2.41	1.00	42.13
1929	3.52	4.66	2.44	7.25	2.51	.94	3.08	1.24	2.79	4.11	2.37	4.29	40.10
1930	2.50	2.40	2.70	2.97	2.69	3.10	1.35	2.41	1.12	1.28	4.76	1.46	28.74*
1931	.92	2.45	2.70	4.95	3.47	3.74	2.58	2.91	1.92	1.35	.70	2.30	29.99
1932	3.61	2.01	4.66	2.62	2.89	3.54	3.03	3.59	1.70	5.48	8.30	1.35	42.78
1933	1.72	2.98	4.49	5.22	2.79	1.23	2.47	11.40	5.62	2.11	.86	3.59	44.48
1934	3.60	2.88	4.31	3.04	5.93	4.11	5.47	2.33	8.17	3.07	4.19	2.20	49.90
1935	1.88	2.37	2.26	2.49	3.24	4.47	3.68	1.77	3.08	1.77	3.78	.88	31.67
1936	5.59	2.98	6.94	2.98	3.00	3.91	2.75	3.84	3.65	3.61	1.52	6.08	46.85
1937	6.13	2.31	2.38	4.09	5.49	5.56	3.96	6.39	4.67	3.21	3.39	2.88	50.46
1938	3.41	2.18	1.77	2.55	2.97	6.07	7.72	4.91	10.74	1.73	2.85	4.60	52.50
1939	3.17	4.82	3.95	6.18	1.42	5.05	2.50	3.14	3.46	4.08	1.67	2.00	41.44
1940	2.58	2.58	6.30	5.96	4.67	3.02	3.36	3.22	2.87	2.13	4.11	2.77	43.57
1941	1.96	2.69	2.46	1.48	2.04	5.07	7.10	3.41	.42	2.03	2.61	3.93	35.20
1942	2.38	3.60	5.33	1.72	3.88	4.32	7.24	4.94	4.18	3.18	4.59	5.12	50.48
1943	2.91	1.88	2.93	2.78	3.52	2.25	3.80	2.40	3.50	7.35	4.26	.76	38.34
1944	2.52	2.15	5.09	3.91	1.76	1.94	1.36	1.44	5.19	1.59	5.70	3.02	35.67
1945	3.91	2.78	1.97	3.77	6.91	4.19	10.21	4.07	5.25	1.81	5.04	4.44	54.35
1946	1.33	2.38	2.00	1.50	5.00	4.30	5.07	2.42	6.07	2.00	1.15	2.40	35.62
1947	3.86	2.33	4.11	5.86	7.06	5.29	6.28	2.20	2.50	2.34	7.97	4.35	54.15
1948	4.04	1.77	3.42	4.92	6.41	5.24	3.41	2.98	1.13	1.93	4.60	7.94	47.79
1949	5.67	3.09	1.88	4.38	6.87	.88	3.78	3.77	3.62	2.40	2.59	3.02	41.88
1950	3.44	4.40	3.51	2.38	5.14	3.91	5.03	2.10	3.06	1.89	5.94	5.06	45.86
1951	5.02	4.71	7.83	3.18	3.46	3.16	5.40	3.99	2.03	4.22	6.78	6.01	55.79
1952	5.19	2.64	7.11	9.47	5.43	6.52	4.87	7.28	5.14	.80	4.64	5.92	65.01
1953	6.64	2.14	8.85	6.66	4.81	1.84	3.68	1.18	1.97	3.34	2.37	5.32	48.80
1954	1.98	2.54	3.98	2.66	6.65	2.25	1.47	7.78	7.12	3.21	7.93	4.27	51.84
1955	.74*	1.53	4.77	3.65	2.01	3.95	2.63	11.74*	2.85	12.75*	6.67	.76	56.05
1956	1.80	4.07	4.21	5.11	3.59	4.12	5.50	2.68	6.09	3.37	2.95	4.79	48.28
1957	2.05	2.31	2.30	4.56	3.03	1.37	3.61	1.73	2.78	4.81	4.21	9.51	42.29
1958	6.17	4.33	5.87	6.27	4.84	3.63	2.05	1.44	6.84	5.84	4.13	1.25	52.66
1959	2.70	2.66	4.66	3.88	.94	5.49	2.46	5.63	1.64	10.97	4.64	4.68	50.35
1960	3.36	.22*	2.85	3.46	4.59	5.02	9.64	5.66	8.26	2.46	2.87	2.94	56.33

Year	Jan	Feb	Mar	Apr	May	June	July	Aug	Sep	Oct	Nov	Dec	Total
1961	3.41	4.41	3.99	5.35	6.47	3.01	2.81	4.03	3.68	2.26	4.27	3.74	47.43
1962	3.41	4.89	1.98	4.41	1.33	3.46	3.17	4.11	2.18	5.39	3.78	3.48	41.59
1963	3.00	2.43	3.30	1.20	1.73	3.60	5.69	2.84	3.56	.12	6.55	2.35	36.37
1964	4.86	2.43	2.10	4.11	2.22	4.09	3.51	1.34	2.02	1.96	2.22	3.82	34.68
1965	3.22	3.97	2.09	2.76	1.54	1.58	3.53	4.19	3.24	3.95	2.31	2.34	34.72
1966	2.53	3.92	2.28	2.46	3.04	.69*	1.16	1.17	7.38	4.96	4.70	3.77	38.06
1967	1.49	2.25	5.63	2.85	3.30	5.38	5.24	6.75	2.50	4.90	3.30	5.90	49.49
1968	2.14	.81	4.73	3.42	6.23	5.71	1.88	4.58	2.94	2.42	5.15	5.04	45.05
1969	2.03	2.65	3.23	4.09	2.68	4.70	4.59	4.58	3.26	2.05	7.28	6.49	47.63
1970	.45	4.28	3.32	3.34	2.82	2.61	2.48	2.57	4.46	3.78	4.85	2.83	37.79
1971	2.42	4.87	4.02	2.94	5.04	1.29	3.84	8.01	6.48	3.21	3.51	3.11	48.74
1972	1.94	5.22	4.52	3.76	8.01	9.56*	2.87	1.56	1.75	5.60	9.01	5.94	59.74
1973	5.32	3.81	3.45	7.43	6.28	6.46	4.54	1.35	2.96	2.39	2.46	8.12	54.57
1974	4.22	2.50	4.82	4.98	4.44	4.67	2.32	3.62	7.27	2.19	2.48	5.27	48.78
1975	5.18	3.51	4.68	2.27	4.67	3.70	7.91	4.72	9.74	4.63	4.41	3.43	58.85
1976	5.06	3.31	2.71	2.97	4.90	3.57	2.73	7.32	3.91	6.21	.57	3.11	46.37
1977	1.49	4.29	6.57	4.47	3.15	3.67	2.19	2.48	7.89	6.84	8.53	4.90	56.47
1978	9.25	1.20	3.39	1.84	9.68	2.34	3.76	5.07	3.79	1.60	2.47	3.60	47.99
1979	11.07	3.56	4.16	5.20	6.10	1.78	1.67	6.10	5.83	6.78	7.42	2.77	62.44
1980	1.54	1.29	7.38	7.68	1.57	4.46	3.40	1.44	1.41	3.51	3.54	1.23	38.45
1981	1.34	8.58*	.59	4.17	5.57	3.77	3.84	1.21	2.26	3.92	1.47	4.66	41.38
1982	3.00	2.28	2.20	4.00	3.00	7.46	3.53	5.18	2.48	1.02	3.93	1.65	40.73
1983	3.79	4.84	8.54	10.16	5.14	2.51	3.27	4.72	2.95	6.40	5.70	11.47*	69.49
1984	1.21	3.99	4.46	6.00	11.18	3.29	8.65	1.86	2.03	1.64	2.06	2.83	49.20
1985	1.10	2.26	2.09	1.65	6.35	5.06	5.91	4.46	5.21	1.95	6.83	2.09	44.96
1986	4.27	3.74	2.47	2.75	1.36	7.01	7.01	3.82	1.15	2.61	4.38	3.94	44.51
1987	4.46	.41	5.70	5.49	1.88	3.27	3.20	4.91	7.90	6.64	2.65	1.91	48.42
1988	2.58	3.32	1.09	2.43	4.17	.53	7.34	4.39	2.60	2.14	8.52	.72*	39.83
1989	1.35	1.99	2.37	3.33	11.09	8.28	2.61	5.60	5.35	7.86	2.83	1.28	53.94
1990	3.89	2.98	3.05	3.17	6.43	3.06	5.25	10.68	1.90	5.84	4.53	7.03	57.81
1991	1.94	1.27	3.55	4.07	4.42	2.64	3.54	5.10	4.48	4.21	1.82	3.54	40.58
1992	2.25	1.51	3.33	2.82	4.49	3.98	5.84	3.29	2.15	1.46	6.17	3.32	40.61
1993	2.79	2.77	5.55	6.05	.68	2.87	1.18	2.35	5.97	5.34	5.42	4.33	45.30
1994	5.51	2.62	4.72	3.69	3.75	7.24	7.72	7.62	4.64	1.57	4.63	3.22	56.93
1995	5.01	1.80	3.09	2.57	2.42	.84	5.83	2.20	3.88	12.21	6.08	2.41	48.34
1996	11.64*	2.58	2.98	6.11	3.32	6.35	9.00	2.85	5.33	5.54	5.52	10.17	71.39*
1997	3.12	2.08	3.69	5.31	3.07	2.74	4.15	5.00	2.10	2.01	6.39	3.56	43.22
1998	4.34	3.61	4.13	4.52	6.23	3.91	2.23	3.08	3.30	4.17	2.56	1.05	46.13
1999	7.81	3.01	8.02	2.34	3.48	.80	1.21	5.40	12.30	2.60	4.58	3.12	54.67
2000	3.57	2.80	3.85	4.16	3.65	7.14	5.03	5.31	6.42	1.43	3.61	5.09	52.06

West Point Monthly Averages (1961-1990)

	Jan	Feb	Mar	Apr	May	June	July	Aug	Sep	Oct	Nov	Dec	Total
	3.35	3.87	3.69	4.05	4.69	4.02	4.00	4.16	4.00	3.83	4.39	3.96	48.01

West Point Monthly Averages (1971-2000)

	Jan	Feb	Mar	Apr	May	June	July	Aug	Sep	Oct	Nov	Dec	Total
	4.12	3.07	4.04	4.28	4.85	4.14	4.38	4.36	4.51	4.12	4.47	3.96	50.30

Total precipitation is estimated from neighboring gauges for one to five months in years:
1866, 1879, 1880, 1881, 1882, 1883, 1884, 1905, 1930, and 1946

APPENDIX Y

FORMER WEATHER STATIONS
AVERAGE TEMPERATURES (°F)
(Uncorrected)

WHITE PLAINS (1862 - 1892)

Jan	Feb	Mar	Apr	May	June	July	Aug	Sep	Oct	Nov	Dec	Annual
29.4	31.0	36.1	49.2	59.9	69.1	73.5	71.6	64.6	54.3	43.3	33.2	51.3

KENSICO (1873 - 1878)

Jan	Feb	Mar	Apr	May	June	July	Aug	Sep	Oct	Nov	Dec	Annual
30.6	29.4	36.8	46.6	61.1	70.0	73.6	72.9	65.4	53.9	42.7	32.2	51.2

MOUNT HOPE (1899 - 1929)

Jan	Feb	Mar	Apr	May	June	July	Aug	Sep	Oct	Nov	Dec	Annual
28.9	28.3	38.1	48.5	59.0	67.6	72.2	70.0	64.1	54.4	42.4	31.5	50.4

MOUNT VERNON (1915 - 1941)

Jan	Feb	Mar	Apr	May	June	July	Aug	Sep	Oct	Nov	Dec	Annual
31.6	31.6	39.5	49.2	56.7	69.1	74.2	72.6	66.4	56.2	44.8	34.9	52.6

OSSINING (1941 - 1973)

Jan	Feb	Mar	Apr	May	June	July	Aug	Sep	Oct	Nov	Dec	Annual
30.2	31.3	39.1	50.5	60.8	70.2	75.8	74.0	67.7	57.0	46.5	34.2	53.1

CHAPPAQUA (1956 - 1974)

Jan	Feb	Mar	Apr	May	June	July	Aug	Sep	Oct	Nov	Dec	Annual
24.9	26.3	34.7	46.8	56.7	66.8	71.6	69.1	62.5	50.8	40.9	29.8	48.4

BEDFORD HILLS (1894 - 1977)

Jan	Feb	Mar	Apr	May	June	July	Aug	Sep	Oct	Nov	Dec	Annual
28.3	28.8	37.9	48.7	59.5	68.2	73.3	71.1	64.6	53.9	42.7	31.6	50.7

SCARSDALE* (1904 - 1990)

Jan	Feb	Mar	Apr	May	June	July	Aug	Sep	Oct	Nov	Dec	Annual
28.6	31.4	39.9	50.1	60.8	69.0	74.2	72.6	65.1	54.2	44.8	33.8	52.0

SHRUB OAK (1950 - 1969)

Jan	Feb	Mar	Apr	May	June	July	Aug	Sep	Oct	Nov	Dec	Annual
26.4	28.4	35.8	48.1	57.4	65.5	69.8	68.2	61.1	51.7	41.0	29.2	48.6

* - 1961 - 1990 average used

APPENDIX Z
MONTHLY PRECIPITATION
DISCONTINUED STATIONS
(Inches)

ARDENIA (Garrison) 1856 - 1890 elevation 157 feet

	Jan	Feb	Mar	Apr	May	Jun	Jul	Aug	Sep	Oct	Nov	Dec	Annual
Average	2.87	3.17	3.75	3.58	3.91	3.58	4.21	4.72	3.85	3.90	3.87	3.16	44.57
Wettest	5.71	9.00	7.77	7.54	8.08	6.54	9.28	13.11	11.56	10.49	8.24	6.47	53.06
Year	1886	1884	1859	1861	1868	1865	1889	1856	1882	1869	1889	1856	1888
Driest	.26	.30	.82	1.29	.49	1.11	1.63	.53	.95	.80	.65	.75	30.80
Year	1873	1856	1885	1882	1887	1888	1868	1876	1884	1879	1882	1861	1880

MOUNT HOPE 1897 - 1929 elevation 200 feet

	Jan	Feb	Mar	Apr	May	Jun	Jul	Aug	Sep	Oct	Nov	Dec	Annual
Average	3.63	3.81	4.23	4.24	4.30	4.11	5.26	5.16	3.68	4.24	3.20	4.13	49.99
Wettest	8.22	7.19	8.20	9.02	7.91	9.44	11.12	11.25	10.00	11.30	7.80	6.72	63.82
Year	1915	1915	1918	1901	1898	1903	1897	1927	1907	1903	1907	1902	1927
Driest	1.59	1.02	1.21	1.95	.78	.94	.79	1.20	.37	.00	.43	1.47	38.53
Year	1922	1901	1924	1900	1903	1901	1910	1899	1914	1924	1903	1896	1924

MOUNT PLEASANT 1831 - 1844 elevation 125 feet

	Jan	Feb	Mar	Apr	May	Jun	Jul	Aug	Sep	Oct	Nov	Dec	Annual
Average	2.16	1.50	2.55	3.58	3.63	3.14	4.46	4.12	3.05	3.23	2.28	2.45	36.15
Wettest	4.50	3.72	5.32	4.94	5.54	6.03	7.23	9.51	5.63	5.88	4.20	5.55	48.86
Year	1841	1832	1837	1835	1834	1834	1839	1932	1839	1931	1932	1839	1832
Driest	.24	.51	1.07	.85	1.18	.67	1.96	.35	.97	1.13	.37	.36	23.31
Year	1844	1844	1839	1844	1843	1844	1838	1834	1835	1839	1844	1843	1844

MOUNT VERNON 1915 - 1941 elevation 155 feet

	Jan	Feb	Mar	Apr	May	Jun	Jul	Aug	Sep	Oct	Nov	Dec	Annual
Average	3.82	3.78	3.59	3.65	3.85	3.74	4.70	4.81	4.01	3.89	3.14	3.46	46.44
Wettest	7.87	7.11	6.62	6.27	5.96	7.34	9.46	12.32	8.15	9.08	7.59	7.45	64.28
Year	1915	1926	1919	1924	1924	1928	1927	1927	1920	1927	1932	1936	1927
Driest	1.47	1.87	.88	1.38	.50	1.78	1.37	1.17	.07	.24	.67	1.57	38.59
Year	1916	1938	1915	1935	1939	1929	1924	1917	1941	1924	1941	1935	1931

NORTH SALEM 1830 - 1860 elevation 361 feet

	Jan	Feb	Mar	Apr	May	Jun	Jul	Aug	Sep	Oct	Nov	Dec	Annual
Average	2.97	2.37	3.20	3.38	4.37	3.41	4.07	4.11	3.09	4.13	3.14	3.20	41.44
Wettest	6.20	5.41	9.55	7.27	7.80	7.02	7.20	12.10	6.63	9.90	5.96	6.92	55.02
Year	1841	1847	1857	1857	1853	1834	1846	1856	1850	1833	1854	1830	1850
Driest	.99	.32	.51	1.23	1.46	1.09	1.32	.23	.35	1.53	.83	.60	33.52
Year	1851	1835	1855	1848	1835	1849	1849	1854	1846	1856	1834	1831	1834

TARRYTOWN 1945 - 1976 & (1860 - 1872) elevation 240 feet

	Jan	Feb	Mar	Apr	May	Jun	Jul	Aug	Sep	Oct	Nov	Dec	Annual
Average	2.70	2.95	3.68	3.89	3.97	3.49	4.53	4.67	3.63	3.37	4.29	3.80	44.97
Wettest	6.39	5.58	10.34	8.20	8.85	14.56	8.91	13.75	10.49	15.62	10.02	9.13	62.18
Year	1949	1960	1953	1952	1946	1972	1945	1955	1868	1955	1972	1973	1972
Driest	.43	.42	1.54	1.24	.99	.37	.77	1.48	.24	.30	.40	.55	29.05
Year	1970	1963	1960	1946	1964	1949	1968	1964	1867	1963	1976	1955	1965

WHITE PLAINS 1854 - 1860, 1873 - 1891 elevation 100 feet

	Jan	Feb	Mar	Apr	May	Jun	Jul	Aug	Sep	Oct	Nov	Dec	Annual
Average	5.50	4.68	4.18	4.01	3.41	3.50	4.99	4.58	3.57	3.87	4.28	4.88	51.45
Wettest	13.70	13.80	12.40	9.68	6.94	7.99	14.07	11.27	9.75	18.90	11.66	12.75	67.92
Year	1863	1863	1876	1888	1857	1887	1889	1856	1882	1877	1889	1872	1882
Driest	1.02	.86	1.02	1.20	.15	.20	2.21	.41	.50	.50		.80	1.55	35.17
Year	1857	1856	1854	1882	1887	1891	1858	1854	1881	1879	1890	1854	1891

YONKERS 1878 - 1943

	Jan	Feb	Mar	Apr	May	Jun	Jul	Aug	Sep	Oct	Nov	Dec	Annual
Average	4.21	3.65	4.20	3.62	3.57	3.80	4.68	4.84	3.73	4.10	3.32	3.71	47.43
Wettest	11.80	10.96	13.25	9.82	8.97	13.16	11.56	16.53	14.70	14.14	8.84	8.58	85.15
Year	1884	1884	1912	1901	1908	1903	1907	1903	1882	1902	1889	1885	1903
Driest	.62	.13	.12	.20	.16	.25	.46	.41	.25	.09	.55	.62	25.45
Year	1911	1914	1915	1896	1903	1901	1924	1923	1914	1920	1908	1907	1921

REFERENCES

Bingham, C., 1963, Probabilities of Weekly Averages of the Daily Temperature Maximum, Minimum, and Range, The Climate of the Northeast, Bulletin 659, Connecticut Agricultural Station, New Haven, CT

Borland, Hal. 1964, *Sundial of the Seasons*, J.P. Lipincott Co., New York, NY

Brumbach, Joseph J., 1965, The Climate of Connecticut, Bulletin 99, Department of Agriculture and Natural Resources, State Library, Hartford, CT

Burroughs, William J., 1992, *Weather Cycles, Real or Imaginary?*, Cambridge University Press, New York, NY

Cable, Mary, 1988, *The Blizzard of 88*, Atheneum Press, New York, NY

Caplovich, Judd, 1987, *Blizzard! The Great Storm of '88*, Vero Publishing Co., Vernon CT

Dineen,R.J., DeSimone, D.J., Hanson, E.L., 1988, Glacial Lake Albany and its Successors in the Hudson Valley, Field Trip Guidebook, AMQUA 1998, ed. J.Brigham-Grette, Contribution No. 63, Dept. of Geology, University of Massachusetts, Amherst, MA

Dethier, B. E., 1966, Precipitation in New York State, Bulletin 1009, Cornell University Agricultural Station, New York State College of Agriculture. Ithaca, NY

Dunlap, D.V., 1965, Probabilities of Extreme Snowfalls and Snow Depth, Bulletin 821, Northeast Regional Research Publication, New Jersey Agricultural Experiment Station, State University of New Jersey, New Brunswick, NJ

Frederick, R.H., Johnson, E.C., MacDonald, H.A., August 1959, Spring and Fall Freezing Temperatures in New York State, Cornell Miscellaneous Bulletin 33, New York State College of Agriculture

Garriot, E., 1906, Cold Waves and Frosts in the United States, Department of Agriculture, Washington, DC

Garwood, A.N. ed., 1996, Weather America, Toucan Valley Publications, Milpitas, CA

Gribbin, J., 1998, *The Case of the Missing Neutrinos and Other Phenomena*, Chapter 6, Fromm International, New York, NY

Gumbel, E.J. 1958, *Statistics of Extremes*, Columbia University Press, New York, NY

Harding, James, C., 1945, Report to Westchester County Board of Supervisors on Storm Water Control, County of Westchester, County Office Building, White Plains, NY

Karl, T.R, Williams Jr, C.N., Young, P.J. & Wendland, W.M., 1986a, A Model to Estimate The Time of Observation Bias Associated with Monthly Mean Maximum, Minimum And Mean Temperatures for the United States, Journal of Climate & Applied Meteorology, v. 25, 145-160

Diaz, H.F. & Kukla, G. 1988, Urbanization: Its Detection in the United States Climate Record, Journal of Climate, v.1, 1099-1123

Jones, P.D., 1989, Urban Bias in Area-Averaged Surface Air Temperature Trends, Bulletin-American Meteorological Society, 70 (3), 265-270

Easterling, D.R., Mason,E.H., Hughes, P.Y., Boden, T.A. & Daniels, R.C., 1996 United States Historical Climate Network Monthly Temperature and Precipitation Data, Publication No. 4500, Carbon Dioxide Information Analysis Center, Oak Ridge National Laboratory, Environmental Sciences Division, 260 p.

Ludlam, David A. 1966, *Early American Winters, 1604 - 1820*, American Meteorological Society, Boston, MA
____ 1968, *Early American Winters II, 1821 - 1870*, American Meteorological Society, Boston, MA

Maciejunes, N.V. & Hall, M.D.,1998, *The Paintings of Charles Burchfield* - North by Midwest, Harry N. Abrams, Inc. Publishers in Association with the Columbus Museum of Art

Mordoff, M.A. 1949, The Climate of New York State, Bulletin 764, Cornell Extension, New York State College of Agriculture, Cornell University, Ithaca, NY

Owenby, J.R. & Exell, D.S., 1992, New York - Monthly Station Normals of Temperature, Precipitation, and Heating and Cooling Degree Days, 1961- 1990, Climatography of the United States, U.S. Dept. of Commerce, National Climatic Data Center, Asheville, NC

Pack, A.B. 1972, Climate of New York, Climatography of the United States No. 60-30, U.S. Department of Commerce, Washington, D.C

Sanders, T.I., 1983, *Greatest American Weather Disasters*, Icarus Press, South Bend, IN 180p.

Schaefer, H.G., 1999, Climate Summary of 1998, The Four Seasons - Journal of the Hudson Valley Weather Observers, vol.9, No. 1

Schmidlin, T.W. 1984, A Temperature Climatology

for New York State, Dissertation, Cornell University

Spar, J. & Mayer, J.A. 1973, Temperature Trends in New York City, A Postscript, Weatherwise, June 1973

Thaler, Jerome S. 1977, *The Westchester Weather Book*, George Candreva Environmental Center, Yorktown Heights, NY, 136 p.
_____ 1978, Climate Summary of Putnam County, Rotary Club of Lake Mahopac, Mahopac, NY
_____ 1979, West Point - 152 Years of Weather Records, Weatherwise, 32, 112-115
_____ 1983, A Cyclical Pattern in 19th and 20th Century Hudson Valley Winter Temperatures, in McCormac, B.M. ed., *Weather and Climate Responses to Solar Variations*, 189-196, Colorado Associated University Press, Boulder, CO, 626 p.
_____ 1987, Hudson Valley Reconstructed Temperature Data Sets: History and Spectral Analysis, in Rampino M.R., Sanders, J.E., Newman, W.S., & Konigsson, L.K., eds *Climate, History, Periodicity and Predictability*, Chap. 3, 70-77, Van Nostrand Reinhold Company, New York, NY, 588 p.
_____ 1989, Hudson Basin Precipitation Regimes, Croton, Esopus and Schoharie Watersheds, Northeastern Environmental Science, 8(2); 106-118
_____ 1996, *Catskill Weather*, Purple Mountain Press, Fleischmanns, NY, 167 p.
_____ 2000, Daily Extremes of Temperature, Precipitation & Snowfall for Selected Hudson Valley Long Term U.S. Cooperative Weather Stations, Unpublished Research Paper
_____ 1998, Hudson Valley Seasonal and Annual Mean Temperatures: History, Trends and Periodicities, Northeastern Geology and Environmental Sciences, 20 (2), 133-144

U.S. Department of Agriculture, Weather Bureau, 1934, Climate Summary of the United States, Section 82: South-Central New York, U.S. Government Printing Office, Washington, DC
_____ 1934, Climate Summary of the United States, Section 83: Eastern New York, U.S. Government Printing Office, Washington, DC
_____ 1894-1897, 1901-1938, Climatological Data: New York, National Climate Center, Asheville, NC

U.S. Department of Commerce, 1956, Substation History: New York, National Climate Center, Asheville, NC
_____ Weather Bureau, 1929-1965, Climatological Data: New York, National Climate Center, Asheville, NC
_____ Environmental Science Services

Administration, 1966-1970, Climatological Data: New York, National Climate Center, Asheville, NC
_____ National Oceanic & Atmospheric Administration, 1971-1998, Climatological Data: New York, National Climate Center, Asheville, NC
_____ 1975, Climate of Carmel, New York, Climatography of the United States No. 20, National Climate Center, Asheville, NC
_____ 1975, Climate of Scarsdale, New York, Climatography of the United States No. 20, National Climate Center, Asheville, NC
_____ Storm Data and Unusual Weather Phenomena, 1959 - 1998, National Climate Data Center, Asheville, NC

U.S. Department of the Interior, 1956, Floods of August 1955 in the Northeastern States, Geological Survey Circular 377, Water Resources Division, Geological Survey, Washington, DC

Vestal, C.K. 1961, Fitting of Climatological Extreme Value Data, U.S. Weather Bureau Climatological Service Memorandum No. 89, Washington, DC

Wilks, D.S. & Cember, R.P., 1993, Atlas of Precipitation Extremes for the Northeastern United States and Southeastern Canada, Publication No. RR 93-5, Northeast Regional Climate Center, Cornell University, Ithaca, NY

INDEX